MEDICAL SCHOOLS
IN THE UNITED STATES
at Mid-Century

MEDICAL SCHOOLS
IN THE UNITED STATES
at Mid-Century

John E. Deitrick, M.D.

and

Robert C. Berson, M.D.

McGraw-Hill Book Company, Inc.,

NEW YORK   TORONTO   LONDON

1953

THE MAPLE PRESS COMPANY, YORK, PA.

*To those teachers who are
interested in the education and
development of young physicians,
and to their students, who are
the physicians of the future.*

STAFF OF SURVEY OF MEDICAL EDUCATION

John E. Deitrick, Director of Study
Robert C. Berson, Associate Director

Estelle W. Brown, Staff Associate
William E. Brown, Staff Associate
Thomas Hale, Jr., Staff Associate
Stockton Kimball, Staff Associate
William F. Norwood, Staff Associate

Paddy Rudd Howes, Writer

FOREWORD

This volume comprises the formal report of the Survey of Medical Education, organized in 1947. It is a factual analysis and evaluation of medical education in the United States at the mid-point of the twentieth century made by chosen representatives of American medical education. Based upon the collection of facts and opinions from the medical schools, and upon visits by Survey groups to a large and representative proportion of those schools, the study has had the full cooperation of their deans, faculties, and students. It is, in effect, the first thorough self-evaluation of medical education in many years.

Since the turn of the century the requirements and content of medical education have increased far beyond what most men could then have envisaged. There are many reasons for this. One has been the effort of medical educators to produce physicians in knowledge and quality calculated to meet the needs of a public expanding not only in numbers but in its desires for high standards of medical care. Another has been the development of the fundamental sciences and their application to medical diagnosis and treatment beyond the concepts of the preatomic age. A third has been the growth of laboratory techniques both in medical practice and in medical research, with consequent increase of what the physician needs to know.

Meanwhile the Second World War and its aftermath created new and augmented old problems in medical education. Among these were the demands of the armed forces upon medical personnel and potential personnel; the increased cost of medical education and the problem of how it could be arrested, reduced, or met; the proper staffing of basic science departments when so few men and women of requisite ability and training could be produced during the war; the question whether specialization in medical education had become excessive; the great increase of administrative work and responsibility thrown upon relatively few experienced medical administrators; the question whether administrative organization and practices are adequate to these new demands; and the effect upon medical education of the development of many medical schools into large, complicated, and often scattered medical centers. Now, at the half-century mark, it seemed high time to take stock by self-examination.

Hence, on the recommendation of the Council on Medical Education and Hospitals of the American Medical Association, the Board of Trustees of the Association voted to embark upon a comprehensive study of medical education, and made generous appropriations for that purpose. Meanwhile similar thinking and activity had developed within the Association of American Medical Colleges, which promptly accepted an invitation of joint sponsorship, and made its own appropriation in support.

A temporary committee, which functioned while the Survey was in its initial stages and which was composed of representatives from the two sponsors, was succeeded by the Survey Committee whose membership is listed elsewhere in this volume. The author of this Foreword, together with the director and members of the staff of the Survey, has worked with this committee through many long and arduous but stimulating meetings.

On October 16, 1948, the committee appointed as Director of the Survey Dr. John E. Deitrick, then Associate Professor of Medicine at Cornell University Medical College. Doctor Deitrick spent the spring and summer of 1949 in developing his staff and program and was joined in September by Dr. Robert C. Berson, then Assistant Dean of the University of Illinois Medical School, as Associate Director.

Early in 1949, it became clear that funds beyond those provided by the two sponsors would be needed to conduct a thorough survey of the whole field. The W. K. Kellogg Foundation responded generously to a request that it finance that phase of the Survey concerned with graduate and postgraduate education. Without this assistance, the Survey must of necessity have been incomplete.

Visits to the medical schools began in September, 1949, and continued until May, 1951, with the following technique: A date was arranged with the dean of the medical school six to eight weeks in advance of the visit by a Survey team. Questionnaire forms were forwarded at once to the school and included sets of questions for the dean and for each of the departments in the school. The answers to these questions were returned to the office of the Survey and were reviewed by the team of men selected to visit that school.

These Survey teams included two or more Survey staff members and one or more carefully chosen medical educators, notably including deans of other medical schools. Every member of the Survey Committee, including the Chairman, participated in one or more visits to medical schools of four to eight days each, depending upon the size and complexity of the school. The first approach was always to the dean. Heads of departments and other faculty members also were interviewed. One member of the team devoted his attention to affiliated hospitals, internships, residencies, and postgraduate educational programs. Representatives of the local medical societies and welfare agencies were consulted, and whenever possible the head of the university and one or more members of its Board of Trustees. The Survey teams always met with younger members of the faculty and with a group of students from the third- and fourth-year classes. Experimental programs in teaching, either planned or in existence, were given special attention. At the end of each survey, a final discussion was held with the dean. Deans, faculty members, and other administrative officers of the medical schools gave remarkable cooperation in terms of interest, time, and energy, and their collective contributions to the Survey were invaluable.

The Survey Committee also arranged for a study of premedical education by a special subcommittee, and Aura E. Severinghaus, Ph.D., Associate Dean of the Faculty of Medicine of Columbia University, accepted the chairmanship of this subcommittee and took full responsibility for its membership and staff. With the help of the Survey Committee, a generous grant was secured from the John and Mary R. Markle Foundation for the support of this study. Dr. Severinghaus's group, though technically a subcommittee of the Survey Committee and in harmony with its objectives, worked with a large degree of independence and initiative. Its report on premedical education, published in a separate volume in conjunction with the Survey, is in content and conclusions the responsibility of the subcommittee alone. The Survey Committee records its appreciation to Dr. Severinghaus and his staff, headed by Dr. Harry J. Carman of Columbia University and Dean William E. Cadbury, Jr. of Haverford College, for their important contribution to medical and general education, and recommends a reading of their separate report.

The Survey Committee believed that its work would gain perspective and public interest through the advice of an Advisory Council composed of leaders from various areas of our national life. Such a Council was formed, with a membership recorded elsewhere in this volume. The Council was asked specifically whether the Survey appeared to be covering the major problems of medical education of interest to the general public; whether those problems were being studied with competence and a proper sense of broad social values; and to what extent and in what manner the findings of the study should be presented to the public. Although it did not prove possible for the Advisory Council to meet as often or with as full attendance as had been hoped, the advice of its members was very valuable and its services warmly appreciated. The reader should understand that members of this Advisory Council are not responsible for the content and opinions of the report.

As the Survey progressed with its studies, it became apparent that its most useful function would be to analyze and define the status of the medical schools as social and educational instruments of modern society. The Survey, therefore, concentrated its efforts first in studying the range of activities in which a modern medical school engages; second, in examining the responsibilities that are being shouldered by the medical schools; and third, in presenting some of the more important problems created for the medical schools by the assumption of these activities and responsibilities. Details of course content and teaching methods were studied, but for the purposes of the

Survey they were considered in terms of their impact on a school as a whole rather than as problems in themselves. They are, however, considered of great importance, and the Survey believes that they should and will be the subjects of continuing study by many groups.

During the years of the Survey activity, several other agencies were also endeavoring to throw light upon various aspects of medical education. The Committee and staff of the Survey kept in informal touch with these other organizations, and full cooperation was given and received. Duplication was thus avoided, and valuable information was exchanged to mutual advantage. Such agencies included the Commission for the Study of Higher Education of the Association of American Universities and the U.S. Public Health Service Surgeon General's Committee on Medical School Grants and Finances. In no case, however, was material given to the Survey in confidence made available without permission.

In July, 1950, the gravity of the Korean War led the Survey Committee to consider whether the situation created by that war should alter the plans for the Survey. In spite of added difficulties, it was agreed to continue without substantial alteration of plans, but it was not found possible to visit each one of the medical schools. Forty-one schools in all were visited by the Survey, and these were carefully selected to comprise a representative group.

The report of Dr. Abraham Flexner to the Carnegie Foundation for the Advancement of Teaching in 1910 was a famous bench mark in medical education. Members of the Survey Committee and staff could not avoid frequent comparisons of their own findings with those of Flexner in 1910. Perhaps the most striking similarities lie in a mutual sense of the practical limitations and possible errors of detail inevitable in so comprehensive and ambitious a survey, and in a mutual confidence that the over-all presentation is dependable. In his introduction to the Flexner report in 1910, President Henry S. Pritchett of the Carnegie Foundation wrote:

"No effort has been spared to procure accurate and detailed information as to the facilities, resources, and methods of instruction of the medical schools. . . . In the immense number of details dealt with, it is altogether impossible to be sure that every minute fact concerning these institutions has been ascertained and set down. While the Foundation cannot hope to obtain in so great an undertaking absolute completeness in every particular . . . the statements which are given here may be confidently accepted as setting forth the essential facts respecting medical education and respecting the institutions which deal with it."

The Survey Committee adopts that statement as appropriate to its own report.

Dr. Pritchett also wrote in 1910:

"Meanwhile the requirements of medical education are enormously increased. The fundamental sciences upon which medical education depends have been greatly extended. The laboratory has come to furnish alike to the physician and to the surgeon a new means for diagnosing and combating disease. The education of the medical practitioner under these changed conditions makes entirely different demands in respect to both preliminary and professional training."

That statement, too, applies to the current situation, although the demands in respect to both preliminary and professional training have increased tremendously in the past 40 years, because of the faster tempo at which knowledge in the fundamental sciences and the uses of the laboratory have advanced.

Contrasts are as striking as similarities. No one could in 1952 read the Flexner report without being impressed at how great has been the progress of medical education in the last 40 years.

Doctor Flexner urged that medical schools be brought under the management and responsibilities of universities. Today this is almost completely the case. In 1910, Dr. Flexner suggested that universities which then possessed medical schools were not giving them an adequate proportion of the university funds; today these medical schools are both a source of pride and a subject of deep financial concern to university officers and trustees. But these contrasts do not indicate any fundamental difference in concepts of medical education between Dr. Flexner and Dr. Pritchett on the one hand and members of this Survey on the other. Both the 1910 and the present report emphasize that quality of personnel rather than quantity of men or money is the first essential in medical education.

The Committee hopes that this Survey report, to which nearly all medical educators have directly or indirectly contributed, will prove of real value, not only to the medical profession but to all higher education and to the general public. Some effects of the report have predated its publication. The infinite number of discussions generated among those engaged in medical education by the questions and activities of the Survey staff, by the ideas and facts received and passed on from school to school, have already played an important part in the constant ferment toward self-improvement in the medical schools. The ideas of the younger men in medical faculties have been brought out and more thoroughly considered by older heads, to mutual benefit.

This report represents the opinions, not always unanimous, of the Director, his associates, and the members of the Survey Committee. The entire manuscript was presented to the Committee and carefully weighed and edited. It is in the nature of such an undertaking that personal variations of opinion must sometimes defer, after thorough discussion, to the conclusions of the majority.

Today's medical students will inevitably determine the quality and nature of the medical care of tomorrow's American citizens. Medical education is thus of the greatest concern to every American. Of this obvious fact the

Survey Committee and staff have been constantly aware. They have tried to present this report in a form and style which will be attractive and intelligible to the average citizen, without diminishing its value to the professional medical man. This has been a special concern of the writer of this Foreword, as the only nonmedical member of the Committee.

So many have contributed to the facts and ideas of this Survey that it is impossible to name and thank all of them, or even to include in this Foreword the names of those whose help was particularly significant. In any such listing the names of Dr. Deitrick and Dr. Berson would clearly lead all the rest. An attempt has been made to record elsewhere in this volume both specific and general thanks, but the list cannot be all-inclusive. We should not, however, omit special mention of Mrs. Paddy Rudd Howes for her valuable assistance in the writing of this report and in seeing the manuscript through to publication.

ALAN VALENTINE, *Chairman*
Survey of Medical Education

AN ACKNOWLEDGEMENT

This report is the result of the efforts of a great number of men and women in medical schools throughout the country who provided the facts on which it is based and who discussed with the Survey teams their problems, opinions, and philosophies regarding medical schools and medical education. To all these persons—too numerous to list—the members of the Survey wish to acknowledge their indebtedness.

Special acknowledgement is due of the contribution made by those men who took time from their medical school duties to serve as volunteer members of Survey teams studying some other school than their own. They included Deans Walter A. Bloedorn, D. Bailey Calvin, C. C. Carpenter, Alan M. Chesney, Sam L. Clark, L. T. Coggeshall, Ward Darley, Stanley Dorst, James M. Faulkner, M. E. Lapham, Vernon W. Lippard, C. N. H. Long, W. S. McEllroy, Currier McEwen, Robert A. Moore, B. O. Raulston, Rolf C. Syvertsen, Edward L. Turner, Joseph T. Wearn, Hugh Wood, Richard Young, and John B. Youmans.

DEFINITIONS

A few terms which have various connotations are here defined according to their usage in this volume.

Full-time Faculty Member

A member of the faculty who devotes all his time to medical school activities, is paid a salary, and receives no fees for other professional services.

Geographic Full-time Faculty Member

A faculty member who, although he spends full time at the medical school and its teaching hospital, devotes part of this time to medical school activities and part to private practice, conducted on the premises, which provides part or all of his income.

Part-time Faculty Member

A member of the faculty who is paid a salary for part-time work in the medical school.

Volunteer Faculty Member

A member of the faculty who receives no financial compensation for his services to the medical school.

FINANCES

Direct Cost

The cost of a research program which is identifiable in the financial records of a medical school. Direct cost includes expenditures for supplies, equipment, travel, and usually the salaries for technical, secretarial, or other personnel.

Indirect Costs

The costs of a research program which are not identifiable in the financial records. They include the time spent on the project by the salaried faculty and other employees, the cost of administration of the funds, building maintenance, and other expenditures not included in "direct cost."

Research Grant

A grant-in-aid for the support of research, given to a medical school

(or other division of a university) or to an individual in a medical
school, by an individual, corporation, foundation, or government agency.
Restricted Funds
Funds whose expenditure is restricted to a specific activity or project.
Teaching Grant
A grant-in-aid for the support of teaching, given to a medical school
(or other division of a university) or to an individual in a medical
school, by an individual, corporation, foundation, or government agency.

INSTITUTIONS

College
An undergraduate college of a university which enrolls students working
toward a Bachelor's degree.
School
A medical school for instruction of undergraduate medical students.
Privately Supported Medical School
A medical school which regularly depends for its major financial support
upon voluntary contributions, income from endowment, and student
fees.
Tax-supported Medical School
A medical school which regularly depends for its major financial support
upon funds raised by taxation.
Teaching Hospital
A hospital utilized by a medical school for a substantial portion of the
clinical instruction of undergraduate medical students.
Affiliated Hospital
A hospital granting certain privileges to a medical school for its teaching
program but functioning as a separate institution.
Associated Hospital
A hospital related to the medical school for the purpose of improving
the quality of the hospital's care of the patient and providing clinical
facilities for the training of interns and residents.
Integrated Hospital
A teaching hospital functioning in close cooperation with a medical
school physically, administratively, and financially, but not owned by the
university or the medical school.
University-owned Hospital
A teaching hospital owned and operated by a university or a medical
school for the purpose of teaching undergraduate students and training
interns and residents.

PATIENTS

Inpatient
A patient admitted to and occupying a bed in a hospital.

Outpatient
>An ambulatory patient who comes to a hospital's clinic for diagnosis and treatment.

PERSONNEL

Ancillary Personnel
>People providing services which supplement and aid in the study and care of the patient. These services include nursing; diagnostic procedures in the fields of pathology, chemistry, physiology, and radiology; as well as social, health, and welfare service.

Technician
>A person trained in the performance of laboratory procedures, including diagnostic and therapeutic techniques.

PROGRAMS AND SERVICES

Inpatient Clerkship
>That part of the medical school curriculum in which the student is introduced to clinical medicine through the study of individual hospitalized patients.

Internship
>A period of hospital training, service, and education, usually of one year's duration, following graduation from medical school.

Mixed Internship
>An internship in which the intern spends periods of time on a limited number of hospital services.

Rotating Internship
>An internship in which the intern spends a period of time varying from a few weeks to two or more months on each of several services of a hospital, such as medicine, surgery, pediatrics, obstetrics, urology, etc.

Straight Internship
>An internship devoted to a single field such as surgery, medicine, pediatrics, etc.

Medical Basic Sciences
>Anatomy, biochemistry, pathology, microbiology, pharmacology, physiology, and other medical sciences which stem from the basic sciences of biology, chemistry, mathematics, and physics.

Project Research
>Research carried on in a medical school, or other institution, with funds provided by an outside agency for the investigation of a specific problem.

Residency
>A period of one to five years of special hospital training, service, and education, following the internship and designed to train the physician in a special field.

STUDENTS

Graduate Student
A student enrolled in a graduate school or medical school as a candidate for the degree of Master of Science or Doctor of Philosophy who takes all or part of his work in one or several departments of the medical school.

Intern
A graduate of a medical school serving his first period of hospital training.

Medical Student
A student enrolled in a medical school as a candidate for the M.D. degree.

Postgraduate Medical Student
A physician enrolled as a student in part-time or full-time special courses, which carry no credit toward a degree.

Resident
A physician serving a more advanced period of training in a hospital than an intern.

CONTENTS

Part 1

INTRODUCTION

1 INTRODUCTION

Medical schools both affect and are affected by the events which determine the history of the nation. Thus the ebb and flow of social, economic, and political forces which have shaped life in the United States over the past 200 years are reflected in the history of the medical schools. These forces, together with the constant advancement in scientific knowledge, have made the medical school of the mid-1950's a highly intricate organization with a multitude of activities and a complex financial structure.

At times of rapid change, the schools' activities progress faster than their policies, and medical education is swept along and molded by the currents at such a rate that its quality may be threatened or damaged. Then the leaders must reset their course. They must examine their policies, restate them in the light of present-day programs, and vigorously pull their activities into proper balance for the future.

Abraham Flexner helped the schools to reset their course in 1910, aided by the Carnegie Foundation for the Advancement of Teaching and in cooperation with the Council on Medical Education of the American Medical Association. And in 1947, the medical profession and medical educators themselves determined that it was time for a reevaluation.

The Survey Committee was instructed to evaluate the present programs of the medical schools and to determine the future responsibilities of medical education in its broadest aspects. The purposes of the Survey were defined as follows:

To improve medical education to better meet the over-all needs of the American people (for the prevention of disease, the restoration, so far as possible, to health of all those who suffer illness or injury, the maintenance of the best standards of physical and mental health of all the people); to assess the degree to which medical schools are meeting the needs of the country for physicians; to promote the advancement of knowledge in the field of medical science; and to better inform the public concerning the nature, content, and purposes of medical education.

The study was to encompass "an inventory of the existing situation, determination of the need for changes and improvements, conclusions and recommendations based on the foregoing, and proposals for ways and means of carrying out the recommendations."

With these objectives, nothing short of a detailed and comprehensive study of the activities of each school included in the Survey, with the aid of its administration, faculty, and students, could result in an understanding of the difficulties and problems of each school and its educational strengths and weaknesses. With the "study" rather than the "survey" approach, therefore, the Survey staff consulted all these groups in each school, as well as many other persons concerned with the medical schools, including university presidents, representatives of the medical profession, and welfare agencies. Facts, opinions, attitudes, and philosophies were collected by means of questionnaires to each school, followed by personal visits to the school by staff members, accompanied by a member of the Survey Committee or some other medical educator serving as a temporary member of the staff.

The cooperation of the medical schools was remarkable. The time and energy that the deans, faculty members, financial officers, and secretaries of the medical schools devoted to the Survey cannot be measured in monetary terms. Any failures or shortcomings of the Survey can in no way be charged to the medical schools.

The staff was unable to devise any precise or useful method for assessing the degree to which medical schools are meeting the needs of the country for physicians. No precise definition exists of the "needs" for physicians, or of the needs as contrasted to the demand, and the Survey was forced to conclude that such a study was not within its province or its resources. It was possible in this respect to study only what the schools were planning in regard to expanding their facilities and enrollments.

The activities of the medical schools fall into three broad categories —education, research, and service. These activities, and the ways in which they are financed, form the subject matter of Chapters 2 to 7. Administrative affairs are discussed in Chapters 7 to 12, and teaching is discussed in Chapters 13 to 16. The final chapter attempts to describe the challenges that must be met before the course of medical education can be set for the future.

The staff accepted as its premises certain principles concerning the education of a physician against which present-day medical education can be measured. These premises, which are concerned with a definition of a medical school and its responsibilities, are set forth in the remainder of this chapter.

BASIC PREMISES

A medical school is an educational institution concerned with a certain body of scientific and empirical knowledge, to which it should continue to make additions, and with which two individuals, the teacher and the student, must deal in order to understand and to help a third person for the purpose of maintaining his health or overcoming his illnesses.

The medical school must accept two major responsibilities in its educational program. The first is to its students and the second, fulfilled through the men it graduates as physicians, is to society. Since the medical school is the only avenue to a career as a physician, the schools are largely responsible for the medical profession. In this respect, the first and paramount consideration is that the students must be the best human material that the faculty can select, regardless of birth, residence, race, creed, or color.

The medical student is the central figure in medical education. Every policy, every activity must be designed and performed with him in view. He has been molded by 20 or more years of development and education, and many of his faults and weaknesses cannot be corrected by four years of medical education. The breadth of the student's point of view and the level at which the medical school can begin its educational program are determined by the type and quality of his preprofessional education. The latter has been the subject of a separate survey, made by a subcommittee, whose report is published in a companion volume.

In the educational program of a medical school, the quality of the faculty and its attitude toward and interest in education are more important than the exact organization of the curriculum. The primary pur-

pose of teaching and of instructional methods is to encourage the student
to develop to the maximum his own latent capacities and interests. The
medical school should offer especially those opportunities, experiences,
and stimuli which it would be impossible for the student to obtain elsewhere. He should be given a firm grasp of the experimental method and
an understanding of the principles and methods of the basic sciences.
While he is in medical school, he must be introduced to sound methods
of studying patients, and he must be given opportunity to apply these
methods under supervision. His instructors should be men who in their
daily work exemplify the highest quality of ethics and professional
medical care.

A curriculum can be sound only if it is designed for the student and
based on sound educational principles. The curriculum must be designed
by the faculty as a whole. Each department must see clearly the complete
sphere of the program before considering its own segment, and with the
student the paramount interest in mind.

Upon graduation from medical school, the young physician should
possess an understanding of science, man and his diseases. He should
have a spirit of curiosity and possess methods of study which produce
accurate observations and facts that may lead to new knowledge and
understanding. It is to be hoped that during his four years of formal
education he will have experienced the satisfaction of facing, studying,
understanding, and mastering by himself problems of science or of a patient's illness. If he has done so, he will be prepared to enter one of the
various fields of medicine, and will continue to gain the satisfaction that
results from constant study and increasing understanding.

The physician today usually practices medicine as an individual, dependent to an increasing degree upon teamwork, and in general attempts to solve problems by utilizing the scientific method. He must
organize his facts, make deductions, reach decisions, and carry out defini-
tive therapy. The better his grasp of the basic sciences, the broader his
factual knowledge, and the more intelligently he organizes this knowledge, the more scientific he will be as a doctor. If, in addition, he has
sympathy for and a broad understanding of people, he will be an excellent physician.

If the Survey was to help to improve medical education, it seemed to
the staff most important to study the medical schools as accurately as
possible against the philosophy expressed in this preamble. Where fac-

tual knowledge was unavailable, inductive reasoning has been used. Weaknesses have been determined, and when possible, methods of correction have been suggested, and problems have been defined and proposed for further study and experimentation. Intelligent and constructive criticism is more likely to result in improvement than laudatory comments, and for this reason elaboration of the many good points and brilliant accomplishments of the medical schools has been omitted.

Part II

THE FUNCTIONS OF THE MEDICAL SCHOOL

2 EDUCATION

Medical education in the early colonies of America was relatively simple. In those days, the student learned from a practitioner who, as his preceptor, taught him his skills and his knowledge. By the time of the American Revolution, however, the shortcomings of preceptorships were becoming recognized and the idea of the medical school was introduced. By 1798 four medical schools were in existence in this country, all of them associated with colleges or universities which provided facilities but no significant financial support. Tuition fees paid for the operating costs.

Nevertheless the concept of endowments for medical schools arose during the Revolutionary period. In 1770 Harvard University, which had no medical school until 12 years later, received a gift for the support of a chair of anatomy and surgery, and thus began the history of philanthropic financial support of the educational activities of medical schools.

This type of financial support grew slowly, however. With a rapidly expanding population due to immigration in the early nineteenth century, the increasing demand for physicians led practitioners of medicine to establish medical schools, and privately owned medical schools became numerous. In many cases financed entirely by tuition, they tended to be commercial enterprises, and the quality of instruction varied. They gave lectures in anatomy, physiology and chemistry, surgery, medicine, therapeutics, midwifery, and diseases of women and children. Dissatisfaction with the low quality of teaching in most medical schools led leaders of the profession in 1847 to found the American Medical Association. Licensing standards for doctors, which had existed as early as 1772 when New Jersey introduced the first state examination, were not highly developed, and by 1850 most states had abandoned them altogether in the wake of the Jacksonian democracy and its abolition of restrictions on individual enterprise. Meanwhile the philosophy was gradually becoming accepted that the medical student should not have to bear the full cost of medical education, and many schools were receiving gifts, grants, state appropriations, and funds raised by lottery.

These events occurred while higher education was still predominately the province of private endeavor or philanthropy. In general, state universities played a minor role in medical education until the beginning of the present century. Among the few exceptions was the University of Michigan medical school which, in 1851, was the first to establish professorships on a salary basis.

It was not until the last two decades of the nineteenth century that a significant number of medical schools began to introduce their students to the study of patients. This method of teaching proved so effective that hospital facilities were seen to be a great advantage to a medical school.

In the meantime, in Europe during the nineteenth century, scientific knowledge developed rapidly. Pathology, physiology, bacteriology, and chemistry became firmly established among the sciences, and by the close of the century appreciation of their value to medicine was growing. Laboratories were essential for the study of these sciences, and they were developed in increasing number. These workshops produced more accurate methods for the study of disease. At the same time they opened the way to more effective methods of teaching which incidentally required more time and equipment.

Gradually a parallel development took place in the United States, and medical schools with access to laboratory and hospital facilities began to assume educational leadership. In 1876, 22 medical schools comprised the basic membership of a new organization, the Association of American Medical Colleges. For a period this organization did not function, but in 1891 it set minimum requirements for admission to membership, and within five years its membership had more than doubled, 55 of the 155 schools then in existence having been admitted to membership by 1896. Efforts to improve medical education also were made through the establishment of licensure requirements, and by 1895 practically every state had its examination board.

In the meantime the universities' growing sense of responsibility for the quality of medical education brought significant progress. A notable example was the establishment in 1895 of a four-year curriculum at Harvard. Because this was an era in which large private fortunes were growing, endowments increased; and in 1893 a school of medicine was founded in Baltimore, endowed by Johns Hopkins with the important proviso that its major preclinical faculty members must devote their full time to teaching and research.

In 1900 the American Medical Association began to publish medical school statistics, and in 1904 it established its Council on Medical Education and Hospitals. This was the year in which the number of medical schools in the United States reached its peak, 160 having come into existence within little more than a century, including eclectic and homeopathic institutions. The Council established minimum standards for an acceptable medical school, inspected the schools, and published a list of schools that met the minimal standards. It played a very active role in bringing the deficiencies of medical education to the attention of the nation.

In 1908 the Carnegie Foundation for the Advancement of Teaching undertook to survey the whole field of medical education in the United States and Canada in order to define its relation to education in general. The Foundation's report, prepared by Abraham Flexner[1] and published in 1910, contained such candid and drastic criticism of the defects of medical education that the weaker schools were unable to continue. Of the recognized schools that survived, some merged for mutual strengthening, and most secured university connections. All became nonprofit institutions. In his preface to the Flexner report, President Pritchett of the Carnegie Foundation anticipated such changes when he stated that "progress for the future would seem to require a very much smaller number of medical schools, better equipped and better conducted than our schools now as a rule are; and the needs of the public would equally require that we have fewer physicians graduated each year, but that these should be better educated and better trained." The decade 1910–1920 marked the establishment of medical education as a university discipline with definite educational standards.

Only the better financed and better led schools were able to develop adequate laboratories and hospital affiliations in order to achieve the

---

[1] FLEXNER, ABRAHAM, "Medical Education in the United States and Canada, A Report to the Carnegie Foundation for the Advancement of Teaching," New York, 1910.

quality of medical education heralded by these events. The number of inferior schools continued to dwindle.

As the schools developed and as teaching in the laboratory and in the hospital became an essential part of medical education, more highly trained assistants were needed both in research and in service activities, and the medical schools' teaching responsibilities increased. With the development of laboratories for research and teaching, the need arose for trained technicians. Part of the responsibility for the training of these technicians was assumed by the medical school faculties, and the training was conducted in their laboratories. The development of bed-side teaching and close affiliations between hospitals and medical schools increased the need for nurses educated to a higher level than formerly. The medical school faculty began to assume the responsibility for part of the teaching of students enrolled in the nursing schools associated with their teaching hospitals, and the trend has continually increased.

Dental schools, the first of which in the United States was established in 1840, were gradually drawn to the universities and medical schools by the growth of scientific knowledge fundamental to both dentistry and medicine. In 1867 Harvard University established its dental school, in which students took the lecture courses in anatomy, chemistry, physiology, and surgery that were required of students of medicine and had access to the dissecting rooms, library, and museums of the medical school. That this pattern was widely adopted is evidenced by the following quotation from the report of the survey of dental education in the United States and Canada, conducted by William J. Gies,[2] which was sponsored and supported in 1926 by the Carnegie Foundation for the Advancement of Teaching. "The teaching of the medical sciences has long been one of the most difficult phases of dental education. For most of the university dental schools, it is now conducted in laboratories in the medical buildings by members of the medical departments."

In 1947, Harlan H. Horner,[3] in a book entitled "Dental Education Today," reported that in 23 of the 40 dental schools the basic sciences were taught in whole or in part by the medical school faculty. Medical

---

[2] GIES, WILLIAM J., "Dental Education in the United States and Canada, A Report to the Carnegie Foundation for the Advancement of Teaching," New York, 1926, p. 193.

[3] HORNER, HARLAN H., "Dental Education Today," Chicago, University of Chicago Press, 1947, p. 70.

faculties served similarly for many schools of pharmacy that were under university supervision.

The medical schools were able to finance these additional responsibilities in the early decades of the twentieth century only because of the rapidly growing wealth of the nation. They received large private gifts or additional state revenue from taxes. On the basis of large philanthropic gifts during this period from such philanthropic agencies as The Rockefeller Foundation, the Carnegie Foundation, and the Commonwealth Fund, the medical schools of the University of Chicago, Columbia, Cornell, Duke, Rochester, Stanford, Washington University, and Yale were either founded or reorganized. In institutions with large yearly incomes from endowments, the costs of medical education and hospital operation were not a major problem. But in less prosperous institutions and those dependent chiefly upon tax support, even though their activities and philosophies developed similarly, their budgets expanded less spectacularly.

The financing of medical schools in the state of Pennsylvania marked a departure from the two patterns of support by taxes and support by private funds. In 1899 this State passed a law enabling the legislature to make biennial grants to all the medical schools of the State to help meet their yearly deficits. Since that time, the medical schools in Pennsylvania have functioned as privately controlled medical schools which develop their own endowments but whose income is supplemented by State appropriations.

Thus, three broad patterns were established for the support of medical schools: endowment income, tax support, and combined endowment and tax support.

With such financial support the medical schools were able to expand their teaching responsibilities and activities in the 1920's and 1930's. Some of the larger and better financed schools developed institutes for service and research in special fields. These institutes offered specialty training in such areas as ophthalmology, urology, psychiatry, and neurology. The training of interns and residents in the university hospital also expanded as research added knowledge and new techniques to be mastered by the young physician.

In the early 1930's, however, the medical schools began to encounter serious financial difficulties. A depression had occurred which resulted in a restriction of endowment income. Even after the immediate effects of the depression had vanished, it was clear that it had left a change in social philosophy which would bring limitations on private fortunes. Rising taxation and curtailment of private wealth made it difficult for privately supported medical schools to increase their endowments for the support of their expanded activities and their new institutes. Many schools were forced to curtail both their activities and their building programs. Between 1931 and 1941 only about one-third of the medical schools carried out any major construction, and only one-fifth of these were privately endowed and controlled.

In 1932, Willard C. Rappleye, director of the Commission on Medical Education, which was organized by the Association of American Medical Colleges for the purpose of studying the educational principles involved in medical education and licensure, devoted five pages of his report to the cost of medical education.[4] It was estimated, he reported, that 13 million dollars per year was being expended by the medical schools with an average cost in 1927 of $704 per student. He stated that no medical school had a comprehensive system of cost accounting and that comparative cost figures were of little value, since some schools included in their totals the instruction of nonmedical students, as well as the research and service activities.

In 1940, Herman Weiskotten, then dean of Syracuse University medical school, published a report of a survey of medical education under the sponsorship of the Council on Medical Education and Hospitals of the American Medical Association.[5] Relatively little of this report was devoted to medical school finances and their complexity. Dr. Weiskotten reported that the total income of 66 four-year medical schools was $22,345,483, with an average cost per student of $1,052. He stated: "It is clear that many of the universities used income from endowment in support of extensive research and in further support of a broadened program of social endeavor. Such universities doubtless performed an important function. If, however, the public is to be expected to maintain its interest in all phases of university activity, it should understand that such expenditure is justifiable."

[4] "Commission on Medical Education, Final Report," New York, Office of the Director of Study, 1932, p. 283.

[5] WEISKOTTEN, H. G., "Medical Education in the United States," Chicago, American Medical Association, 1940, pp. 23, 102.

EXPANSION IN RECENT YEARS

The Second World War placed tremendous strains on the structure of medical education. The output of physicians was increased by extending the school year to 12 months and graduating a class every three instead of every four years. Faculties were depleted as members entered the armed forces, and the training of teachers was markedly hampered by draft regulations. The medical schools increased their income through the additional tuition fees received for the 12 months of instruction, and the Federal government paid a large percentage of the fees. Some faculty vacancies could not be filled, new equipment was unobtainable, and in a number of schools income exceeded expenditures. In spite of this improved financial state, medical educators stated emphatically that the quality of medical instruction suffered.

Following the Second World War, taxation continued to increase and inflation appeared. Medical school and hospital costs rose rapidly. In one private school with a university-owned hospital, for instance, the hospital costs increased 63 per cent and medical school costs increased 36 per cent between 1945 and 1948. The problem reached such proportions that it was given widespread attention, and finally the Federal government became concerned. In a monograph entitled "The Nation's Health,"[6] the Federal Security Administrator stressed the inadequate financial support of the medical schools and their inability to meet the needs of the nation for physicians and health personnel. State and private institutions were subjected to a growing demand for expansion of student enrollments, both to accommodate the larger number of applicants and to increase the supply of physicians. In response to these needs, the medical schools increased their enrollments from 22,739 in 1947–48 to 25,103 in 1949–50.[7]

Resident training and postgraduate medical education were also ex-

[6] EWING, OSCAR R., "The Nation's Health, A Ten Year Program (Report to the President by the Federal Security Administrator)," Washington, D.C., U.S. Government Printing Office, 1948.

[7] Latest enrollment figure reported by the Council on Medical Education and Hospitals of the American Medical Association is 27,076 for the year 1951–52. [ANDERSON, D. G., F. R. MANLOVE, and ANNE TIPNER, Medical Education in the United States and Canada, *Journal of the American Medical Association,* Vol. 150, p. 109 (Sept. 13), 1952.]

panded. Many physicians, having been impressed while they were in the armed forces with the favored position given to medical specialists, on their return to civilian life sought education and training in order to qualify as specialists. Others returned to their medical schools to be brought up to date in the latest medical knowledge in postgraduate courses. The residency and fellowship training programs in all hospitals expanded from an enrollment of 5,487 in 1940–41 to 8,930 in 1945–46 and to 18,669 in 1950. At the same time attendance at postgraduate courses increased from a total of 59,811 in 1946 to 75,318 in 1950.[8]

The educational responsibilities of the medical schools in the year 1949–50, according to the Council on Medical Education and Hospitals, included, in addition to the teaching of 25,103 medical students, the instruction of 32,506 other students in the categories shown in Table 1.

Table 1. OTHER STUDENTS FOR WHOM MEDICAL SCHOOLS WERE RESPON-
SIBLE, 1949–50

Part-time or special medical students working toward M.D. degree.............	110
Physicians enrolled for advanced degrees..................................	1,125
Other graduate students working for degrees in medical basic sciences.........	2,094
Nonmedical students taking medical courses..............................	2,720
Physicians enrolled in refresher or continuation courses.....................	17,930
Physicians enrolled in formal basic science courses in preparation for specialty board certification..	1,087
Physicians holding appointments as fellows...............................	1,135
Interns for whose instruction and supervision the medical school was primarily responsible...	1,960
Residents for whose instruction and supervision the medical school was primarily responsible...	4,345
Total...	32,506

Source: Anderson, D. G., and Anne Tipner, Medical Education in the United States and Canada, *Journal of the American Medical Association*, Vol. 144, p. 124 (Sept. 9), 1950.

The Council failed to include in its report a large number of dental, pharmacy, nursing, and technical students. It did report a total of 2,720 "nonmedical students taking medical courses," under which heading it is presumed that some of these students are included.[8] However, according to statistics reported by Horner,[9] as early as 1944 approximately

[8] ANDERSON, D. G., and ANNE TIPNER, Medical Education in the United States and Canada, *Journal of the American Medical Association,* Vol. 144, p. 109 (Sept. 9), 1950.

[9] HORNER, HARLAN H., "Dental Education Today," Chicago, University of Chicago Press, 1947, pp. 70, 168, 217.

2,000 dental students alone were receiving part of their instruction from full-time members of medical school faculties. When, in 1950–51, the Council for the first time asked the schools for this information, it reported a total of 16,948 students in the four hitherto unreported groups, including 3,854 dental students.[10] In addition it reported a total of 9,838 "nonmedical students taking medical courses." In view of these facts it is obvious that the figures reported to the Council were not complete. It will be seen later that most medical schools found it difficult to supply similar data to the Survey and that very few had records readily available.

THE COST OF MEDICAL EDUCATION

By 1950 the costs of these expanded programs, accentuated by inflation, had reached staggering proportions. In 1927 the cost of operating the medical schools of the United States was estimated at about $13,000,000, a sum which included at least a part of the expenditures for the teaching hospitals.[11] In 1951, the 79 medical schools spent more than $106,000,000, excluding hospital costs. In 1927 the cost of educating a medical student was estimated at $700.[11] A committee appointed by the Surgeon General of the U.S. Public Health Service reported an average cost of $2,285 per student for the year 1947–48,[12] and in 1949 the Council on Medical Education and Hospitals estimated the average expenditure per student to be $2,577 per year.[13] The estimated cost of educating a medical student had increased 250 per cent in 23 years while the cost of operating the medical schools had increased at least 700 per cent.

These increased costs have been of growing concern to medical

[10] ANDERSON, D. G., F. R. MANLOVE, and ANNE TIPNER, Medical Education in the United States and Canada, *Journal of the American Medical Association,* Vol. 147, p. 131 (Sept. 8), 1951.

[11] "Commission on Medical Education, Final Report," New York, Office of the Director of Study, 1932.

[12] Federal Security Agency, Public Health Service, "Report by the Surgeon General's Committee on Medical School Grants and Finances," Part II, Financial Status and Needs of Medical Schools, Washington, D.C., U.S. Government Printing Office, 1951, p. 3.

[13] ANDERSON, D. G., and ANNE TIPNER, Medical Education in the United States and Canada, *Journal of the American Medical Association,* Vol. 141, p. 43 (Sept. 3), 1949.

schools and universities and to interested private citizens. They have overtaxed the financial capacities of universities and have brought the charge that the costs of the medical schools are limiting the development of other university programs. Some university authorities have raised the question of reducing the cost of medical education, but the medical schools have replied that this is impossible without lowering its quality.

None of the recent attempts to solve this financial problem, or even to determine its exact dimensions, have brought conclusive results. The Survey, searching for the most helpful and logical approach, decided to discover exactly what activities this $106,000,000 expenditure supported. Basing its study on the assumption, already mentioned, that the major activities of a medical school are education, research, and medical service, the Survey has endeavored to relate these activities to the budgets.

In studying the educational activities of a medical school, it was necessary to know how many students of all kinds were receiving instruction from the medical school faculty. The dean of the medical school and the head of each department were therefore asked for this information. The form in which the question was worded appears in Table 2. The Survey had difficulty in securing this information, however, not because of lack of cooperation, but because medical school officers were unable to answer the question. Very few had records readily available of the number of nonmedical students enrolled in courses taught by the medical school faculty. Some had apparently never asked themselves this important question. The reply of one dean of a tax-supported school is typical. After discussing the problem of the teaching of nonmedical students, he attempted to gather the desired information and then wrote as follows:

These 2,224 other students represent a rough approximation of the number of individuals who take work at the School of Medicine. In addition to the regularly enrolled students in the School of Medicine, the number corresponds closely with the figure of about 2,000 the Dean gathered three or four months ago when he was compiling data for the Legislature. Without a great deal of work and expenditure of staff time in the Graduate School and the College of Arts and Sciences, it is not possible to obtain more accurate figures for the above students.

Many deans replied by stating that the information could be obtained from the individual departments of the medical school.

In the time available for the study of each medical school, it was impossible to determine which nonmedical students were enrolled in more than one course in the medical school, or the exact number of hours of instruction devoted by medical school teachers to such students. Since the number of nonmedical students taught by the medical schools could not be determined more accurately, the material presented here indicates only the approximate magnitude of the teaching load carried by medical faculties beyond the instruction of their own students.

Table 2. FORM OF THE SURVEY'S QUESTION TO EACH MEDICAL SCHOOL REGARDING NUMBERS AND CATEGORIES OF STUDENTS TAUGHT BY THE MEDICAL FACULTY

In addition to medical students, how many students in the following categories were taught by the faculty, for how many *class hours*, and what were the total tuition fees received by the *medical school* for this instruction?

	Number of students		Course hours, 1949	Total tuition fees paid by the student	Total amount of tuition fees received by the medical school
	1939	1949			
College students (biology majors, etc.).............					
Nursing students...........					
Dental students............					
Pharmacy students.........					
Technicians...............					
Graduate students (M.S. and Ph.D.).................					
Postgraduate..............					
Fellows...................					
Interns...................					
Assistant residents.........					
Residents.................					
Others...................					

A typical example is that of a privately supported medical school, which revealed that, in addition to the teaching of 191 medical students, it gave all the training received by 50 interns and residents, all the instruction received by 8 technicians and 10 graduate students, plus instruction to 160 postgraduate students in courses of about one week's duration, and part of the instruction of 45 nursing students. This school did not have a large budget, and full-time faculty members were supported in only one clinical department.

A second privately supported school reported that, in addition to the teaching of 481 medical students, its faculty gave all the training received by 129 interns and residents and 36 fellows, all the instruction of 48 technicians and 52 graduate students, plus part of the instruction of 522 nursing students and 150 dental students. This medical school is a division of a large private university with very little endowment. A campaign is now under way for improving the financial position of the medical school.

A third school, tax-supported, reported that, in addition to teaching 293 medical students, it was responsible for the training of 89 interns and residents and the instruction of 25 technicians, 34 graduate students, 147 postgraduate students, 141 occupational- and physical-therapy students, and 100 nursing students, as well as of 460 students enrolled in the college of the university.

In another instance, the department of anatomy in a tax-supported school supplied the detailed information which appears in Table 3. This department gave 124,968 student hours of instruction to nonmedical students, graduate and postgraduate medical students and 125,-548 hours to medical students. The same school was able to give the complete breakdown of instruction of nonmedical students by each department of the medical school which is summarized in Table 4. The figures showed that the school gave 612,129 hours of instruction to 3,818 nonmedical students. In addition, the Survey calculated that the medical school provided 500,000 hours of instruction to the 452 medical students enrolled. These 500,000 hours included both direct and indirect instruction. By hours of indirect instruction is meant the clinical clerkship hours during which a student may work for several hours a day without continuous direct supervision.

Table 5 shows the other students, and the number in each category, taught by the medical school faculties in six schools. Three schools were tax-supported, and three were privately supported. Accurate information as to the amount of instruction given to these students by the faculty was obtainable only for one school. Teaching hours for this school are analyzed in Table 4.

A study of 37 four-year medical schools revealed that they gave instruction to 11,741 medical students and a part of the instruction re-

Table 3. TEACHING RESPONSIBILITIES OF DEPARTMENT OF ANATOMY IN A
TYPICAL TAX-SUPPORTED SCHOOL, 1948–49

	Students	Course hours	Student hours
Courses for Medical Students			
Human gross anatomy........................	145	300	43,500
Microscopical and developmental anatomy......	145	252	36,540
Neuroanatomy	145	132	19,140
Topographical anatomy.......................	145	84	12,180
Applied anatomy............................	117	64	7,488
Otolaryngology and ophthalmology............	110	20	2,200
Surgical anatomy (elective)..................	50	90	4,500
	857	942	125,548
Courses for Nonmedical Students			
Anatomy for nurses.........................	80	144	11,520
Anatomy for dental hygienists................	40	144	5,760
Anatomy for physical education students........	55	144	7,920
Human gross anatomy for dental students.......	96	256	24,576
Microscopical anatomy for dental students.......	96	192	18,432
Applied anatomy of the head and neck..........	80	64	5,120
	447	944	73,328
Graduate Courses			
Human gross anatomy.......................	5	300	1,500
Microscopical and developmental anatomy......	6	252	1,512
Neuroanatomy..............................	13	132	1,716
Morphology of special regions*...............	10x2	200	4,000
Anatomy and function of the vocal apparatus....	6	120	720
Neuroanatomy of the vocal mechanism.........	6	40	240
Surgical anatomy of head and neck for graduates in dentistry.............................	40	64	2,560
Advanced human neuroanatomy...............	25	64	1,600
Advanced course in surgical anatomy*..........	20x2	128	5,120
Comparative vertebrate neuroanatomy...........	15	80	1,200
Preresearch course in morphology of the nervous system*.................................	7x2	200	2,800
Research work in neuroanatomy*...............	7x2	200	2,800
Research work in gross anatomy*...............	1x2	200	400
Research work in histology*...................	2x2	128	512
Research work in embryology*................	2x2	200	800
	214	2,308	27,480
Postgraduate Courses			
Advanced surgical anatomy....................	100	144	14,400
Ophthalmology section.......................	5	48	240
Orthopedic section..........................	5	48	240
Postgraduate gross anatomy..................	30	192	5,760
Postgraduate neuroanatomy...................	30	32	960
Postgraduate microscopical anatomy............	35	32	1,120
Postgraduate seminar course in heart development	36	40	1,440
	241	536	24,160
Totals.................................	1,759	4,730	250,516

* Courses run both semesters.

ceived by 36,000 other students. Of these 36,000 other students, approximately 18,000 were interns, residents, fellows, graduate students, and postgraduate students, who for practical purposes received all their training or instruction from the medical school faculties, and most of whom were graduates of the same medical schools. The other half were nursing, dental, pharmacy, technical, and miscellaneous graduate and undergraduate college students.

Table 4. TEACHING HOURS PER YEAR DEVOTED TO MEDICAL AND NON-MEDICAL STUDENTS IN SAME TAX-SUPPORTED SCHOOL AS IN TABLE 3

Department	Students	Teaching hours
Nonmedical Students		
Anatomy..............................	867	274,400
Physiology...........................	380	25,100
Pharmacology.........................	270	43,045
Physiological chemistry...............	515	43,968
Bacteriology.........................	1,003	185,092
Pediatrics...........................	298	24,992
Psychiatry and neurology.............	184	12,912
Ophthalmology........................	125	1,000
Radiology and physical medicine......	176	1,620
	3,818	612,129
Medical Students......................	452	500,000
	452	500,000
Total.........................	4,270	1,112,129

Heretofore, in estimating the costs of medical education, the extent to which the medical schools contribute to other educational programs of the parent institutions has apparently been ignored. This is not surprising when, as the Survey discovered, the heads of many medical schools have not analyzed the expenditures of their instructional budgets and do not know how much is expended on the undergraduate medical students and how much on the other students. Perhaps this is why even the parent universities have apparently never looked clearly at the facts.

In 1951, for instance, the Commission on Financing Higher Education issued a statement regarding the cost of the medical school to the university in which it obviously assumed that the instructional budget was expended only on the undergraduate medical student. The state-

Table 5. SIX EXAMPLES OF THE NUMBERS OF STUDENTS OTHER THAN
MEDICAL STUDENTS TAUGHT BY MEDICAL SCHOOL FACULTIES

Privately Supported School

College students..............	40
Nursing students.............	49
Dental students..............	63
Pharmacy students...........	60
Technicians..................	22
Interns......................	62
Assistant residents...........	55
Residents....................	14
Graduate students............	24
Postgraduate students.........	70
Fellows.....................	10
Others......................	66
	535

Privately Supported School

Interns......................	38
Assistant residents...........	42
Residents....................	7
Postgraduates................	474
Fellows.....................	24
College students (undergraduate)	345†
Graduate students (Master's)...	163†
Graduate students (Ph.D.).....	15†
	1,108

Privately Supported School

Public health................	44
Undergraduates..............	5
Graduate students............	83
Interns......................	46
Assistant residents...........	73
Residents....................	24
Fellows.....................	14
Nurses (a part of education)....	225
Postgraduate—19 courses (range 3 to 54 hr. of teaching)......	642
	1,156

*Tax-supported School**

Dental students..............	608
Nursing students.............	1,357
Medical technicians...........	211
Occupational therapists........	74
Dental hygienists.............	87
Embalmers..................	90
Speech pathologists...........	18
Physical ed. students..........	73
Pharmacists..................	238
Veterinary med. students.......	93
Agric. and economics.........	55
College of science, literature, and the arts....................	143
Graduate students............	421
Mortuary science.............	80
College of education..........	19
Interns.....................	10
Assistant residents............	14
Postgraduate.................	90
Fellows.....................	21
Others.....................	60
Physical therapists...........	11
College students.............	7
Residents...................	38
	3,818

Tax-supported School

Nursing students.............	110
Pharmacy students...........	102
Technicians.................	13
Interns.....................	7
Assistant residents...........	27
Residents...................	6
Graduate students............	3
Fellows.....................	10
Special students..............	3
Postgraduate students (4 days)..	203
Cancer refresher (2 days).......	121
Alcoholism (2 days)...........	130
Mental hygiene (2 days).......	500
	1,235

Tax-supported School

College students..............	1,123
Nursing students.............	189
Pharmacy students...........	53
Technicians..................	23
Interns.....................	25
Residents...................	61
Graduate students............	20
Postgraduate students.........	80
Fellows.....................	12
	1,586

Note: These "other students" are not full-time students in the medical schools. Medical student enrollments varied in the six schools between 300 and 500.

* Teaching hours analyzed in Table 4.

† Estimated by the dean.

ment, published under the sponsorship of the Association of American Universities, read as follows:

A sampling of 18 private universities and 18 public universities points up the fact that medical education constitutes the most pressing single financial problem of those institutions of higher learning which have a medical school. In two-thirds of the private universities the medical school required from 20 to 38 per cent of the instructional budget; in each of these instances the *medical students* constituted only from 3 to 14 per cent of the student body [of the university]. In over half of the public universities the medical school budget was from 20 to 30 per cent of the instructional budget, while the medical students made up from 2 to 7 per cent of the total number of students.[14]

This statement is not compatible with the facts collected by the Survey. Nothing is said in it about the great number of other students whose teaching is included in the instructional budget of the medical school. By extension, it could be assumed that the teaching of all the other students was in some way necessary to the education of the medical student—which is, of course, untrue.

It is the conclusion of the Survey that only a few medical schools and universities have studied this problem in detail. Few of them have an accurate conception of the total educational services of the medical school faculty; few have evaluated the material contribution made by the medical school to other educational programs of the parent institution. It appears that both university and medical school officers still consider that the medical student is either the major or the only item of expense in the medical schools' costs of instruction.

It would also be necessary to take into account the large amount of assistance the medical schools receive from the volunteer faculty members. Because these physicians receive no salary, their work is usually ignored in discussions of costs. But they do carry a large portion of the teaching of medical students, the training of interns and residents, and a small portion of the teaching of students in other categories. Few medical schools could operate their present programs without the services of the volunteer faculty.

Although most medical schools receive the tuition fees paid by medical students, they rarely receive a portion of the tuition fees paid to the university by the nonmedical students enrolled in courses at the med-

[14] "Financing Medical Education, a Statement by the Commission on Financing Higher Education," New York, 1951. (Pamphlet.)

ical school. It could be estimated with fairness that the tuition income of the 41 medical schools studied in the Survey could be increased by at least one-third if the proper proportion of their nonmedical tuition fees reverted directly to the medical school. If it is claimed that the medical school receives these fees indirectly in its university appropriation, the administrative and finance officers of the university should clearly understand that the university appropriation includes such fees and is not derived entirely from endowment income.

From the facts already presented, it is obvious that the problem of financing the educational programs of the medical schools cannot be intelligently appreciated unless the amount of time, energy, and expense devoted by the medical schools to students in all the categories is known and evaluated. Without this information it is impossible to compute the cost of educating a medical student with any degree of accuracy.

THE QUALITY OF MEDICAL TEACHING

Of greater importance than the effect of these broad educational programs on the cost of medical education, however, is their effect on the education of the medical student.

The magnitude of the instructional load of the faculty in its teaching of other students is a serious threat to the quality of medical teaching. In the opinion of some faculty members, the quality has already deteriorated. For example, in one state medical school that was studied, animal experiments had been practically eliminated from the medical students' course in biochemistry because the staff had not had time for proper supervision. The professor of biochemistry was responsible for courses for 75 dental students, 48 physical-education students, 90 nursing students, 38 dental-hygiene students, 14 technicians, 30 graduate students, and 38 postgraduate medical students, in addition to the undergraduate medical students enrolled in the school. His staff consisted of six full-time faculty members and five part-time assistants. The professor expressed the wish that his staff could devote more time and thought to teaching, but said that at present this was impossible. Faculty members in other departments made similar statements. They mentioned new laboratory methods and new teaching methods that should be introduced into their courses, but stated that the present work load of the staff made these changes impossible. They were forced to make use of part-time student assistants for much of the instruction given to non-medical students. This is an old medical school with an excellent reputation, and its yearly budget exceeds two million dollars. At the time of the Survey the administration had definite plans for expanding the enrollment of medical students.

The example cited is not unusual. The same situation was encountered in varying degrees in 10 medical schools during the course of the Survey. Tax-supported schools and those located on the campuses of parent universities most frequently revealed this problem. The 16 tax-supported medical schools with a total enrollment of 5,106 medical students gave additional instruction to a total of approximately 23,000 other students. Twenty-two private medical schools in which 6,635 medical students were enrolled gave additional instruction to approximately 13,500 other students.

The location of a medical school with respect to the university raises an old but still serious problem. In the past the theory has been that the medical school greatly benefited both academically and in its research activities by being on the university campus. This theory is still sound: but in practice the load of other university instruction is in several instances becoming a burden to the medical school and impairing the education of the medical student.

CONCLUSIONS

1. Medical schools gained university status within the first half of the century.
2. Medical schools are teaching centers for many categories of students other than medical students.
3. The estimated costs of operating these expanded centers have risen about 700 per cent in a period of 23 years.
4. The expanded educational programs of some universities jeopardize the education of the medical student.
5. The problem of analyzing the costs of the educational programs of medical schools cannot be intelligently approached unless the time, energy, and money expended by the medical schools on students in all categories is known and evaluated.
6. The cost of educating a medical student is only one of many items involved in the expense of maintaining the educational program of

a medical school. There is a misconception that the medical student is the only important item of expense.

7. The majority of medical schools maintain a large percentage of their teaching programs through the use of volunteer faculty members.

RECOMMENDATIONS

1. There is urgent need for each school to evaluate the quality, quantity, and cost of its instruction.
2. Universities, together with their medical schools, would do well to study the time, energy, and money devoted by the medical school to the instruction of all categories of students.
3. When such studies have been carried out, they should be utilized to inform the public concerning what it is asked to support under the term "medical education."

3 RESEARCH

Experimental investigation, or research, is now one of the three major activities of a modern medical school. It is the principal means by which the medical school fulfills its fundamental obligation for the advancement of knowledge, and it requires a substantial portion of the time of the faculty and comparable shares of the funds of the institutions. The best teaching is done where a well-balanced research program is carried on.

In medicine, investigation and good medical practice are fundamentally one in spirit, method, and object. The good practitioner must carefully study his patient, institute proper treatment, and accurately determine its effects. As science advances, new tools constantly become available which improve the effectiveness of each of these steps. Knowledge derived from the study of patients constantly gives rise to new clues, investigation of which proves fruitful. Therefore the practitioners and investigators of the future must be taught to be alert, systematic, thorough, and critically open-minded. Their teachers must be men with clear-cut educational ideals and exacting habits of thought, and must work with curiosity and enthusiasm for learning. Productive research is the most effective intellectual pursuit a teacher can pursue in order to cultivate these characteristics.

The concept of a university has always included an obligation for the advancement of knowledge, and the medical school shares this responsibility. Research, however, has not always been a major activity of the medical schools. For several centuries after the universities were founded, experimental investigation did not exist, and when it was first developed it was not accepted as an appropriate university responsibility.

The experimental philosophy had its earliest development in the sixteenth century in the hands of men working independently of the universities. One of the characteristics of such early investigators was that they could work almost single-handed; a minimum of improvised space and homemade equipment, coupled with a rare combination of knowledge, imagination and perseverance, were sufficient. This experimental investigation was, from the beginning, increasingly effective in advancing knowledge, and the practical benefits were soon apparent. By the middle of the eighteenth century educated men accepted it as a scholarly pursuit, but the number of workers was small and most of them were working outside the universities.

Two factors operated to bring experimental investigation into the universities. First, advances in science and progress in technology made it necessary for investigators to collaborate with each other in the use of more complicated and expensive equipment and to have ready access to the increasing body of scientific knowledge that could effectively be brought together in libraries. These requirements made necessary new and expanded methods of financing research. Then, when experimental investigation had proved to be an important means of advancing knowledge, it became logically necessary for the universities to adopt it, and to establish laboratories and scientific libraries.

By the middle of the nineteenth century experimental investigation had become firmly established in the universities on the continent of Europe and in Great Britain. Professors of chemistry, of physics, and of the natural sciences were actively engaged in research, and the budgets of the universities had been expanded to meet their requirements in equipment, supplies, libraries, and maintenance. In America, however, as long as medical schools adhered to the pattern of ungraded curricula taught by practicing physicians, there was little opportunity for scientific investigation by members of the faculty, and the research carried on was supported by their own personal funds and done in their own time. With the establishment of laboratories of physiology, chemistry, pathology, and bacteriology, the schools appointed faculty members of special competence in these fields. When these professors were placed on a full-time basis—a trend which began at the University of Michigan and was given added impetus with the establishment of the Johns Hopkins Medical School in 1893—their opportunity for investigation was vastly increased.

The Flexner report[1] in 1910 argued eloquently and effectively for medical research carried on by the faculty of the medical school. At that time a few of the stronger schools encouraged and supported substantial amounts of research and selected their faculties accordingly. Stimulated by the Flexner report and the demonstrated effectiveness of this policy in advancing knowledge and in graduating high-quality physicians, many schools made increasing efforts to support research and to appoint to their faculties productive scientists. This policy was prominent after the First World War in the establishment of such new schools as the University of Rochester, Duke University, and the University of Chicago. The wealth of these schools made possible the maintenance of research laboratories and the support of faculty members from the general funds of the medical school.

Thus, in the 40-year period from 1890 to 1930, a new and enlarged method of financing medical research in this country was developed which consisted essentially in its becoming domesticated in the academic scene of the medical schools. The faculty became the scientific investigators, and the budget of the medical school paid for their salaries, equipment, and supplies. The medical schools and universities were in turn supported by large gifts from individuals or from foundations, or by appropriations of tax funds for the same purposes.

In 1932 the Commission on Medical Education[2] called attention to the fact that in some schools "large funds are devoted to research alone"; but eight years later, according to Weiskotten,[3] "relatively little attention was paid to the segregation of expenditures for research," and "departmental budgets in by far the greater number of institutions included the cost of both teaching and research."

Nevertheless, during the 1920's and 1930's certain developments led some of the schools to separate in their budgets the funds for part of their research. In certain of the schools research expanded to such a degree that budgetary separation of some research ventures was necessary for successful administration. The schools found that they could readily

[1] FLEXNER, ABRAHAM, "Medical Education in the United States and Canada, A Report to the Carnegie Foundation for the Advancement of Teaching," New York, 1910.
[2] "Commission on Medical Education, Final Report," New York, Office of the Director of Study, 1932, p. 285.
[3] WEISKOTTEN, H. G., "Medical Education in the United States," prepared for the Council on Medical Education and Hospitals of the American Medical Association, Chicago, American Medical Association, 1940, p. 111.

secure funds from certain outside agencies, such as The Rockefeller Foundation and the Commonwealth Fund, for the support of specific research ventures, and that the accounting for these funds was simplified by separate handling. Often, too, the donor made separate accounting a condition of the gift.

The outbreak of the Second World War led agencies of the Federal government to secure the cooperation of medical schools in seeking answers to wartime medical problems. The fact that these agencies were supported by Federal funds and were responsible for special programs accelerated the trend toward separate budgets for part of the research carried on by medical schools.

By the end of the Second World War the importance of medical research, and the special competence of the medical school faculties in this field, were becoming so broadly and fully appreciated that many forces in society began to come to the aid of the university in the financial support of this increasingly expensive activity. Many private organizations, such as the National Foundation for Infantile Paralysis, the American Heart Association, the American Cancer Society, the Life Insurance Research Fund, the Nutrition Foundation, Inc., and other philanthropic agencies as well as industrial firms in the health field gave money for the support of medical research. The Congress appropriated tax funds through several agencies of the Federal government for the same purpose. Not all the research to whose support they contributed was in the medical schools, but a large portion of it was.

In general, the pattern for making these funds available to the medical schools was that of awarding grants of limited duration for specific projects. This pattern was not new; it had been highly developed in wartime programs. It was adopted by most of these organizations because it had proved to be of merit, and because their funds had been raised for stated purposes and by methods that did not guarantee their annual replacement.

In this way the medical schools, in the postwar years, found that they had some 80-odd separate allies aiding the support of their research work. Without such strong assistance the schools would have been unable to maintain their research programs, since the general rise in prices and the demands of other activities put heavy strains on the financial resources of the universities. By the mid-point of the twentieth century, the pattern of establishing separate budgets for funds restricted to research had thus become widespread and well established. A study of medical schools' grants and finances in 1948 made by the Surgeon General's Committee on Medical School Grants and Finances[4] revealed that in that year all but two of the 70 four-year medical schools and all but three of the 7 two-year medical schools reported the existence of such separate budgets.

It is important to emphasize that, although separate budgets for funds restricted to research are well established and growing, the medical schools also make from their own regular budgets large financial contributions to the support of research. Restricted funds do not cover all research costs. As the Surgeon General's Committee pointed out, "the research program of any medical school incurs indirect costs that are as surely a cost of research as are the direct costs. Indirect costs include such things as a share of the general administrative expenses of running the medical school, and the consumption of goods and services not directly charged to research—such as heat, light, maintenance of grounds and buildings, and use of the library."[5] Such costs will vary, of course, with the nature of the project. Detailed analyses carried out by the U.S. Navy and by the National Foundation for Infantile Paralysis have revealed that indirect costs of some grants amount to 30 to 50 per cent of the salary budget supported by these grants. The U.S. Public Health Service has allowed 8 per cent overhead to the medical school on the total amount of its grants, and clearly recognizes that this amount does not cover all indirect costs.

It is also important to emphasize that the research programs which these funds help to support make important contributions to the educational programs of the medical schools. In a number of medical schools within the past decade, the availability of financial support for research has brought about a marked improvement in the faculty and in the teaching program. The contributions may take several forms: the research program may be an additional inducement which attracts or holds able faculty members; it may permit a member of the research team to take a small but important part in some teaching program; or the contribution may lie in the stimulation that faculty members receive through in-

[4] Federal Security Agency, Public Health Service.

[5] Federal Security Agency, Public Health Service, "Report by the Surgeon General's Committee on Medical School Grants and Finances," Part I, Washington, D.C., U.S. Government Printing Office, 1951, p. 18.

formal contact with members of the research team. Any or all of these contributions are worth while. Occasionally members of the faculty receive some of their salaries from grants, but this practice is not widely followed. Expressing these contributions in quantitative terms is difficult if not impossible.

The essential role of research in graduate programs of the medical school is discussed elsewhere.

EXPENDITURES OF SPECIAL RESEARCH FUNDS

Four considerations led the present survey to take special interest in the funds restricted to research expended by medical schools. First, scientific investigation has become the principal means by which the medical schools add to knowledge. Secondly, the amount of these funds has increased enormously within the last decade. Thirdly, as described by the Surgeon General's Committee on Medical School Grants and Finances, restricted funds usually provide for only the direct costs of research to which they contribute, while many indirect costs are still carried as general or educational expense on the regular budgets of the medical schools. Fourthly, the time and energy of the faculty—most important ingredients in these research programs—are the primary assets of a medical school for all its activities.

Four steps were taken by the Survey in order to study this facet of the medical schools' activities. Financial data on each of the 41 schools included in the Survey were collected for the year in which the school was visited, and then studied in detail; an estimate of the amount of salaried time devoted to research by each member of the faculty during the year in which the school was visited was obtained from the head of each department; opinions regarding each school's research programs and the influence of those programs on the school as a whole were obtained in interviews with the administration, the faculty, and the students. Lastly, an attempt was made to collect data on the income and expense of all 79 medical schools for the fiscal year 1950–51 that were entirely comparable to data used by the Surgeon General's Committee on Medical School Grants and Finances.

The Survey was keenly aware of the limitations of this method of study. However, the limitations were inevitable in a survey in which the main purpose was to study medical education and the schools in which it was carried out. Since the faculty is one of the prime assets of a school, it is essential to know what portion of the faculty's time is devoted to research. The number of dollars expended on research is of little help in measuring the quality of the work or its value to medical education and to society, but the number of dollars does indicate to some degree the magnitude of the research activity and its relations to other medical school activities.

In this report two classifications of expenditures have been used. The first, "general operating expense," includes all expenditures reported by the medical schools except those specifically designated as restricted to research, support of hospitals or clinics, or the construction of new buildings. This inclusive classification is used because the medical schools are committed to these expenditures in the support of their general programs. The funds that make these expenditures possible come in the form of tuition and student fees, endowment income, appropriations of tax funds, general university funds transferred to the medical school, and gifts and grants that are either restricted to teaching or unrestricted.

It proved convenient to use a second classification of expenditures which was developed by the Surgeon General's Committee on Medical School Grants and Finances and used in its report under the heading "research budgeted separately." This Committee, pointing out that such a classification represented only a first approximation and did not permit precise comparison of schools, allowed the Survey access to its material. For the convenience of the business officers of the medical schools, who had had experience in supplying financial information in the "research budgeted separately" classification, the Survey used the same classification but chose to label it "funds restricted to research." This classification includes Federal government grants, Federal government contracts, and other research funds budgeted separately. It represents funds restricted to the support of certain research activities, and most of those funds are supplied by agencies outside the medical schools. However, the classification by no means represents all the medical schools' expenditures in support of research.

Data on general operating expenses and on funds restricted to research for the fiscal years 1940–41, 1947–48, and 1950–51 were available for 59 four-year and 6 two-year medical schools. Figure 1 shows the relations of these two items of expense for each of the three fiscal years as revealed by the total figures for the 59 schools. Funds for general operating expense rose from 24.2 million dollars in 1940–41 to 57.8 million dollars in 1950–51, an increase of nearly 140 per cent. In the same period, funds restricted to research rose from 3.1 million dollars to 27.9 million dollars, an increase of almost 800 per cent. Funds restricted to research in 1940–41 are probably underestimated since a few schools included such funds in their general operating expenditures. It is believed that this error is small.

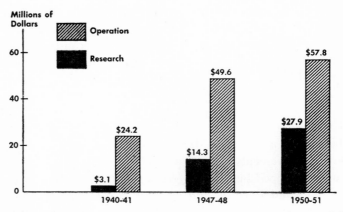

Figure 1. Total general operating expenditures and total expenditures of funds restricted to research of 59 four-year medical schools in fiscal years 1940–41, 1947–48, and 1950–51. Figures for 1940–41 and 1947–48 computed from those of the Surgeon General's Committee on Medical School Grants and Finances.

When the figures for tax-supported and privately supported schools are compared (Figure 2), several interesting facts come to light. It is found that privately supported schools expend larger sums from funds restricted to research than do tax-supported schools. In the 22 tax-supported schools, funds restricted to research in 1940–41 totaled only $849,000. By 1950–51, however, this figure had risen to $8,407,000, increasing nearly 900 per cent in 10 years while the general operating expense increased only about 200 per cent. During the same period, in the 37 privately supported schools the expenditures of funds restricted to research rose from $2,314,000 to $19,474,000, an increase of over 700 per cent, while the general operating expenses increased only about 100 per cent.

To state it differently, in the tax-supported schools funds restricted to research increased nearly tenfold in 10 years while the general operating expense less than tripled. In the privately supported schools, the funds restricted to research increased more than eightfold, while the general operating expense slightly more than doubled.

In the six two-year medical schools, the general operating expense rose from $380,000 in 1940–41 to $1,404,000 in 1950–51; in the same period funds restricted to research rose from $10,000 to $236,000. In 1940–41, only one two-year school had funds restricted to research, but in 1950–51 all six of the schools had such funds.

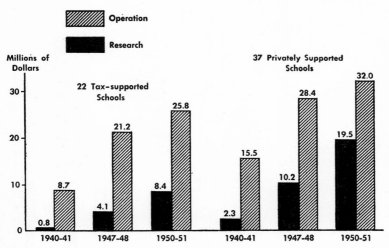

Figure 2. Total general operating expenditures and total expenditures of funds restricted to research of 22 tax-supported and of 37 privately supported schools in fiscal years 1940–41, 1947–48, and 1950–51. Figures for 1940–41 and 1947–48 computed from those of the Surgeon General's Committee on Medical School Grants and Finances.

Thirty-two of the 59 four-year schools were included in the Survey and were studied in more detail. These 32 schools fall into three groups according to the amount of funds restricted to research. Their general operating expenses and funds restricted to research are shown in Figure 3 and Table 6.

In Group I are seven schools which had very small or no funds restricted to research in 1940–41 and individually still less than $125,000 of such funds in 1950–51. All these schools had been hard pressed for funds and had had difficulty in holding small faculties together and in operating educational programs of adequate quality. Only three of these schools had been able to increase their general funds adequately, and this increase had occurred only in the last four years. The majority of the clinical faculty members in this group of schools had had neither the time nor the reputations to attract funds for research.

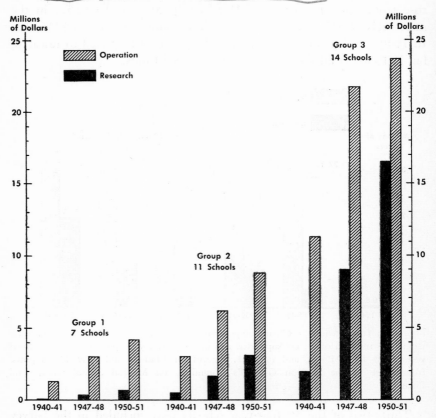

Figure 3. Total basic operating funds and funds restricted to research in three groups of medical schools, 1940–41, 1947–48, and 1950–51. Group I is comprised of schools which in 1940–41 had little or no funds restricted to research and in 1950–51 had less than $125,000 per school. Group II is comprised of schools which in 1940–41 had limited funds restricted to research and by 1950–51 still had less than $500,000 per school. Group III is comprised of 14 schools which together in 1940–41 expended almost 80 per cent and in 1950–51 approximately 82 per cent of the total funds restricted to research for all 32 schools. Figures for 1940–41 and 1947–48 computed from those of the Surgeon General's Committee on Medical School Grants and Finances.

Table 6. FUNDS RESTRICTED TO RESEARCH AND GENERAL OPERATING FUNDS
IN 32 FOUR-YEAR MEDICAL SCHOOLS GROUPED ACCORDING
TO MAGNITUDE OF RESEARCH FUNDS

	1940–41		1947–48		1950–51	
	Funds restricted to research	*General operating funds*	*Funds restricted to research*	*General operating funds*	*Funds restricted to research*	*General operating funds*
Group I (7 schools)	$ 3,495	$ 197,615	$ 22,214	$ 276,640	$ 122,442	$ 342,483
	0	132,403	11,012	247,695	71,713	344,132
	0	102,705	31,005	320,096	65,809	350,747
	17,252	155,633	79,574	354,738	120,669	467,555
	0	91,867	0	341,654	41,918	632,131
	782	313,385	65,444	544,405	107,317	862,402
	17,464	303,143	92,647	914,470	87,945	1,149,585
Total........	$ 38,993	$ 1,296,751	$ 301,896	$ 2,999,698	$ 617,813	$ 4,149,035
Group II (11 schools)	0	182,638	50,765	475,436	420,154	429,867
	4,720	235,328	129,111	503,677	343,454	495,957
	40,439	104,994	24,806	260,718	176,386	541,405
	20,482	193,794	109,175	506,339	148,454	603,093
	4,472	154,681	121,031	367,632	209,084	625,308
	143,280	389,325	199,903	549,587	229,264	681,741
	83,555	445,514	369,601	605,399	273,719	793,516
	54,522	435,826	191,722	670,128	339,108	941,216
	0	216,967	234,852	559,512	330,197	1,118,376
	0	135,837	45,971	337,582	192,642	1,178,738
	101,935	437,870	151,683	1,314,167	381,295	1,377,007
Total........	$ 453,405	$ 2,932,774	$1,628,620	$ 6,150,177	$ 3,043,757	$ 8,786,224
Group III (14 schools)	94,755	467,299	554,072	837,732	717,020	900,179
	4,474	756,111	1,440,944	1,296,790	2,328,240	1,120,526
	118,538	657,344	484,803	1,010,885	1,622,627	1,128,811
	132,392	359,793	573,707	961,935	1,066,427	1,150,927
	197,551	637,062	966,487	1,096,918	1,329,754	1,180,911
	143,953	462,534	443,324	672,828	686,376	1,204,637
	377,411	739,201	915,869	1,445,134	1,578,438	1,369,691
	125,280	768,709	406,025	1,740,663	776,161	1,583,551
	0	383,959	248,559	1,260,291	516,956	1,604,155
	389,419	847,231	616,922	1,430,067	1,118,288	1,709,392
	190,494	968,849	506,014	1,550,619	817,596	2,077,499
	59,072	772,652	292,716	2,205,636	663,465	2,606,641
	0	2,246,187	619,878	3,311,102	2,305,945	2,701,846
	132,672	1,231,108	909,399	3,018,053	1,062,953	3,465,633
Totals.......	$1,966,011	$11,298,039	$8,978,719	$21,838,653	$16,590,246	$23,804,399

In Group II are 11 schools which in 1941 had limited funds restricted to research and by 1950–51 still had less than $500,000 per school even though these funds had increased remarkably. Several of the schools had undergone major reorganization, and funds for general expenses had expanded markedly. New staff appointments had increased the number of full-time faculty members. In general the tax-supported schools were more fortunate in this respect than the privately supported schools, many of which receive little financial support from their universities. The salaries of only a small number of clinical faculty members were carried on the budgets. These men earned their living from the practice of medicine and devoted what time they could to the medical school; there was little opportunity for them to participate in research.

In Group III[6] are 14 schools which accounted for most of the funds restricted to research expended by all 32 schools. Nine of these schools were privately supported, and five were tax-supported. In 1940–41 this group spent almost two million dollars in funds restricted to research, or about 80 per cent of the total of $2,458,000 in this category expended by all 32 schools. By 1950–51, although expenditures by the schools in Group II had also shown a marked increase, the Group III schools spent more than $16\frac{1}{2}$ million dollars, or approximately 82 per cent of the total of $20,252,000. Examples of both privately supported and tax-supported schools in each of the three groups are presented in Figure 4. Their general operating expenses and funds restricted to research are given for the fiscal years 1940–41, 1947–48, and 1950–51. These examples demonstrate the variations encountered in the schools with respect to the growth of and the relations between these two expense items.

Indirect Costs

The importance of the indirect costs to the schools in carrying these funds restricted to research is decidedly different for the three groups of schools. These indirect costs may include that fraction of the faculty members' time that is paid for by the medical school but spent on the research projects, as well as maintenance of buildings and laboratories

[6] Two schools, each expending two million dollars or more per year of funds restricted to research, were not included in Group III because their financial data could not be handled in a manner similar to that of the other schools.

which house the projects, and library, administration, and business office expenses, all of which are essential.

To the schools in Group I, these indirect costs of research cause little concern because the expenditures are small. To the schools in Group II, this question is of somewhat greater importance, but it is probably not yet a pressing problem. In Group III, however, because of the magnitude of the funds restricted to research, the problem of indirect costs becomes vital when general operating income remains relatively stationary or even shrinks. Many of these schools support some of the research

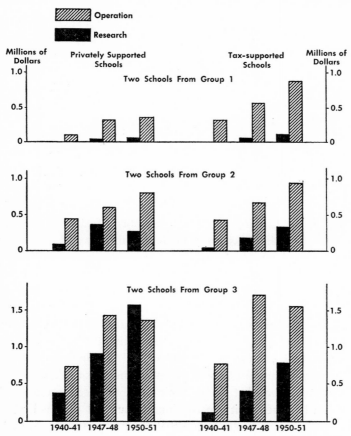

Figure 4. Six examples of the growth, over a 10-year period, of basic operating expense and funds restricted to research, taken from the three groups of schools in Figure 3. Figures for 1940–41 and 1947–48 computed from those of the Surgeon General's Committee on Medical School Grants and Finances.

of their faculty members through their departmental budgets as well as meeting the indirect costs of the research projects. The heads of the departments of the 14 schools in this group estimated that approximately $3,500,000 of their collective salary budgets derived from general operating funds was devoted to research. If the fact determined by several studies is accepted, that research funds may cover less than half of the indirect costs, it is seen that the remainder must come from general operating expenses.

It is clear that in half of the schools in Group III, if indirect costs were considered, the sum of all monies (including funds restricted to research, those portions of departmental budgets expended on faculty salaries for research, and all other indirect costs) expended on research already surpasses their expenditures on other activities. In 1951 the combined general operating budgets of Group III schools totaled 211 per cent of the 1940–41 figure. During the same period, however, the cost-of-living index as compiled by the U.S. Bureau of Labor Statistics rose to 186 per cent of the figure for the 1935–39 period.[7] The goods and services purchased by the schools must have increased correspondingly. Therefore it may be assumed that the remaining 25 per cent of the increase in funds has been available to finance (1) the indirect costs of rapidly expanding research programs, (2) the instruction of a 12 per cent larger medical-student body, and (3) all the other expanded activities such as the training of a large number of students in ancillary health fields, consultative services to the community and the nation, and postgraduate medical education. The conclusion drawn is that in these schools all activities except research are less well financed in terms of dollar purchasing value than they were in 1941. Although research does strengthen many of the other activities of a medical school, the question arises whether these schools can afford, without weakening their other activities, the amount of research that they are now handling.

In one of these schools endowment capital is being used to meet operating expenses, and in another, general university funds are being used to such an extent that the governing board is deeply concerned with the question of whether it can continue to support the medical school. Two deans from this group stated that their schools had refused large research funds because they could not afford to accept the grants.

[7] The cost-of-living index of 186 per cent in 1950 represents an 86 per cent increase over 1939.

Granting agencies, recognizing that every research grant adds to overhead costs, have attempted to meet these costs in part in various ways. The Office of Naval Research has accepted charges for all indirect costs; the U.S. Public Health Service has set an arbitrary figure of 8 per cent of the total grant; the American Cancer Society has accepted charges of 5 per cent of the grant; and the Veterans Administration has set its figure at 10 per cent. The Atomic Energy Commission has paid all salaries but has allowed nothing for other indirect costs. The National Foundation for Infantile Paralysis has worked out a formula which attempts to meet all indirect costs involved in its grants. Only one of these methods of financing research grants meets the total estimated costs.

H. M. Weaver,[8] director of research for the National Foundation for Infantile Paralysis, has pointed out that many of our schools of medicine are today more nearly institutions for the conduct of research than they are schools for the education of the medical student, largely because acceptance of grants-in-aid for research necessitates expenditures, on indirect costs, of the schools' funds for their other activities. In an effort to determine a formula that would facilitate payment by granting agencies of additional sums to the grantees to defray 90 per cent of the indirect costs of conducting the programs, he has analyzed 91 heterogeneous research programs in 33 institutions. As a result of this study he has suggested that a sum equal to 46.0 per cent of the total grant be added when the grant is $10,000 or less and that when the grant is over this amount the percentage be diminished.[9] He has proposed also that some national organization extend his study to several hundred grants and develop a sliding scale for determining accurately the amount of the indirect costs for grants-in-aid of all sizes.

More accurate studies of indirect costs are essential, but in addition a different philosophy must be developed in the policies of granting agencies. Methods of financing research must be found which will strengthen the general budget of the medical school. The alternative is for the schools to curtail their research activities in order to permit adequate support of their educational and service activities.

[8] WEAVER, H. M., A Proposal for Defraying the Cost of Conducting Programs of Research, *Journal of Medical Education,* Vol. 27, p. 316 (September), 1952.

[9] Forty-six per cent of the first $10,000 and 38.0 per cent of all remaining, when the grant is between $10,001 and $30,000; and 46.0 per cent of the first $10,000, 38.0 per cent of the next $20,000, and 6.0 per cent of all remaining, when the grant is over $30,000.

HAZARDS IN PROJECT RESEARCH GRANTS

The Factor of Freedom

The effect on both the university and the medical school of the support of research through project grants extends far beyond the question of finances. Such methods of support inevitably lead to direction of research by agencies outside the medical school and result in regimentation of the faculty and loss of freedom to follow their bent and their own clues to new knowledge. In carrying out project research, the investigator's freedom to pursue paths is inhibited. He is investigating "to order," as it were. The compulsion and lack of freedom increase when he is compelled to report the results of his research to the grantor at regular intervals. Rheumatism and arthritis are cases in point. Although national organizations have existed for the support of research in these two diseases for several years, it was not through their efforts that ACTH and cortisone were developed. Instead, it was through the freedom of men of curiosity and perseverance to explore the adrenal and pituitary glands because of their intrinsic interest that this most effective means of treating rheumatism yet known was produced. The same is true of the discovery of penicillin and of many other advances in medicine. The men who created the knowledge had no reason to know what diseases their research would benefit. Having created the knowledge, they went on to further exploration, and it is not unfair to anticipate that such freely pursued research will create still further knowledge of tremendous importance. Meantime, project research will continue to attack primarily the problems of current interest to the public.

The principle must not be forgotten that all knowledge is potentially valuable, and that it is impossible to step away at any point in its creation and assign to it absolute values on a monetary basis or in terms of human welfare. This, in essence, is what is required by the granting agencies who make periodic progress reports a provision of the grant. Evaluation of a research project by the investigator is a constant process, but the injection of a third party into the evaluation process implies an obligation to the grantee to defend the value of his work to the grantor, and this again has a stifling effect on the potentials of the investigator and his work.

The advantages of freedom have been well stated by Mees and Leer-makers[10] in a discussion of industrial scientific research:

> The preeminence of the universities in scientific work will continue as long as the research work in university departments continues free from any external direction or organization. Compared with other agencies for the prosecution of scientific research—research institutes, technological institutes, industrial laboratories—universities are at a disadvantage. The investigators are often burdened with administration and with teaching; they are, on the whole, poorly paid; and it is difficult for them to obtain funds for equipment. Clearly, they should not have been able to advance knowledge as rapidly or as widely as the professional research workers of the industrial laboratories or the research institutes. But they are *free*—they can explore unpromising paths and make experiments that any administrator would regard as useless, and sometimes those experiments succeed and those paths lead to new fields of knowledge.
>
> The danger is that this great advantage of the universities may be lost. During the Second World War, the universities abandoned their unordered system of inquiry and organized their research work along the lines dictated by the requirements of the armed forces. There is a real danger that this direction of the work of the universities may continue in times of peace as part of a national directing and organizing system. If this change occurs, the disadvantages will remain and the overwhelming advantage of freedom will disappear.

Isolation from Teaching

There is a second hazard to carefully planned research projects with large sums for their support. There is a tendency to isolate the project or develop a research institute. This pattern is rapidly developing. Many schools have large research projects, housed in separate buildings, for the investigation of such subjects as cardiovascular disease, cancer, infantile paralysis, diseases of metabolism, or diseases of the blood. There is a definite tendency for workers in these institutes to become divorced from teaching. One dean interviewed during the Survey stated that when a faculty member became engaged in an expanding research project it became necessary to employ new faculty members to take over his teaching and other responsibilities in the medical school. In numerous schools, students repeatedly said they wished they could be told about the work being carried on by the medical school in these institutes. This is a serious defect in a total research program of a school. If students' interest

[10] MEES, C. E. K., and LEERMAKERS, J. A., "The Organization of Industrial Scientific Research," New York, McGraw-Hill Book Company, Inc., 1950, p. 14.

in, and curiosity about, the unknown are not stimulated, the school is failing to meet one of its most important objectives. Research is sharpened and the research worker is himself stimulated by close contact with students and by their questions and criticisms.

Much has been said about the great benefits of research to teaching but little about the drive and energy brought to research in an educational institution by the constant inflow of young men with active minds. Very few institutes can compete with this advantage of an educational institution. The policy of most institutes is to select men with already proved ability. It is a well-known fact that, for many men in research, their early years are the most productive and by the time their ability has become recognized their productivity is declining. A school has the advantage of always putting young men to the test and observing their development. Any method of supporting research in educational institutions which does not promote such an environment is misguided and should be avoided by the schools or discarded if it is the practice.

Relation to Over-all Program

There is one further danger of project research to the medical schools. Granting agencies do not always have sufficient knowledge about an individual medical school to determine its strengths and weaknesses. In one school a large grant had been made for cancer teaching and research, and since the funds were sufficient, a department of oncology was established. In this school the basic budget did not allow the maintenance of any full-time men in the departments of surgery, pediatrics, and psychiatry. Through the research grant from an outside donor, however, the school was able to employ two full-time men to teach and explore in a relatively highly specialized field that was not related to the primary needs of the school's program. In another instance a medical school had inadequate facilities and the student classrooms were housed in temporary wartime buildings. Grants to this school ranging from $25,000 to more than $100,000 supported institutes at some distance from the medical school. These institutes were supplied with the finest of equipment and adequate technical staff while the departments of the medical school had difficulty in maintaining adequate space and equipment for the teaching of the student.

Although such projects may strengthen certain small areas in a medical school, they certainly add little to its over-all strength or balance. They are of little direct value to the medical student's education, and they do not promote the research freedom essential for the faculty of an educational institution. This danger was of greatest significance in those schools with small operating budgets and relatively small amounts of research money. However, it was not limited to schools in this group. One of the largest and wealthiest schools carrying well over a million dollars of research grants was having extreme difficulty in financing a medical basic science department and had had to dip into capital funds in order to reorganize another.

In all 41 schools visited by the Survey these various dangers were real and present. There was ample evidence that research workers were being isolated from teaching, that their work was being unconsciously directed by granting agencies, and that the quality of teaching was beginning to suffer in some instances. The degree to which these factors were apparent in different schools varied widely. The greatest dangers appeared to be in those schools with the largest research funds. This fact is disturbing because from these schools have come the vast majority of significant contributions to medical knowledge in this country, as well as most of the training of young men for teaching and research. Success of these schools has encouraged others to foster research and has given rise to growing public confidence in research in medicine. The general trend is for more and more medical schools to follow the leadership established by these great institutions. It is therefore felt that their problems are of the greatest significance for the future. Their need is for institutional—not project—support.

CONCLUSIONS

1. Research is an essential activity of any medical school. It is the means whereby the schools seek to discharge their obligation for the advancement of knowledge, and within the first half of the century it has become one of their three major activities.
2. The medical schools make a unique contribution to research by constantly introducing young men to the field in an environment where scholars and students with curiosity mix freely.

3. Eighty or more Federal and private agencies are aiding in the support of medical school research programs which enrich medical education.

4. Privately supported medical schools expend far larger sums restricted to research than do tax-supported schools.

5. Research grants tend to gravitate to those schools in which the general operating funds are sufficient to support full-time or part-time paid faculty members with demonstrated ability in research.

6. In 59 four-year medical schools, funds restricted to the support of research (exclusive of building construction) in 1950–51 had increased to almost nine times the 1940–41 figure, while funds for general expense had increased to almost two and one-half times the 1940–41 figure.

7. Unfortunately, present methods of financing research in medical schools have not been evaluated from the standpoint of the objectives of the school or the effects on the other activities. At present they exert undue influence upon the research and educational program of the school and threaten the financial support of its other activities.

8. Safeguards have not been set up to protect the freedom that is necessary in the creation of new knowledge.

9. Methods of determining indirect costs of research are not well established. Figures reported were extremely variable, ranging from 15 to more than 50 per cent of research grants.

10. The indirect costs of large research grants, which, to a considerable extent, under present methods, are borne by the medical schools from general funds, may be a serious threat to the financial stability of the school. This is especially true of privately supported medical schools.

11. The medical schools surveyed fell into three groups according to the amount of their funds restricted to research. In the first group, the schools had a great need for research funds. In the second group, there was apparently some balance between the research funds and the general funds for the maintenance of the schools, although the indirect costs of research were beginning to be an important problem. In the third and largest group, the research activity had developed to such a degree that supporting it threatened the other activities of the schools.

RECOMMENDATIONS

1. Every medical school, after clearly weighing its objectives, should decide what research it should undertake in terms of educational ideals, in order to strengthen its educational and research programs.
2. Research activities should not be expanded to the point where supporting them jeopardizes the support of the other activities that are essential to the school's objectives.
3. Those schools in which the research activity is relatively undeveloped should attempt to develop it; but they should do so wisely by first strengthening their basic operating budgets.
4. Medical schools, realizing the potential hazards to their freedom that lie in project research grants (in which a third party helps to initiate and evaluate the work), should make their position clear to granting agencies and should elect to undertake only those forms of research which will best help in attaining the objectives of the institution.
5. Agencies making research grants should use them, whenever possible, to strengthen the basic programs of the schools—a policy which will in the long run be of the greatest value to the agencies' objectives.
6. The medical schools must adopt a clear-cut policy defining the exact composition of indirect costs of research.
7. The indirect costs of every research project that is contemplated should be clearly set forth for the information of the granting agency concerned, and when the agency does not meet them in their entirety, the medical school should carefully consider whether it can afford them without jeopardizing other activities.

4 SERVICE

Service, in the sense in which the word is used to describe the third major activity of a modern medical school, is comprised of the care of the sick and the provision of other health services for the community. Medical schools in the United States have not always served in this capacity. During the Revolutionary period, a few medical schools gave some clinical instruction in hospitals with which they had agreements, but during the early part of the nineteenth century many schools had no hospital affiliations and their teaching was entirely didactic. Such clinical instruction as the students received they obtained from preceptors, who usually were not members of a medical school faculty. In such a setting, the medical school provided little or no direct medical care for patients.

A change in this pattern came about with the growth and the development of hospitals. The Pennsylvania Hospital, established in 1751 in Philadelphia, was the first institution of its kind in the colonies. Intended primarily for the care of transient and indigent sick persons, the hospital gave opportunity for professor-preceptors to walk the wards with their pupils and house physicians. Similar institutions were opened in New York, Boston, and elsewhere after the Revolutionary War, and at them, as well as at the Pennsylvania Hospital, indigent patients in particular were demonstrated to the students.

As medical school enrollments increased, hospital trustees resisted the influx of students onto the wards and questioned its advantages to the patient. The better medical educators campaigned relentlessly to convince them that properly supervised clinical instruction not only did not endanger their charity patients, but often improved the care provided for them, with the result that by the end of the nineteenth century many municipal and private hospitals permitted teaching on their ward patients.

The acceptance of the student by the hospitals raised a serious problem of hospital staff and medical school faculty relationships. The hospitals, being separate institutions, appointed their own staff members; the medical schools, in order to ensure that the students were freely accepted on the wards, found it necessary to appoint the staff members to faculty positions. Thus came about the situation described by Flexner[1] in 1910: "Clinical faculties are organized on a personal rather than on a scientific or educational basis. . . . It just happens that some competent teachers find themselves in prominent hospital positions; but the system is not designed to pick them out."

Two solutions to the problem were adopted. In one solution, some of the universities and medical schools, to whose officers the educational advantage of closely relating the classroom, laboratory, and hospital were apparent, constructed their own university hospitals with funds derived either from private sources or from tax monies. In the second solution, many hospitals, having become aware of the improvement in the quality of patient care resulting from medical school affiliation, permitted the medical schools to appoint their medical staffs. By these new arrangements, not only did the medical schools assume responsibility for providing professional care of indigent patients, but they also provided hospital care for these patients in their own hospitals. Thus the medical schools became more firmly entrenched in the field of medical service.

At the same time, this development added greatly to the costs of maintaining those schools which owned hospitals, and posed complex problems for the administrative heads of the universities and the medical schools. The dean of one medical school concerned with medical school–hospital relations said in the late 1920's that he had attempted to so intermix the budgets of the medical school and hospital that the university would never be able to separate them.

THE MEDICAL CENTER

A further development of the medical schools' service activity came about with the establishment of medical centers in the third decade of

---

[1] FLEXNER, ABRAHAM, "Medical Education in the United States and Canada, A Report to the Carnegie Foundation for the Advancement of Teaching," New York, p. 276.

the century. Because of the phenomenal success of the methods used by the medical school in the study and treatment of the sick, the hospitals utilized in teaching quickly became identified with a high quality of medical care. Recognizing the fact that through the research carried on in the medical school the teaching hospitals were able to render services not offered by the average hospital, large privately endowed hospitals joined with medical schools to construct common facilities. In New York, the Presbyterian Hospital joined with Columbia University and the New York Hospital joined with Cornell University; in St. Louis, the Barnes Hospital joined with Washington University; in Cleveland, the Lakeside Hospital joined with Western Reserve University; and in other cities, privately endowed hospitals joined with medical schools. This not only improved hospital care but tremendously strengthened the medical schools and gave them an opportunity and facilities such as they had never had before. State schools, such as the University of Michigan and the University of Wisconsin, followed a similar pattern when large tax-supported hospitals were constructed as units of the medical schools. Separate hospitals were developed for such specialties as orthopedics, ophthalmology, neurology, and psychiatry, and as they attracted funds for new facilities and for clinical research, the medical centers steadily gained in strength.

Some hospitals in the medical centers assumed the responsibility for financing ward or charity beds for the teaching of medical students. Frequently they provided classrooms and laboratories for the students, as well as research laboratories for the clinical faculty members, who were also the medical staff of the hospital. The financial arrangements between medical school and hospital became so complex that it appeared impossible to separate the costs.

Those universities owning hospitals frequently charged the cost of certain hospital operations to the medical school budget. If the hospital ran a deficit, this was met by the university's appropriation to the medical school. The same was true in tax-supported medical schools with university-owned hospitals. The opinion was generally held by medical school and hospital administrators that the hospital costs could not be sharply separated from those of the medical schools, although in some instances attempts were made to keep in a separate budget the expenses that obviously belonged to the hospital.

During the Second World War, however, hospital accounting practices underwent a change of considerable significance to the medical schools. The principle of requiring third parties to pay the cost of hospital care had long been accepted in certain regions; but it was not accepted generally by hospitals until, in 1943, the Emergency Maternal and Infant Care Program was established by the Federal government authorized by the Social Security Act. Under this program, money was available to state health agencies for the provision of medical and hospital care for the wives and infants of enlisted men in the armed forces. Hospital service was on a contract basis between the state agency and the participating hospital, and payment was made to the hospital on the basis of per diem costs. These costs included charges for all services except professional fees. The hospitals were forced to submit actual operating costs to state health agencies, and in order to submit comparable figures it was essential to adopt a common formula for deriving them. The formula adopted has become known as the "government reimbursable cost formula." The new accounting practices made necessary by the EMIC programs and other factors led university-owned and affiliated teaching hospitals to attempt to separate hospital from medical school costs.

Thus, by the fourth decade of the twentieth century, two significant changes were taking place in medical school budgets. The costs of hospital maintenance were being distinguished from the costs of the medical school, and as described in the previous chapter, the same phenomenon occurred in the field of research when research grant funds appeared as distinct items in the budgets.

Following the Second World War, hospital costs became a major problem to the university and affiliated teaching hospitals. Those hospitals relying upon endowment income and gifts for the financing of care for indigent patients found it impossible to meet the rising costs caused by inflation. Many found themselves with operating deficits of one-quarter to one-half million dollars. Endowed hospitals were forced to use capital funds, and some university-owned hospitals became a drain on university funds. The problem is typified by the following example.

Thirty-five years ago, one university made an agreement with a privately owned hospital to help underwrite a portion of the costs of the hospital which the school utilized as its major teaching unit. By 1947, the university was contributing more than $300,000 per year to this institution, and the total medical school deficit reached almost one-half million dollars. In 1915 the hospital had contracted with the city in which it is located to provide hospital care for patients suffering from contagious diseases. Four dollars per day was allowed the hospital for the care of each of these patients. By 1948 the hospital cost for such patients was more than four times this amount. At the time the hospital and medical school were visited by the Survey, both institutions were attempting to arrive at a new contract with the city for increasing the allotment to $8 or $12 per day. The medical school was also studying its agreement with the hospital, and new arrangements were being worked out which would reduce the amount the medical school contributed to the hospital. In many instances such situations caused friction between hospital and medical school. In the example cited, the medical school felt that the hospital and the city should assume larger financial responsibilities; on the other hand, those hospitals which maintained ward teaching beds urged the medical schools to make larger contributions to the hospital. In considering this common problem, many medical schools and hospitals are looking to their communities for aid in meeting the costs of hospital care for indigent patients.

SERVICE AND THE EDUCATIONAL OBJECTIVE

While medical schools and their teaching hospitals were encountering these serious financial difficulties, the public demand for their services was increasing. Medical centers had proved their value in terms of improved medical service. The concept of a medical center rendering many types of medical service had been promoted by several medical schools. Tax-supported schools had generally rendered some direct medical services to their communities or to their states, but they were constantly being asked to expand this service as the public grew to expect direct and supervised medical care from the medical school.

The new philosophy is illustrated in a report published by the regents of one state university which included the following statement: "University personnel and activities constitute many resources that are of potential importance to our community welfare. Consequently, the medical school has extended its interests beyond the limits of its classrooms to the end that its many resources may be made of maximum use to the people of our state." This medical school supervised or had affiliations with 14 hospitals whose primary function was patient care.

One private medical school specifically stated that one of its major objectives was a community medical-care program.

The philosophy, propounded by national organizations and leaders in the health professions, soon reached the level of the Federal government. In 1948, a report to the President by the Federal Security Administrator stressed the point that financially the medical schools were unable to meet the need of the nation for physicians, and at the same time promulgated the need for large medical centers, with a medical school becoming the hub of each center. The President was advised that the nation's total health resources could best be utilized by a program of Federal-state-community action to develop a system of hospitals and health centers closely integrated with a medical school and medical center in their respective regions, to provide smaller nearby hospitals with various services and professional personnel for patients who required special care.

The Veterans Administration, in reorganizing its medical-care program following the Second World War, established the policy of affiliating its hospitals with medical schools for the purpose of improving the quality of medical care. It constructed many of its hospitals in close physical relationship to a medical school. Affiliations were established with the medical school through a "dean's committee" appointed by the dean of the medical school. The committee has the responsibility for selecting all professional medical personnel for the Veterans Hospital. In addition, it organizes and supervises a residency training program and selects the residents. The dean of the medical school usually acts as an administrative officer for these programs. The school receives no compensation for these services, but the faculty members who serve as consultants or attending physicians are paid as individuals. The medical school may, if it wishes, make use of the Veterans Hospital for the instruction of medical students. In such affiliations, the medical schools are rendering an important service to a national medical-care program.

The concept of expanding the influence and responsibility of medical schools for patient care was discussed in 1951 in the publication entitled "Financial Status and Needs of Medical Schools," which was a preliminary report by the Surgeon General's Committee on Medical School Grants and Finances. It stated:

The entire problem of extending the influence of medical schools is becoming of increasing importance. Active regional programs in New England,

New York, Michigan, Virginia, and other areas demonstrate the weight attached to these plans by many medical educators and medical administrators. The rapid growth of hospital facilities under provisions of the Hospital Survey and Construction Act will increase the demand for leadership and direction from medical schools.

. . . About 30 deans reported to us that a shortage of general funds is the major barrier to the development of these activities. . . . It is clear that an expanding concept of the function of medical schools as part of the community is evolving out of the initiative and experience of the schools themselves. These experiments have proved to be productive, and we foresee a growth of this movement.[2]

Obviously these statements represent a radical change in the fundamental concept of the function of a medical school. The medical schools, organized originally as educational institutions, are developing into medical-service centers with constantly expanding responsibilities in the health field. Not only does the public expect these institutions to set standards of medical care, but in addition it expects them to provide and supervise the hospital care for large population areas as well as for national medical-service programs.

The faculty of a medical school may function in many other service areas, and it usually does. In addition to rendering free professional service to patients, individual members render consultative services to Federal, state, city, and community health and welfare agencies. They also may serve on editorial boards of lay health publications and professional and research journals.

The Survey decided to limit its study of services mainly to free professional medical service rendered to patients. Information concerning other services was, however, recorded when it was available. A method was devised for estimating the quantity of free professional service provided by each medical school included in the Survey. Professional medical service was defined, for the purpose of the Survey, as the service rendered to patients by the faculty for which no fee was collected by the faculty member or by the medical school. The information was obtained either from the dean of the medical school or from the administrator of the teaching hospital. The following examples show the categories and the magnitude of these professional medical services.

[2] Federal Security Agency, Public Health Service, "Report by the Surgeon General's Committee on Medical School Grants and Finances," Part I, Washington, D.C., U.S. Government Printing Office, 1951, p. 37.

One privately supported medical school owned and operated its own university hospital and an outpatient clinic. In addition, it had close teaching affiliations with two hospitals in which it supervised the medical care of charity patients. In 1949 the patient load for which the school was responsible totaled 12,859 outpatient admissions, 26,554 return outpatient visits, and 4,949 new hospital admissions with 67,435 hospital patient days. No charge was made for the professional service given to any of these patients. For providing this service, the school depended almost entirely on volunteer members of the clinical faculty and residents in training.

A second privately supported medical school utilized three city hospitals and three privately owned hospitals for teaching. This school reported 18,418 new outpatient admissions, 226,204 return outpatient visits, and 38,919 new hospital admissions with 747,193 days of hospital care. The school had a fairly large nucleus of paid clinical faculty members, but for the professional care of patients it relied chiefly on volunteer faculty members and residents in training.

A third institution, tax-supported, reported 6,179 new patients in the outpatient department, 53,612 return outpatient visits, and 12,573 new hospital admissions with 197,875 hospital patient days. The faculty of this school was predominately on a full-time or geographic full-time basis, and little of the professional care was given by volunteer faculty members.

The magnitude of the free professional service given by the clinical faculties of 35 medical schools has been estimated on the basis of information supplied by each school. It amounted to 591,430 new outpatients, 527,147 new hospital admissions, 3,652,113 return visits to the outpatient department, and 6,493,695 hospital days of service. These are minimal figures, since 11 of the schools were unable to supply complete statistics.

In order to put an approximate dollar value on these services and permit a view of the contribution in relation to the financial picture, the Survey has applied to these figures the scale of professional fees utilized by the Veterans Administration for the payment of private physicians in its home-care program. The professional fees allowed are $7 for the examination of a new patient, $4 for each visit of the physician to a hospital patient, and $3 for an office visit, which corresponds to an outpatient visit. On the basis of this scale of fees, the value of the professional service rendered to indigent patients by the faculties of these 35 medical schools is approximately 45 million dollars. It is estimated that the 72 four-year medical schools contribute annually approximately 100 million dollars worth of professional service. The value of this service, which is rendered as a by-product of medical education, approaches the total of 106 million dollars expended on all activities other than hospitals by the medical schools of the United States. This is highly significant when it is viewed in relation to the high costs of maintaining medical schools. Today the medical schools and their paid and volunteer faculty members receive little or no direct income from this service.

The other services provided by the medical schools such as consultations at the Federal, state, city, and community levels, and service on editorial boards of publications, should not be overlooked. The Survey staff was not able to obtain a dollar formula which could be applied to them, but it is self-evident that they are extremely valuable to the public. At the same time they are time-consuming for the faculty. Many faculty members who were interviewed estimated that one-tenth to one-fifth of their time was expended in serving on advisory committees and in giving consultative services. The dean of one medical school had kept a record of the time devoted by his faculty as consultants to Federal agencies. On the basis of the salaries paid to these men, it had cost the medical school $60,000 in one year to make these consultations possible.

The effect of such activities on the student and his education is of prime importance. The fact that these service functions require so much of the time and energy of the faculty causes their magnitude to become an important problem to the medical school and the university. If service expands, the faculty must expand accordingly; otherwise the time and energy devoted by the faculty to educational activities diminishes. Service is not synonymous with education, and the primary objectives of service institutions and universities are not the same. Medical schools educate and train men for service in the future, and service institutions must perform their primary function as direct service in the immediate present.

The magnitude of free professional service is remarkable. It would be impossible to provide it were it not for the large number of physicians who serve voluntarily as faculty members. These physicians, as members of the staffs of the teaching hospitals, render service in return for the benefits of being associated with an educational institution. No other profession or group of educational schools matches this achievement. Medical schools as they exist in the middle of the twentieth century represent one of the greater philanthropic groups of institutions in the United States.

CONCLUSIONS

1. The medical schools of the United States first provided extensive free professional medical care of patients with the introduction of bedside teaching in the nineteenth century.
2. With the establishment of teaching hospitals owned by or affiliated with the university, part of the costs of these hospitals was assumed by medical schools.
3. At the mid-point of the twentieth century, service costs are being separated from the costs of maintaining medical schools. However, the separation is incomplete. Some medical schools are spending from their general funds for the maintenance of hospital and outpatient facilities for charity patients, and conversely some hospitals are supporting educational activities.
4. The second and third decades of the twentieth century marked the establishment of medical centers in which medical schools expanded their service functions and increased opportunities for clinical training. At the middle of the century these centers are being asked to extend their services to large community areas and to supervise and assume responsibilities for national medical-care programs.
5. The over-all magnitude, worth, and costs of the service activities of the medical schools have not been properly evaluated. The value of free professional service alone is estimated to equal 100 million dollars per year. This figure approaches the total sum expended by the medical schools on all their activities. It would be impossible for the medical schools to render this service were it not for the large number of physicians who serve on faculties without pay.
6. The extent and complexity of a medical school's service activities make it unusual and not strictly comparable with other schools in a university.
7. The already enormous and rapid growth of the service activities of the medical schools is a drain on the time and energy of the faculties and on the finances of many schools. The extension of service activ-

ities beyond those needed to support a medical school's educational program already threatens the education of the medical student.

RECOMMENDATIONS

1. The value of all services provided by a medical school should be studied, and their costs to the school should be determined.
2. The public should be informed concerning the cost and the value of the service rendered by medical schools. The communities in which medical schools are located cannot be expected to support these services intelligently unless their cost and their value are clearly understood.
3. The medical schools should thoughtfully consider their role in the field of medical service. Medical service is not synonymous with medical education.

Part III

THE FINANCES OF THE MEDICAL SCHOOL

5 THE COST OF EDUCATING A
MEDICAL STUDENT

The major activities described in previous chapters indicate that the medical schools have become educational centers for physicians and for ancillary health personnel and have assumed increasing responsibilities for research and medical service. The cost factors in medical education and in maintaining medical schools can be considered against this background.

The Commission on Medical Education in its report[1] in 1932 recognized to some extent the complicated fiscal problems of the medical schools. Weiskotten[2] in 1936 gave the average cost of educating a medical student as $1,052 per year but noted that medical school funds were frequently utilized for the support of other broad problems of social endeavor. Since the Second World War the high costs of medical education have been repeatedly emphasized and have attracted the attention of national educational organizations, governmental agencies, and legislators as well as the public. The Council on Medical Education and Hospitals[3] in 1949 reported that the expenditures per student by the medical schools ranged from $917 to $9,500 per year. In 1951, a committee appointed by the Surgeon General of the U.S. Public Health

[1] "Commission on Medical Education, Final Report," New York, Office of Director of Study, 1932.
[2] WEISKOTTEN, H. G., "Medical Education in the United States and Canada," Chicago, American Medical Association, 1940, p. 113.
[3] ANDERSON, D. G., and ANNE TIPNER, Medical Education in the United States and Canada, *Journal of the American Medical Association,* Vol. 141, p. 43 (Sept. 3), 1949.

Service estimated the range to be from $754 to $8,257 per student.[4] The National Fund for Medical Education, Inc., gave the four-year cost of training a typical student at a larger medical school as $13,356[5] or an average cost per year of $3,339. On the basis of such figures it has become generally accepted that medical education is the most expensive form of professional education.

From these estimates of the average cost of educating a medical student, it has been assumed that the high cost of educating a medical student was primarily responsible for the expanding budgets of the medical schools. The organizations making the studies utilized the conventional method of subtracting from the total budget of the medical school the cost of hospital maintenance, certain noneducational expenses, and research grants, and dividing the remainder by the number of medical students. This method, although it may have been adequate in the past, cannot be applied to the modern medical school with its extensive activities. It takes for granted that the same situation prevails in the mid-twentieth century as existed when the schools were engaged only in the instruction of the medical student and provided little or no instruction for other students.

A VIEW OF COSTS IN RELATION TO ACTIVITIES

In the modern medical school, in order to understand costs it is necessary to view the budget in relation to the activities of the school rather than to the number of medical students. To obtain a realistic picture, the Survey compiled activity tables for each of the 41 medical schools. On each table was shown the total budget of the school for the year in which it was surveyed. Hospital expenses were subtracted from the total budget, and the remaining figure represented the sum available for support of the three major activities as well as the minor activities, which vary from school to school. The educational activities were listed in terms of the number of medical students and other students receiving instruction from the school. Research activities were

[4] Federal Security Agency, Public Health Service, "Report of the Surgeon General's Committee on Medical School Grants and Finances," Part II, Financial Status and Needs of Medical Schools, Washington, D.C., U.S. Government Printing Office, 1951, p. 29.

[5] "Medical Education in the United States," New York, National Fund for Medical Education, Inc., 1950, p. 14.

listed in terms of research grants and the amount of faculty salaries which, according to the department heads' estimates, was expended on research. The service activities were listed in terms of the amount of free professional care given to inpatients and outpatients. Four schools are illustrated in Tables 7 to 10.

Table 7. ACTIVITIES AND FUNDS FOR THEIR MAINTENANCE AT A PRIVATELY SUPPORTED MEDICAL SCHOOL WITH A RELATIVELY SMALL BUDGET

Budget

Total budget...........................	$991,365
Hospital expense........................	75,065
Balance for mai ntenance of activities..............	$916,300

Activities

Education	*Research*	*Service**
Medical students.................. 191	Research grants....... $211,167	Value of free professional
Other students, who received part or all of	Estimated faculty salary	service rendered by medi-
their instruction from the medical	for research......... 90,000†	cal school faculty
school faculty		New hospital admissions
Interns and residents........ 50		4,949 @ $7 = $34,643
Graduate students........... 10		Total patient days
Technicians................. 8		62,486 @ $4 = 249,944
Postgraduate students........ 160		New OPD admissions
Nurses..................... 45		12,859 @ $7 = 90,013
Total other students........... 273		Return OPD visits
		26,554 @ $3 = 79,662
		$454,262

* The cost, if any, of providing this professional service is not identified in the budget. All dollar values for professional service calculated on the basis of VA home-care rates: $7 for new patients, $3 for return office visits, $4 a day for hospital visits.

† Based on department heads' estimates of faculty time spent on research.

Table 7 was compiled from the figures supplied by a privately owned medical school with a total budget of $991,365.01. After deducting hospital expenses, $916,299.25 remained for the support of all its activities. The three major activities are shown. One hundred and ninety-one medical students and 273 other students received all or a portion of their instruction from the medical school faculty. Approximately one-third of the total budget was accounted for by research grants and by that portion of the faculty salary budget estimated to be expended on research. The free professional service is valued at $454,262 according to the Veterans Administration scale of professional fees.

Table 8 was compiled from information supplied by a tax-supported

Table 8. ACTIVITIES AND FUNDS FOR THEIR MAINTENANCE AT A TAX-
SUPPORTED MEDICAL SCHOOL WITH A RELATIVELY SMALL BUDGET

Budget

Total budget..........................	$652,086
Hospital expense.......................	32,354
Balance for maintenance of activities................	$619,732

Education	*Research*	*Service**
Medical students................ 231 Other students, who received part or all of their instruction from the medical school faculty Nurses.................... 110 Pharmacy students......... 102 Technicians.............. 13 Interns.................. 7 Assistant residents.......... 27 Residents................ 6 Graduate students......... 13 Fellows and special students. 13 Postgraduate students (2- to 4-day courses)........ <u>954</u> Total other students........ 1,245	Research grants..... $32,897.58 Estimated faculty sal- ary for research.... $60,000.00†	Value of free professional service rendered by the medical school faculty New hospital admissions 5,439 @ $7 = $38,073 Hospital patient days 66,528 @ $4 = 266,112 New OPD admissions 4,984 @ $7 = 34,888 Return OPD visits 73,661 @ $3 = 220,983 Home delivery service 1,625 @ $50 = <u>81,250</u> $641,306

* The cost, if any, of providing this professional service is not identified in the budget. All dollar values
for professional service calculated on VA home-care rates: $7 for new patients, $3 for return office visits,
$4 a day for hospital visits.

† Based on department heads' estimates of faculty time spent on research.

school with a total budget of $652,086. After deducting hospital ex-
pense, the sum of $619,732 remained for the support of the school's
activities. The faculty carried a large teaching load of other students and
gave free professional service equal in value to the total budget of the
school. Research grants accounted for a relatively small amount of the
budget.

Table 9 shows information obtained from a large privately owned
medical school with a total budget of $2,671,728. The sum of
$2,517,353 remained after deducting hospital expenses. The school
trained a large number of graduate students in the basic science departments and a relatively large number of interns and residents in its teaching hospital. Approximately one-half of the budget was accounted for
by research grants and that portion of the salary budget estimated to be
expended on research. Research had been a major activity of the school
for more than 20 years. Professional service was valued at $682,113.

Table 9. ACTIVITIES AND FUNDS FOR THEIR MAINTENANCE AT A PRIVATELY
SUPPORTED MEDICAL SCHOOL WITH A RELATIVELY LARGE BUDGET

Budget

Total budget............................	$2,671,728
Hospital expense.........................	154,375
Balance for maintenance of activities..............	$2,517,353

Education	Research	Service*
Medical students................. 231	Research grants..... $1,234,194	Value of free professional
Other students who received part or all of	Estimated faculty sal-	service rendered by the
their instruction from the medical	ary for research.... 200,000†	medical school faculty
school faculty		New hospital admissions
Public health............. 44		6,565 @ $7 = $45,955
Undergraduates........... 5		Total patient days
Graduate students.......... 83		97,918 @ $4 = 391,672
Interns................... 46		New OPD admissions
Assistant residents.......... 73		3,982 @ $7 = 27,874
Residents................. 24		Return OPD visits
Fellows................... 14		72,204 @ $3 = 216,612
Nurses (a part of ed.)....... 225		$682,113
Postgraduate—19 courses		
(range 3 to 54 hr. of		
teaching)............. 642		
Total other students.......... 1,156		

* The cost, if any, of providing this professional service is not identified in the budget. All dollar values
for professional service calculated on VA home-care rates: $7 for new patients, $3 for return office visits,
$4 a day for hospital visits.
 † Based on department heads' estimates of faculty time spent on research.

Table 10 shows information from a tax-supported school with a
budget of $4,608,749, of which $2,912,716 remained after deducting
hospital expense. In its educational activities, this school carried a portion of the basic science teaching of the dental and pharmacy schools of
the university. Approximately $900,000 of the budget was accounted
for by research grants and faculty salaries devoted to research. Free professional service was valued at $1,741,090, although this was probably
underestimated because the school was unable to supply the Survey with
information on one hospital utilized in teaching.

These four typical examples, chosen to represent schools with large
and with small budgets, illustrate the magnitude of the activities supported by the expenditures of the medical schools. No matter what the
size of the budget, the contribution the school makes by its activities
stands out vividly in all four of the tables. Obviously, every dollar invested in a medical school produces a tremendous return to society in

terms of the value of the school's activities. Despite this fact, it is the public impression that all medical schools are expensive institutions to maintain.

The Survey next compared its study of the activities of each school with the costs of educating a medical student at the same schools, as

Table 10. ACTIVITIES AND FUNDS FOR THEIR MAINTENANCE AT A TAX-SUPPORTED MEDICAL SCHOOL WITH A RELATIVELY LARGE BUDGET

Budget

Total budget...................... $4,608,749
Hospital expense................... 1,696,033
Balance for maintenance of activities.............. $2,912,716

Education	Research	Service*
Medical students.................. 656	Research grants....... $595,405	Free professional service rendered by the medical school faculty
Other students who received part or all of their instruction from the medical school faculty	Estimated faculty salary for research......... 290,000†	New hospital admissions
Dental students............ 200		11,921 @ $7 = $83,447
Pharmacy students........... 84		Total patient days
Interns.................... 23		153,621 @ $4 = 614,484
Residents.................. 56		New OPD admissions
Graduate students (M.S. and Ph.D.).................. 161		35,405 @ $7 = 247,835
Postgraduate............... 168		Return OPD visits
Fellows.................... 63		265,108 @ $3 = 795,324
Total other students........... 755		$1,741,090

* The cost, if any, of maintaining this professional service is not identified in the budget. All dollar values for professional service calculated on VA home-care rates: $7 for new patients, $3 for return office visits, $4 a day for hospital visits.

† Based on department heads' estimates of faculty time spent on research.

computed by several national organizations. It was immediately apparent that, in computing the cost of medical education, these groups had not considered many important factors. The three examples set forth in Table 11 illustrate the extent of the inaccuracy. In the first school, for instance, at which the Surgeon General's Committee on Medical School Grants and Finances reported in 1950 that the basic operating expense per student was $2,411,[6] this government agency had ignored in its calculations the fact that the expenditures included the instruction of 996

[6] Federal Security Agency, Public Health Service, "Financial Status and Needs of Medical Schools, A Preliminary Report by the Surgeon General's Committee on Medical School Grants and Finances," Washington, D.C., 1950, p. 84.

other students, the faculty time devoted to research totaling $180,000 in terms of salaries, and the costs of providing a great amount of free professional care for patients. (It is also interesting to note that application of the Veterans Administration scale of fees would place a value or $1,083,400 on the free professional care provided to patients by this school.) The table also shows that, although the organization estimated the "basic operating cost per student" at approximately the same figure for the three schools, it omitted from its calculations widely varying numbers of other students.

Table 11. THREE EXAMPLES* OF ITEMS THAT, ALTHOUGH SUPPORTED BY THE BUDGETS OF THE SCHOOLS, HAVE BEEN ERRONEOUSLY IGNORED IN DETERMINING COST OF MEDICAL EDUCATION

	School A	School B	School C
Education			
College students....................	460	0	362
Ancillary health personnel..............	266	0	569
Graduate students and fellows..........	34	51	222
Postgraduate students (M.D.)..........	147	368	2,097
Interns and residents trained...........	89	146	220
Research			
Faculty salary spent on research, according to department heads................	$180,000	$125,000	$200,000
Service			
New admissions to outpatient department and hospital..................	18,752	31,008	52,944
Hospital patient-days.................	197,875	259,532	259,745
Return visits to outpatient department...	53,612	258,686	213,517

* Selected because estimates of "basic operating expense per medical student" were almost exactly the same for all three schools. Note wide variations in size of activities omitted from the calculations.

MISCONCEPTIONS

Methods used in the past for determining the costs of educating a medical student have ignored all the items listed in Table 11. The effect of these methods has been to charge to the cost of educating a medical student all indirect costs of research, the costs of providing professional service to indigent patients, and the cost of instruction of nonmedical students in all categories. The fact that the research and service activities are essential to the education of many other categories of students receiving instruction from the medical school has been entirely disregarded. These methods imply that the education of a medical student is the major if not the only cost factor in the activities and maintenance of a medical school, except for separately budgeted research, hospital costs, and relatively small sums spent on noneducational activities.

It is plain that all the figures that have been published on the cost of educating a medical student are misleading. They are not compatible with the facts. Arrival at any acceptable figures requires first a thorough understanding of all the activities of a medical school; second, precise definition and measurement of these activities; and third, clear decision as to which, and how much of each, of the activities are essential to the education of a medical student. The fourth essential step is to redesign the budgets and accounting practices so that they reflect the quantity and cost of the several activities.

The lack of accurate information concerning the activities of medical schools and the cost of educating a medical student have led the public, boards of trustees, university administrators, and medical schools themselves into misconceptions and confusion. The confusion in the minds of university boards of trustees and university presidents is illustrated in Table 12, in which are set forth the activities and the funds available to support them at one of the privately supported medical schools. The total expense budget for this school for the year 1949 was $1,040,775, of which $61,091 was spent in making up the deficit of operating the university-controlled hospital, leaving $979,684 for the support of all the other activities of the medical school. The school gave all the instruction received by 240 medical students and part or all of the instruction received by 742 other students, including 354 college students. Its research grants totaled $256,296, and according to the department heads' estimates, the faculty time devoted to research accounted for $160,000 of the salary budget. The school provided a large amount of free professional care for indigent patients. The board of trustees of this university is acutely aware of the "high costs" of medical education. At the time of the Survey team's visit, the board was debating whether it could afford to continue to maintain the medical school. When this table was shown to the board, the chairman of the committee responsible for the medical school stated that the 354 college students should be charged to the cost of medical education, because he had the impression that many

Table 12. ACTIVITIES AND FUNDS FOR THEIR MAINTENANCE AT A PRIVATELY
SUPPORTED MEDICAL SCHOOL (AT WHICH UNIVERSITY AUTHORITIES
REVEALED CONFUSION OVER COSTS)

Budget

Total budget.......................... $1,040,775
Hospital expense....................... 61,091
Balance for maintenance of activities................ $979,684

Education	Research	Service*
Medical students............... 240 Other students who received part or all of their instruction from the medi- cal school faculty College students (one or more courses).......... 354 Nursing students (one or more courses)'.......... 69 Graduate students........ 60 Postgraduate students..... 112 Fellows.................. 29 Interns.................. 45 Assistant residents........ 60 Residents............... 13 Total other students......... 742	Research grants...... $256,296.00 Estimated faculty sal- ary for research..... 160,000.00	Free professional service ren- dered by the medical school faculty New hospital admissions 18,955 @ $7 = $132,685 Total patient days 247,147 @ $4 = 988,588 Return OPD visits 115,449 @ $3 = 346,347 $1,467,620

* The cost, if any, of providing this professional service is not identified in the budget. All dollar values
for professional service calculated on VA home-care rates: $7 for new patients, $3 for return office visits,
$4 a day for hospital visits.

of them were premedical students. The president of the university stated
that the medical school was receiving one-eighth of the total university
budget, although it taught only 240 (one twenty-fifth) of the 6,000 students enrolled.

The breakdown of the $1,040,000 budget of ths school according
to the sources of its funds (Table 13) shows that $198,000 was ob-

Table 13. BREAKDOWN OF MEDICAL SCHOOL BUDGET ACCORDING TO
SOURCES OF FUNDS
(Same School as Table 12)

Funds Obtained by Medical School
Medical student tuition fees............... $198,000
Research grants to medical school.......... 256,000
Gifts to medical school................... 253,000
    Total... $ 707,000
Funds Obtained by University......................... 333,000
    Total budget..................................... $1,040,000

tained from medical-student tuition fees, $256,000 from separately budgeted research funds granted specifically to the medical school, and $253,000 was received in gifts and grants given specifically to the medical school for instructional or general purposes. Since the university handles the finances of the medical school, all these items go into general university income. In the last analysis, however, the medical school received specifically from the university funds only $333,000. This sum was only one-twentieth of the total university budget.

The medical school income, exclusive of gifts and grants, was, therefore, $333,000 from university funds and $198,000 from tuition fees— a total of $531,000. Of this amount, the sum of $61,000 was spent in meeting the deficit of the university hospital and clinics; another $70,000 was spent in maintaining services in a city and county hospital for welfare patients where some teaching was done. The remainder, $400,000, may be said to have been spent on all other activities carried on by the faculty. These activities included all the education of 240 medical students and a portion of the education of 354 college students, 69 nurses, 60 graduate students, 112 postgraduate students, 29 fellows, 45 interns, 60 assistant residents, and 13 residents. The $400,000 also supported research facilities and a portion of the faculty salary budget which was expended on research. And it maintained free professional service to the extent of 18,955 new hospital admissions, a total of 247,147 patient days, and 115,449 return outpatient department visits during the year, with a total value of $1,467,620. In addition, the faculty members served on important national and local committees dealing with health problems.

It would appear that the university is receiving a large return for its expenditures on the medical school, and that the public both locally and nationally receives tremendous benefits from the school. However, the administration of the university, and even the university president, obviously had never viewed the medical school from this point of view, nor had the community been made aware of the value of the free professional care of patients contributed by the medical school faculty. It was amazing to find that the board of trustees and the president of this university had been extremely hesitant to undertake a fund-raising campaign for the medical school. In view of the tremendous contributions of such an institution, the value of the educational, research, and service functions of the school should have provided an excellent basis on which to approach various segments of society for additional support.

COSTS IN RELATION TO VALUE

The public is thoroughly indoctrinated with the idea that medical schools and medical education are very expensive. One hundred and six million dollars, the sum expended by all medical schools in 1950, is considered a large sum for the support of one form of professional education. However, the Survey data reveal that medical schools are unique in the university family of schools, in that the education of the physician is only one of its many educational responsibilities. In addition to education, the 106 million dollars supports research and services which are of tremendous value. Medical school costs are actually very low in comparison to the value of their products. One hundred and six million dollars is only 8.2 per cent as much as the nation spent on jewelry, or 1.3 per cent of the sum spent on alcoholic beverages in 1949. There is little doubt that not only can the public afford to support the medical schools as they exist today, but they can well afford to greatly increase their support. The medical schools have not informed the people of the value of their activities. Until this is done intelligent support cannot be expected.

CONCLUSIONS

1. In order to understand the financial problems of the medical schools, their expenditures must be considered in relation to their activities.
2. The budgets and accounting practices of medical schools have not been devised for the purpose of determining the costs of educating a medical student.
3. The term "cost of medical education," as used today, is a broadly inclusive term without precise meaning. It often includes the education of many other categories of students in addition to medical students. The term is so vague that it cannot be used intelligently in discussing the costs of educating a medical student.
4. Estimates of the cost of educating a medical student that have been published are misleadingly high and are not compatible with the facts revealed by the Survey.
5. The cost of educating a medical student mounts as the quality of instruction is improved, but it is only one factor contributing to the "high costs" of maintaining medical schools. Other major factors are:

    a. Rapidly expanding research activities with large indirect costs carried by the medical schools.

    b. Increased instructional costs due to broadened programs for educating many categories of students.

    c. The development of medical schools as the hubs of medical-service centers.

    d. Growing consultative services for national and local health and welfare agencies.

    e. Rising prices of goods and services purchased by the medical schools.

6. Medical school costs are small in comparison with the values of their activities. The dollars invested in a medical school bring manifold return values to society.

RECOMMENDATIONS

1. In discussing costs, the term "medical education" should apply only to the education of a student of medicine. The term "health-personnel education" could be used to cover the education of all students in related health fields. Students in nonhealth fields should not be included in the terms "medical education" and "health-personnel education."

2. The medical schools should reorganize their accounting practices so that the separate costs of their various activities can be determined.

3. The various figures purporting to show the cost of educating a medical student are misleading and should not be relied upon. A realistic determination requires a clear decision as to which of the activities of the schools are essential to the education of a medical student and in what amount, which are activities undertaken by the schools primarily as a service to the public, and which of them are services to the university as a whole or to other colleges on the campus.

4. The public should be fully and accurately informed concerning the values and costs of the medical schools' multiple activities. Intelligent financial support cannot be effected until this has been accomplished.

6 THE FUNDS AND HOW THEY ARE SPENT

Medical schools are sensitive to social changes. Thus, in the postwar years, the schools shared with the rest of the nation the problems and the responsibilities of peacetime adjustment. There were demands to admit more students, to undertake more research projects, and to expand medical service activities. At the same time, there was renewed and widespread concern over whether the schools were adequately financed to meet the increased demands placed upon them, especially in view of the inflationary trend and the "high costs" of medical education. Many methods of aiding the medical schools were proposed, and some that have been put into operation are resulting in a good response in contributions from the interested public.

It was in this setting that the Survey sought information from the medical schools regarding their expenditures and income. Were the schools adequately financed to support, at a high level of quality, the activities they were attempting? And, perhaps more important, just which of their activities require financial support and which of them are the most important in relation to the school's objectives? In respect to the latter, in the present pattern of the schools' expanding activities, each school must decide whether the education of the undergraduate medical student is its prime objective and what and how much of its activities are essential to that objective.

The Survey could not answer these questions for all the schools without making impractical generalizations. It attempted to collect information regarding the income received by the schools for their major activities, and regarding their expenditures on each activity also, for the five

years prior to 1950. In spite of excellent cooperation from the administrative officers, however, the administrative policies and accounting methods frequently provided no way of knowing on what activity income from
any certain source was spent. Overlapping and lack of uniformity created
problems. Among those deans who found their financial records insuffi-
ciently informative to provide replies to the Survey's questions were
four of the wealthiest and largest privately supported schools and three
large tax-supported schools.

For these reasons, the Survey discarded the plan of studying the trends
in 41 medical schools over a five-year period, and sent questionnaires to
all 79 medical schools regarding their finances in 1950–51. By this
means, the 1950–51 data for 76 schools presented in this chapter were
obtained. It was necessary to discard the data from three of the 79
schools, either because it was impossible to interpret them or because the
school was unique in some respect and therefore could not be compared
with the other schools.

By utilizing the information for 1940–41 and 1947–48 made available by the Surgeon General's Committee on Medical School Grants and
Finances, the Survey was also enabled to study the trends in the finances
of 59 schools over a 10-year period. These trends are described and
analyzed in this chapter.

It cannot be emphasized too strongly, however, that the same factors
responsible for the fallacies in estimates of the cost of educating a medical student also operate to confuse the picture of the school's finances.
Accounting policies varied from year to year and from school to school,
and this lack of uniformity alone constituted a variability that detracted
from the value of the statistical data. Again from the statistical point of
view, the fact that the needs of the privately supported schools are usually different from those of the tax-supported schools, and that within
each group many other variations exist, made impossible the analysis of
the data in terms of statistical means or medians.

The material is presented here with a warning, therefore, that conclusions drawn from it as to the exact financial needs of the medical
schools would be fallacious. Before any such conclusions can be drawn,
it must be known which of the activities is in need of financial support.
Is it the schools' educational activity that is poorly supported? And if so,
is it the instruction of the medical student or that of the other students?
Is it the service activity that most importantly needs support? Or is it
research, and if so, what type of research is most important as an ac-

tivity of the medical school? All these unanswered questions are challenging the medical schools of the nation.

1950–51 EXPENDITURES OF 76 MEDICAL SCHOOLS

The expenditures of 76 schools appear in Table 14, where they are broken down into instruction, research, administration, maintenance, and all other expenditures except hospitals and clinics. Expenditures on hospitals and

Table 14. 1950–51 EXPENDITURES OF 76* MEDICAL SCHOOLS

30 *Tax-supported Schools*			
Instructional activities..............................		$22,766,000	
Research activities			
Federal funds.........................	$ 5,771,000		
All other funds........................	4,522,000		
Total..		10,293,000	
Administration (including share of university expense)....		2,986,000	
Maintenance..		4,570,000	
All other items except hospitals and clinics..............		2,650,000	
Total..			$ 43,265,000
40 *Privately Supported Schools*			
Instructional activities..............................		$22,355,000	
Research activities			
Federal funds.........................	$10,726,000		
All other funds........................	10,634,000		
Total..		21,360,000	
Administration (including share of university expense)....		4,718,000	
Maintenance..		4,054,000	
All other items except hospitals and clinics..............		3,513,000	
Total..			56,000,000
6 *Two-year Schools*†			
Instructional activities..............................		$ 1,031,000	
Research activities			
Federal funds.........................	$ 160,000		
All other funds........................	76,000		
Total..		236,000	
Administration (including share of university expense)....		134,000	
Maintenance..		85,000	
All other items except hospitals and clinics..............		154,000	
Total..			1,640,000
Total 76 medical schools.....................................			$100,905,000
Hospitals and clinics, 76 medical schools..........................			$ 49,245,000

* Only 76 of the 79 medical schools are included here because of factors which made breakdowns for three schools impossible to compare with the others. Total expenditures of the 79 schools exceeded $106,000,000, exclusive of hospitals and clinics.

† All two-year schools but one are tax-supported.

clinics were removed from the totals because of the wide variations that existed in this category.

The figures reported as research expenditures do not include the salaries and other indirect costs, which are charged to instruction, administration, and maintenance, so that in reality the schools are spending larger sums on research than the figures indicate.

Of the total of $100,905,000 expended by the 76 medical schools (Table 15), 45.7 per cent ($46,152,000) was classified "For Instructional Purposes," and 31.6 per cent ($31,889,000) was classified "Restricted to Re-

Table 15. EXPENDITURES, AND PERCENTAGE ON EACH ACTIVITY, OF 76 MEDICAL SCHOOLS, 1950–51

	Expenditures	Per cent of total
Instruction	$ 46,152,000	45.7
Research	31,889,000	31.6
Administration	7,838,000	7.8
Maintenance	8,709,000	8.6
All other expenditures except hospitals and clinics	6,317,000	6.3
Total expenditures, 76 medical schools	$100,905,000	100.0

search"; administration accounted for 7.8 per cent ($7,838,000), maintenance for 8.6 per cent ($8,709,000), and all other expenditures except hospitals and clinics accounted for 6.3 per cent ($6,317,000) of the total expenditures.

Several interesting facts become apparent when the expenditures on in-

Table 16. INSTRUCTION AND RESEARCH EXPENDITURES OF 76 MEDICAL SCHOOLS, 1950–51

	Instructional activities	Research activities		
		Federal funds	Other funds	Total research funds
30 Tax-supported schools	$22,766,000	$ 5,771,000	$ 4,522,000	$10,293,000
40 Privately supported schools	22,355,000	10,726,000	10,634,000	21,360,000
6 Two-year schools	1,031,000	160,000	76,000	236,000
Total 76 medical schools	$46,152,000	$16,657,000	$15,232,000	$31,889,000

struction and on research are compared (Table 16). The 76 schools spent approximately three-fourths as much on research (excluding indirect costs) as they spent on instruction. Of the 76 schools, 70 were four-year medical schools. The 40 privately supported schools in this group spent approximately the same amount (22 million dollars) on instruction as did the 30 tax-supported schools. It would seem that the tax-supported schools are spending on the average more on instruction than the privately supported schools. This conclusion means little. As pointed out in Chapter 2, "Education," the tax-supported schools are responsible for the instruction of approximately twice as many other students as the privately supported schools. The 40 privately supported schools spent the same amount on research as they spent on instruction, and 50 per cent of their funds for research were derived from Federal sources. The tax-supported schools spent half as much on research as they spent on instruction. The six two-year schools spent on research less than one-fourth the amount they spent on instruction.

The 40 privately supported schools in 1950–51 spent Federal funds for the support of research in twice the amount spent by the 30 tax-supported schools. It is a historical fact that the privately supported medical schools have made greater research contributions than the tax-supported schools. Because of their emphasis on research, their facilities and their potential research manpower have been greater.

1950–51 INCOME OF 76 MEDICAL SCHOOLS

Income of the 76 schools in 1950–51, exclusive of hospitals and clinics, totaled $103,544,000 (Table 17). Of this sum, 50.1 per cent ($51,839,-000) came from tax monies, 17.5 per cent ($18,164,000) came from private sources in the form of gifts and grants, 15.2 per cent ($15,769,000) came from tuition, 11.9 per cent ($12,286,000) was endowment income, and the remaining 5.3 per cent ($5,486,000) was classified as income from all other sources except hospitals and clinics (Table 18).

Federal funds ($20,765,000) played a large part in the financial support of the 76 medical schools in 1950–51, totaling two million dollars more than the gifts and grants from private sources and eight million dollars more than income from endowment (Table 19). The privately supported schools received a higher proportion of Federal funds than the tax-supported schools, but the tax-supported schools received a higher proportion of tax monies from the state, county, and city. Privately supported schools received a much higher proportion of endowment income and of gifts and grants from private sources than the tax-supported schools. In the six two-year schools, of which only one is privately supported, tax monies constituted by far the largest source of income, and most of these funds derived from state rather than Federal sources.

Table 17. 1950–51 INCOME OF 76* MEDICAL SCHOOLS

30 *Tax-supported Schools*
- Tuition... $ 4,509,000
- Endowment..................................... 1,056,000
- Tax Monies
  - Federal.............................. $ 7,899,000
  - State................................ 24,648,000
  - County or city....................... 1,566,000
  - Total....................................... 34,113,000
- Gifts and grants from private sources.................. 5,390,000
- All other sources but hospitals and clinics.............. 1,605,000
  - Total...................................... $ 46,673,000

40 *Privately Supported Schools*
- Tuition.. $11,097,000
- Endowment..................................... 11,154,000
- Tax monies
  - Federal.............................. $12,685,000
  - State................................ 3,717,000
  - County or city....................... 62,000
  - Total....................................... 16,464,000
- Gifts and grants from private sources.................. 12,646,000
- All other sources but hospitals and clinics.............. 3,851,000
  - Total...................................... 55,212,000

6 *Two-year Schools*†
- Tuition.. $ 163,000
- Endowment..................................... 76,000
- Tax monies
  - Federal.............................. $ 181,000
  - State................................ 1,081,000
  - County or city....................... 0
  - Total....................................... 1,262,000
- Gifts and grants from private sources.................. 128,000
- All other sources but hospitals and clinics.............. 30,000
  - Total...................................... 1,659,000

Total 76 medical schools....................................... $103,544,000

Hospitals and clinics, 76 medical schools............................ $ 43,554,000

* Only 76 of the 79 medical schools are included here because of factors which made breakdowns for three schools impossible to compare with the others.

† All two-year schools but one are tax-supported.

Table 18. 1950–51 INCOME, AND PERCENTAGE SUPPLIED BY EACH SOURCE, OF 76 MEDICAL SCHOOLS

	Income	Per cent of total income
Tuition...	$ 15,769,000	15.2
Endowment...	12,286,000	11.9
Tax monies...	51,839,000	50.1
Gifts and grants from private sources..................	18,164,000	17.5
All other income except from hospitals and clinics........	5,486,000	5.3
Total income, 76 schools.........................	$103,544,000	100.0

Table 19. 1950–51 INCOME OF 76 MEDICAL SCHOOLS FROM TAX MONIES, ENDOWMENT, AND GIFTS AND GRANTS FROM PRIVATE SOURCES

	Tax monies				Endowment	Gifts and grants from private sources
	Federal	State	City or county	Total		
30 Tax-supported schools.....	$ 7,899,000	$24,648,000	$1,566,000	$34,113,000	$ 1,056,000	$ 5,390,000
40 Privately supported schools.....	12,685,000	3,717,000	62,000	16,464,000	11,154,000	12,646,000
6 Two-year schools.....	181,000	1,081,000	0	1,262,000	76,000	128,000
Total 76 medical schools	$20,765,000	$29,446,000	$1,628,000	$51,839,000	$12,286,000	$18,164,000

TRENDS IN THE FINANCIAL SUPPORT
OF 59 MEDICAL SCHOOLS

In spite of the limitations already described, the schools' records of their expenditures offer the statistician more promise of dependability, because of the sharper definition of the various items of expense, than do the records of their income. Records of expenditures were more often classified according to the activity on which funds were expended than according to their source and the activity for which they were designated.

In many schools, income from most sources is pooled by the university and allocated according to the needs of the various colleges.

Because many tax-supported institutions are forbidden by law to incur a deficit, the magnitude of their expenditures is strictly determined by their income—a condition which is seldom found to the same degree in privately supported schools. Nevertheless, no attempt should be made to compare income with expenditures, since the balance between the two seldom represents either a true surplus or a true deficit. Income received in one year is not necessarily spent in that year; expenditures in one year may be from income in an earlier year.

The Survey was not concerned with balances, but with trends in the financial support of medical schools. Although both expenditures and income show trends, income is more important in revealing the value placed on specific activities by the public.

By utilizing the information for 1940–41 and 1947–48 made available by the Surgeon General's Committee on Medical School Grants and Finances, and comparable statistics collected by means of questionnaires to all the schools, the Survey was enabled to study the trends in the expenditures and income of 59 of the medical schools over the last decade of the half century. Only 59 schools supplied comparable data for the three fiscal years.

As mentioned earlier, for purposes of fairer comparison the figures for hospitals and clinics have been removed from the totals presented in this chapter because the great variations in this category detracted from the value of the statistics. The variations depended upon whether the medical schools owned the teaching hospitals, and also upon how sharply the financial records at hospitals were separated from those of the medical schools. In the latter respect, sometimes the records were inextricably interwoven, but more recently the trend has been toward a sharp differentiation between the two.

It must be remembered that the sums reported as expenditures on research do not include all the research expenditures of the schools. They include expenditures of funds that were restricted to research at their source; they do not include the indirect costs charged to the instructional, administration, and maintenance budgets.

EXPENDITURES, 1940–41 TO 1950–51

Exclusive of hospitals and clinics, the total expenditures of the 59 medical schools, of which 22 were tax-supported and 37 were privately supported, rose from $27,354,000 in 1940–41 to $85,743,000 in 1950–51, or more than tripled (Figure 5). In the 22 tax-supported schools, these expenditures rose from $9,549,000 in 1940–41 to $34,223,000 in 1950–51, increasing almost fourfold in the 10 years; in the 37 privately supported schools, they rose from $17,805,000 in 1940–41 to $51,520,000 in 1950–51, or nearly tripled.

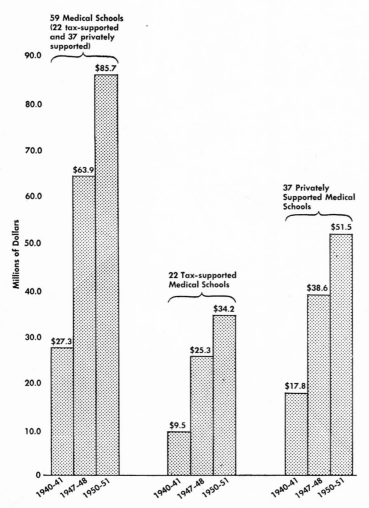

Figure 5. Total expenditures on all activities except hospitals and clinics of 59 medical schools (22 tax-supported and 37 privately supported) in fiscal years 1940–41, 1947–48, and 1950–51. Figures for 1940–41 and 1947–48 computed from those of the Surgeon General's Committee on Medical School Grants and Finances.

22 Tax-supported Schools

Expenditures on instruction, research, maintenance, and administration—the four main items of expenditure after deducting expenditures on hospitals and clinics—rose at different rates (Figure 6). Instructional expenditures rose from $5,336,000 to $17,655,000, more than tripling in the 10-year period. Expenditures on research (excluding indirect costs) rose from $849,000 to $8,407,000, or increased tenfold. Expenditures on administra-

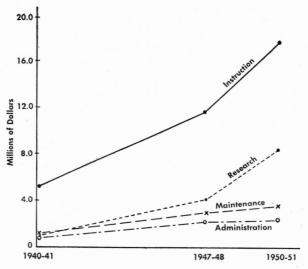

Figure 6. Expenditures of 22 tax-supported medical schools on four major items (instruction, research, maintenance, and administration) in fiscal years 1940–41, 1947–48, and 1950–51. Figures for 1940–41 and 1947–48 computed from those of the Surgeon General's Committee on Medical School Grants and Finances.

tion rose from $869,000 to $2,317,000, or approximately tripled; expenditures on maintenance rose from $1,101,000 to $3,710,000, or approximately tripled.

The fact that the expenditures on any one activity have increased does not necessarily mean that that activity was better financed in 1950–51 than in 1940–41. Any such claim, to be valid, must have taken into account the expansion of the activity during a period when the purchasing power of the dollar was decreasing.

A more reliable indication of how well an activity has fared financially is obtained by comparing its expenditures in relation to the total expenditures over the 10-year period. The percentages of the total expenditures spent on the several activities reveal shifts in their emphasis in the total medical school program (Table 20). Thus it is found that the expenditures on instruction fell, in the 10-year period, from 55.9 per cent to 51.6 per cent of the total expenditures for the year. Expenditures on research rose from 8.9 per cent to 24.6 per cent of the total expenditures. Expenditures on maintenance fell from 11.5 per cent to 10.8 per cent, and expenditures on administration fell from 9.1 per cent to 6.8 per cent of the total expenditures.

Table 20. SHIFTS IN EMPHASIS ON ACTIVITIES OF 22 TAX-SUPPORTED MEDICAL SCHOOLS AS SHOWN BY RATIOS OF EXPENDITURES, 1940–41, 1947–48, AND 1950–51

Activity	Expenditure as Per cent of Total		
	1940–41*	1947–48*	1950–51
Instruction..	55.9	47.3	51.6
Research..	8.9	16.2	24.6
Administration (including share of university expense)	9.1	9.3	6.8
Maintenance.......................................	11.5	11.4	10.8
All other items† except hospitals and clinics..........	14.6	15.8	6.2
	100.0	100.0	100.0

* Figures for 1940–41 and 1947–48 computed from those of the Surgeon General's Committee on Medical School Grants and Finances.

† Includes libraries, separately organized postgraduate education, student health service, and miscellaneous other items.

37 Privately Supported Schools

Again in the privately supported schools, the major expenditures rose at different rates (Figure 7). Instructional expenditures increased from $10,465,000 to $20,715,000, or approximately doubled. Research expenditures (excluding indirect costs) rose from $2,313,000 to $19,474,000, or increased more than eightfold. Expenditures on administration in 1950–51 were approximately two-and-one-half times the 1940–41 figure, while expenditures on maintenance were approximately twice the 1940–41 figure.

At the same time, instructional expenditures fell from 58.8 per cent to 40.2 per cent of the total expenditures for the year (Table 21). Research expenditures rose from 13.0 per cent to 37.8 per cent of the total expenditures. Expenditures on administration fell from 10.1 per cent to 8.7 per cent of the total, and expenditures on maintenance fell from 7.8 per cent to 6.9 per cent of the total.

As is shown in Chapter 7, "Administration," the administration percentage of the general operating expenses rose slightly in the 10-year period.

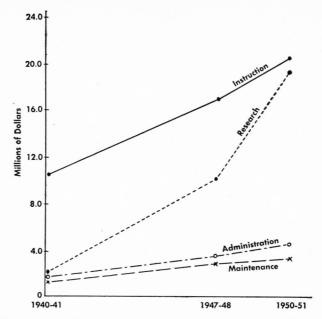

Figure 7. Expenditures of 37 privately supported medical schools on four major items (instruction, research, maintenance, and administration) in 1940–41, 1947–48, and 1950–51. Figures for 1940–41 and 1947–48 computed from those of the Surgeon General's Committee on Medical School Grants and Finances.

Table 21. SHIFTS IN EMPHASIS ON ACTIVITIES OF 37 PRIVATELY SUPPORTED MEDICAL SCHOOLS AS SHOWN BY RATIOS OF EXPENDITURES, 1940–41, 1947–48, AND 1950–51

Activity	Expenditure as Per cent of Total		
	1940–41*	1947–48*	1950–51
Instruction..	58.8	44.2	40.2
Research...	13.0	26.4	37.8
Administration (including share of university expense)	10.1	9.8	8.7
Maintenance.......................................	7.8	8.3	6.9
All other items† except hospitals and clinics..........	10.3	11.3	6.4
	100.0	100.0	100.0

* Figures for 1940–41 and 1947–48 computed from those of the Surgeon General's Committee on Medical School Grants and Finances.

† Includes libraries, separately organized postgraduate education, student health service, and miscellaneous other items.

INCOME, 1940–41 TO 1950–51

The total income of the 59 medical schools rose from $25,934,000 in 1940–41 to $86,837,000 in 1950–51 (Figure 8). In the 22 tax-supported schools, total income rose from $10,130,000 to $36,500,000, or increased nearly fourfold. In the 37 privately supported schools, total income rose from $15,804,000 to $50,337,000, or more than tripled in the 10-year period.

Income of the medical schools comes mainly from four sources: tuition fees, endowment, gifts and grants from private sources, and tax monies. Much of it, therefore, accrues from the good will and generosity of the interested public.

22 Tax-supported Schools

In the 22 tax-supported schools (Figure 9), income from tuition fees rose from $2,021,000 in 1940–41 to $3,770,000 in 1950–51, or less than doubled. Income from Federal, state, county, and city tax monies rose from $4,984,000 in 1940–41 to $25,672,000 in 1950–51, or increased more than fivefold. Funds from private sources in the form of gifts and grants rose from $1,159,000 in 1940–41 to $4,588,000 in 1950–51, or increased nearly fourfold. Endowment income usually constitutes only a small percentage of the total income of tax-supported schools, and for this reason, as well as because of some doubt as to the comparability of the 1947–48 and 1950–51 figures, endowment income is not shown on the graph.

As stated earlier, these increases do not indicate that the schools were more adequately supported in 1950–51 than in 1940–41. Tax-supported schools today have sources of income which in most instances are not available to privately supported schools. Although the incomes of tax-supported

Table 22. THE CHANGING RATIOS IN SOURCES OF INCOME OF 22 TAX-SUPPORTED MEDICAL SCHOOLS, 1940–41, 1947–48, AND 1950–51

Source	Income as Per cent of Total		
	1940–41*	1947–48*	1950–51
Tuition (all categories)............................	20.0	12.3	10.3
Tax monies (Federal, state, county, city).............	49.2	53.3	70.3
Gifts and grants from private sources................	11.4	11.4	12.6
All other sources (including endowment) but hospitals and clinics......................................	19.4	23.0	6.8
	100.0	100.0	100.0

* Figures for 1940–41 and 1947–48 computed from those of the Surgeon General's Committee on Medical School Grants and Finances.

schools appear to be large, many instances were encountered during the Survey in which the funds were not adequate for the support of the activities the schools were attempting to carry on. These data do, however, reveal trends in the financial support of the medical schools when the shifts in the proportions derived from the various sources of income are examined (Table 22). Tuition fees, for instance, constituted 20.0 per cent of the total in-

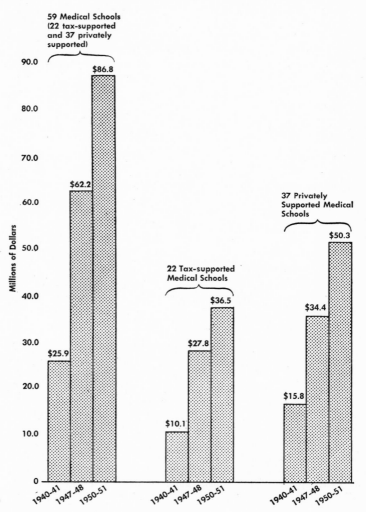

Figure 8. Total income from all sources except hospitals and clinics of 59 medical schools (22 tax-supported and 37 privately supported) in fiscal years 1940–41, 1947–48, and 1950–51. Figures for 1940–41 and 1947–48 computed from those of the Surgeon General's Committee on Medical School Grants and Finances.

come in 1940–41 but only 10.3 per cent in 1950–51. Tax monies from Federal, state, county, and city sources rose from 49.2 per cent of the 1940–41 total to 70.3 per cent of the 1950–51 total. Gifts and grants from private sources rose from 11.4 per cent of the 1940–41 total to 12.6 per cent of the 1950–51 total.

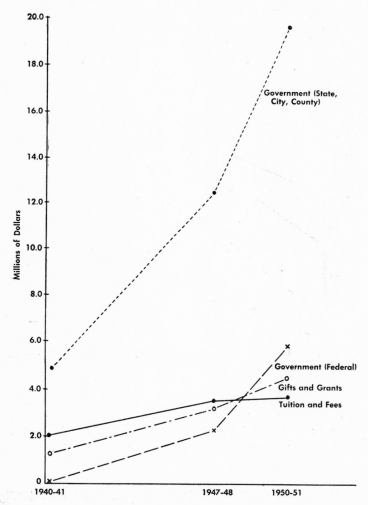

Figure 9. Ten-year trend in income from four principal sources for 22 tax-supported schools. For reasons explained in the text, endowment income is not included in this graph, but is shown in Tables 24 and 25. Figures for 1940–41 and 1947–48 computed from those of the Surgeon General's Committee on Medical School Grants and Finances.

37 Privately Supported Schools

Income from tuition rose in the 37 privately supported schools from $5,559,000 in 1940–41 to $10,170,000 in 1950–51, or nearly doubled. Income from Federal, state, county, and city tax monies rose from $413,000 in 1940–41 to $15,362,000 in 1950–51, or increased in 10 years to thirty-seven times the 1940–41 figure. Gifts and grants from private sources rose

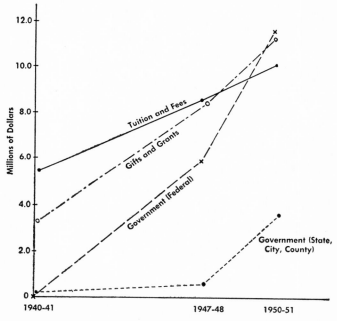

Figure 10. Ten-year trend in income from four principal sources for 37 privately supported medical schools. For reasons explained in the text, endowment income is not included in this graph, but is shown in Tables 24 and 25. The sharp increase in state, city, and county funds between 1947 and 1950 is accounted for largely by state funds appropriated to the medical schools in Pennsylvania, and the two privately supported schools in New York State which were becoming state supported between 1947 and 1950. Figures for 1940–41 and 1947–48 computed from those of the Surgeon General's Committee on Medical School Grants and Finances.

from $3,335,000 to $11,347,000, or increased more than threefold (Figure 10).

Thus tuition fell from 35.2 per cent of the 1940–41 total income to 20.0 per cent of the 1950–51 total income (Table 23); income from tax monies rose from 2.6 per cent to 30.5 per cent; and gifts and grants from private

Table 23. THE CHANGING RATIOS IN SOURCES OF INCOME OF 37 PRIVATELY
SUPPORTED MEDICAL SCHOOLS, 1940–41, 1947–48, AND 1950–51

Source	Income as Per cent of Total		
	1940–41*	1947–48*	1950–51
Tuition (all categories)............................	35.2	24.7	20.0
Tax monies (Federal, state, county, city).............	2.6	19.3	30.5
Gifts and grants from private sources................	21.1	24.5	22.5
All other sources (including endowment income†) but hospitals and clinics...........................	41.1	31.5	27.0
	100.0	100.0	100.0

* Figures for 1940–41 and 1947–48 computed from those of the Surgeon General's Committee on Medical School Grants and Finances.
† For endowment income, see Tables 24 and 25.

sources remained about the same, changing from 21.1 per cent in 1940–41 to 22.5 per cent in 1950–51.

The Survey, in its questionnaire to the schools, obtained separate figures for income from endowments specifically designated for the medical schools by their donors and income that was allocated to the schools from general university endowments. When these two types of endowment income are added and considered as the total 1950–51 endowment income, the figure obtained constitutes a sharp increase over the 1947–48 figure for endowment income reported by the Surgeon General's Committee on Medical School Grants and Finances. Some doubt arises as to the comparability of the two sets of figures, and the Survey has therefore refrained from plotting a curve to show the trend in endowment income. With that reservation, however, it can

Table 24. ENDOWMENT INCOME COMPARED WITH TOTAL INCOME EXCLUSIVE
OF HOSPITALS AND CLINICS AT 59 FOUR-YEAR MEDICAL SCHOOLS,
1940–41 AND 1947–48

	1940–41		1947–48	
	Endow-ment income	Total income	Endow-ment income	Total income
22 Tax-supported schools.............	$ 416,000	$10,130,000	$ 533,000	$27,755,000
37 Privately supported schools.........	4,274,000	20,129,000	5,756,000	34,423,000
Total 59 four-year medical schools....	$4,690,000	$30,259,000	$6,289,000	$62,178,000

Source: The Surgeon General's Committee on Medical School Grants and Finances.

be stated that endowment income, which in 1940–41 constituted more than one-fourth of the total income of the privately supported medical schools, in 1947–48 constituted less than one-seventh of the total income (Table 24); and that in 1950–51, according to the Survey's figures, total endowment income constituted one-fifth of the total income, and income from endowments specifically designated for the medical school constituted one-seventh of that total income (Table 25).

Table 25. ENDOWMENT INCOME COMPARED WITH TOTAL INCOME EXCLUSIVE OF HOSPITALS AND CLINICS AT 59 FOUR-YEAR MEDICAL SCHOOLS, 1950–51

	From medical school endowments	From university endowments	Total endowment income	Total income
22 Tax-supported schools...............	$ 681,000	$ 262,000	$ 943,000	$36,500,000
37 Privately supported schools.........	7,041,000	3,063,000	10,104,000	50,337,000
Total 59 four-year medical schools....	$7,722,000	$3,325,000	$11,047,000	$86,837,000

THE TRENDS ANALYZED

In both tax-supported and privately supported schools, the income from *tuition* almost doubled during the 10-year period 1940–41 to 1950–51, although it rose only moderately compared with other sources of income. It is impossible fairly to relate this increase to any increase in medical-student enrollment since some of the tuition came from students in many other categories.

Income from *gifts and grants from private sources* increased almost equally in the tax-supported and privately supported schools, the figure in 1950–51 being nearly four times larger in the tax-supported schools and about three-and-a-half times larger in the privately supported schools than the respective figures in 1940–41.

INCOME FROM TAX MONIES

The greatest change occurred in the income from tax monies (Table 26). Federal, state, and county or city tax funds served as a source of income to all 59 schools in 1950–51 and totaled slightly more than $41,034,000, while the total income of the same schools from all sources other than hospitals and clinics totaled $86,837,000. Of the $50,337,000 total income (excluding hospitals and clinics) of the 37 privately supported schools, $15,362,000 (or 30.5 per cent) was accounted for by Federal, state, city, and county tax appropriations. In 1940–41, the same schools reported only $413,000 (or 2.6 per cent) of such funds out of

Table 26. TOTAL INCOME FROM TAX APPROPRIATIONS OF 59 MEDICAL SCHOOLS, 1940–41, 1947–48, AND 1950–51

	1940–41*	1947–48*	1950–51
22 *Tax-supported Schools*			
Federal funds..	0	$ 2,240,000	$ 5,967,000
State funds....	$4,682,000	12,039,000	18,139,000
County or city funds.....	302,000	539,000	1,566,000
Total.......	$4,984,000	$14,818,000	$25,672,000
37 *Privately Supported Schools*			
Federal funds..	$185,000†	$5,917,000	$11,583,000
State funds....	218,000	721,000	3,717,000
County or city funds.....	10,000	4,000	62,000
Total.......	413,000	6,642,000	15,362,000
Total 59 medical schools..	$5,397,000	$21,460,000	$41,034,000

* Figures for 1940–41 and 1947–48 computed from those of the Surgeon General's Committee on Medical School Grants and Finances.
† $152,000 of this amount went to one medical school.

their total income of $15,804,000 from all sources but hospitals and clinics.

Total tax appropriations for the tax-supported schools, including Federal, state, city, and county, increased more than fivefold in the 1940–41 to 1950–51 decade. More significant, however, is the trend in the privately supported schools, where tax monies available for their support increased almost fortyfold.

Federal funds for research in the medical schools increased, in the tax-supported schools, from zero in 1940–41 to $4,907,000 in 1950–51, and in the privately supported schools from an estimated $33,000 or less to $9,585,000 during the same period. In 1950–51 both groups of schools received more funds for research from Federal than from private sources, but the 37 privately supported schools received nearly twice as much in Federal funds for research as did the 22 tax-supported schools.

Federal grants for instructional purposes in the tax-supported schools rose from zero in 1940–41 to $1,060,000 in 1950–51, and in the privately supported schools from $152,000 (one medical school only) in 1940–41 to $1,998,000 in 1950–51 (Table 27).

Table 27. GIFTS AND GRANTS (FEDERAL AND PRIVATE) FOR RESEARCH COMPARED WITH THOSE RESTRICTED TO OR AVAILABLE FOR INSTRUCTION, AT 59 FOUR-YEAR MEDICAL SCHOOLS, 1951

	Restricted to research	*Restricted to or available for instruction*	*Totals*
22 *Tax-supported Schools*			
From Federal government...	$4,907,000	$1,060,000	$ 5,967,000
From private sources.......	3,320,000	1,268,000	4,588,000
Total................	$8,227,000	$2,328,000	
37 *Privately Supported Schools*			
From Federal government...	$9,585,000	$1,998,000	11,583,000
From private sources.......	8,737,000	2,610,000	11,347,000
Total................	18,322,000	4,608,000	
Total 59 four-year medical schools................	$26,549,000	$6,936,000	$33,485,000

Federal grants for instructional purposes are a relatively new source of income for the medical schools. It is true that for some time before 1940–41 there had been occasional gifts of this nature, but they were received by only a few schools at irregular intervals and in varying amounts. After the Second World War, however, interest was focused upon several special categories of disease; to some extent it was this interest that led to the increase in gifts from a number of sources for instruction in these special fields.

The U.S. Public Health Service has been the largest source of teaching grants. Congress makes appropriations to the U.S. Public Health Service from funds that are earmarked for that government agency in the national budget, and from these funds, USPHS makes grants to the medical schools for teaching in the fields of cancer, cardiovascular disease, and mental health. It is clear that the growth of income that initiates in this manner remains to be determined, as do the purposes for which that income is to be utilized. The future growth of this source of income for the medical schools cannot be anticipated by studying the trend over a short period.

TRENDS IN THE SUPPORT OF THE ACTIVITIES

The changing ratios in the sources of income and in the expenditures of the medical schools must reflect to some extent the values the administrative officers—since it is they who expend the money or seek additional income—place upon the schools' activities, each in relation to the other activities and in relation to the schools' objectives. The changing ratios also reflect the value the public places upon each of the activities of the schools, since it is from the public that the medical schools derive their income.

EDUCATION

The increase in support of the educational activity of the medical schools does not in any way mean that such activities were better financed in 1950–51 than they were in 1940–41. The data for the two years cannot be compared, since no accurate information could be obtained for 1940–41—and indeed for 1950–51, as pointed out in an earlier chapter —concerning the numbers of students in all the various categories receiving instruction in the medical schools. It must be remembered also that the expenditures of medical schools are affected by the cost of living, which increased 86 per cent in the period under consideration. Although the private schools were spending approximately 100 per cent more in 1950–51 than they were in 1940–41, a large percentage of that increase can be accounted for by the increase in the cost of living. In terms of purchasing power, therefore, the schools were expending only a small percentage more on instruction in 1950–51 than 10 years earlier.

RESEARCH

Research, as has already been mentioned in Chapter 3, receives greater emphasis, judged by the increasingly larger sums flowing to it from the public, and being expended upon it, than any other activity of the medical schools. If this trend continues, it will create a serious imbalance in the activities of the schools.

SERVICE

Little can be said about expenditures on medical service and the cost of professional care of patients. The expenditures on hospitals, and the income derived from them, are so variable from school to school that no attempt was made to analyze such figures.

HOW THE AMERICAN PUBLIC SUPPORTS MEDICAL EDUCATION

The costs of the medical schools are a part of the public's expenditures for health care. Whether these expenditures come from the people as private citizens or as taxpayers, the amount of the national expenditure for health is determined by the value the people place upon health in relation to other goods and services that they purchase. Obviously, therefore, the ability of the medical schools to prove their value to the public determines how much their share will be of the national expenditures on health care.

The 106 million dollars spent in 1950–51 by the 79 medical schools to maintain those activities which are the backbone of the nation's health is a very small sum in comparison with the 8.5 billion dollars which, according to the U.S. Department of Commerce, was spent by the American people on medical services. This 8.5 billion dollars does not include the tax monies that the people expended on health. Without the medical schools there would be no physicians to provide professional medical care, medical research would practically cease, and the education and training of ancillary health personnel would be greatly diminished. It would seem, therefore, from this study of the total expenditures of the schools, that, contrary to the popular belief that the medical schools are expensive institutions to maintain, in actuality they are relatively inexpensive.

The schools have failed to educate the public to the value of all the activities of the medical schools in terms of the people's health, and Federal and state governments have been spending taxpayers' money on the medical schools in accordance with their own evaluation of the various activities. To continue in this fashion is to invite further Federal support—and eventual Federal control—of the medical schools.

TAXATION

The trend to the financing of medical schools through tax monies is unmistakable. Although the medical schools' income from tax funds has already outstripped all other sources of income, new methods of increasing their income from taxation are constantly being proposed, and some have been put into effect. In West Virginia a tax on soft drinks and in Arkansas a tax on cigarettes have been levied to provide funds for the support of the respective medical schools. The proposal has been made that a tax of $100 be levied on every physician for the support of all medical schools.

Concern at the national level has led to the introduction into Congress of bills for the purpose of providing support for the medical schools. The argument is that not only have the schools been unable to expand sufficiently to meet the civilian and the military needs of the nation for physicians, but they are unable to finance their present activities adequately. The most recent bill was based on the premise that funds were necessary to meet an emergency, and a five-year period was set as the duration of Federal support. Funds would be distributed to the medical schools in proportion to the size of the medical-student enrollment. The schools would receive $500 for each medical student and, as an incentive to expansion, a bonus of $1,000 for each additional medical student above the usual enrollment figure. The administrations of the majority of the medical schools endorsed the principle of Federal support of medical education. Amendments to the bill, however, proposed in Washington, brought opposition from many of those same schools on the basis that a new proposal to provide $200 per student enrolled and $2,200 for each new student placed greater emphasis upon expansion than upon improving the quality of instruction.

PHILANTHROPY

Gifts and grants from private sources have shown a remarkable growth in the past 10 years, increasing approximately fourfold in both the tax-supported and the privately supported medical schools. In 1950–51 such funds accounted for more than one-fifth of all the income of the privately supported schools and one-eighth of the income of the tax-supported schools. Most of these funds are given by philanthropic foundations, industry, the alumni of the medical schools, and other individual donors. In 1950–51 more than three-fourths of the funds from such gifts and grants were designated for research purposes (Table 28). A few foundations have helped the schools by designating their funds for special instructional progress and the training and development of faculty members.

Although large private fortunes are diminishing, *endowment income* of the medical schools nevertheless increased considerably between 1940 and 1950. The future of this source of income depends upon the social and economic trends of the country and public understanding.

Table 28. INCOME, RESTRICTED TO RESEARCH AND UNRESTRICTED, FROM GIFTS AND GRANTS FROM PRIVATE SOURCES, OF 59 FOUR-YEAR MEDICAL SCHOOLS, 1951

	Restricted to research	*Unrestricted*	*Total*
22 Tax-supported schools..................	$ 3,320,000	$1,268,000	$ 4,588,000
37 Privately supported schools.............	8,737,000	2,610,000	11,347,000
Total 59 four-year medical schools........	$12,057,000	$3,878,000	$15,935,000

Many medical schools have organized their *alumni* for the purpose of obtaining yearly contributions to the medical school, and others are doing so. One of the appeals has been on the basis that the alumnus has paid only a fraction of the cost of his medical education and, therefore, should recognize a moral obligation to his school. A few of these plans are producing from several thousand to as much as $100,000 per year per school. In the majority of the schools, however, little income is obtained from this source.

Another new venture in this direction was the establishment, in 1949, of the National Fund for Medical Education, Inc., initiated by leaders in university and medical education and the medical profession for improving the financial support of the medical schools. In a booklet entitled "Medical Education in the United States," this organization proposed "that America's great corporations be invited to take the lead in this movement to forge a pattern of practical benevolence in support of medical education," and stressed the importance of enlisting private support in order to make it unnecessary for Federal and state government to "step into the breach on an extensive and permanent basis." It warned that "federal grants-in-aid may be forthcoming, at least temporarily," and emphasized the desirability of stimulating private sources of support also, in order to create "a balance between two great sources of support—a balance under which the academic freedom essential to scientific medical education will be preserved."

In 1951, the American Medical Education Foundation was established by the American Medical Association for the support of all the medical schools in the United States. The Board of Trustees of the A.M.A. appropriated half a million dollars as a nucleus of this fund for the first year, and a similar sum in the second year, and all members of the A.M.A. are being asked to contribute to the fund on a yearly basis. All sums are to be distributed to the medical schools without restriction. The Foundation and the Fund cooperate closely and, in 1951, distributed approximately $15,000 to each four-year school and $7,500 to each two-year school. The combined goal of the two organizations is to raise annually for the medical schools the sum of five million dollars.

Current or yearly gifts and grants, such as may be obtained from the National Fund, alumni, or friends of the medical schools, are an increasingly important and valuable source of income. Such gifts and grants are not yet so stable a source of income as tuition and endowment income. It should be realized that tax funds are also relatively unstable. The majority of tax-supported schools receive their funds every two years, and the appropriations may be increased or decreased by decisions beyond the control of the institution. A typical example was a school which reported to the Survey that in the face of an expanding educational program planned over a four-year period, and in spite of rising prices, it had received a 5 per cent cut in its budget by the state legislature.

The contributions of their *time and services by the voluntary faculty members* are an important asset to medical schools. In many medical schools one-fourth to three-quarters of the faculty members serve on a volunteer basis and receive no compensation from the school. It is estimated that 10 to 15 per cent of all practicing physicians now serve on medical school faculties or on the teaching staffs of their hospitals. The value of these men's services has never been computed in dollars. Their contributed services, however, make the medical school unique in the family of university professional schools.

PAYMENT FOR SERVICES RENDERED

Tuition

Tuition income represents payment for services rendered to students. During the ten-year period 1940–41 to 1950–51, income from tuition and fees almost doubled in both the tax-supported and the privately supported medical schools.

From the observation that income from student tuition fees provides a declining percentage of medical school income, it should not be deduced that tuition fee income is increasingly failing to meet the "costs of medical education." Such a deduction would be illogical. The declining percentage contributed by tuition fees to the medical school budget in recent years has resulted from the great increase in the total income from other sources, such as tax monies and gifts or grants for special purposes, many of which are not directly helpful, if helpful at all, to the education of the medical student and are frequently for research purposes only.

The cost of medical education obviously can be expected to fluctuate with the cost of living, and when tuition fees are compared with the cost of living over the 10-year period, it is found that the average medical-student tuition fee in 1951 stood at 158 per cent of the 1939–40 figure,[1] while the cost of living stood at 186 per cent of the 1939–40 figure. Thus the average student tuition fee has lagged behind the cost of living, which inevitably has affected the costs of the medical school and will do so in the future. Even this comparison is misleading, however, since no school has as yet defined precisely what items of its expenditures can legitimately be said to constitute the cost of educating a medical student.

It has been seriously proposed that privately supported and tax-supported schools charge tuition fees that will more nearly cover the full cost of educating a medical student, and one privately supported school has recently raised its tuition to $1,200 per year. Tuition fees ranging from $1,500 to $3,000 per year have been discussed. The Board of Control for Southern Regional Education has been paying $1,500 per year to cooperating medical schools admitting certain out-of-state students.

[1] ANDERSON, D. G., F. R. MANLOVE, and ANNE TIPNER, Medical Education in the United States and Canada, *Journal of the American Medical Association,* Vol. 147, p. 153 (Sept. 8), 1951.

In the West also there is a regional plan under which some states without medical schools have agreed to pay to medical schools in other states the sum of $2,600 per year for every resident of their states whom they admit as students. Many schools are considering higher tuition fees with concomitant increases in scholarships and loan funds for those students unable to meet tuition charges.

The proposal to increase tuition to meet the costs of education more adequately is defendable on a business basis, but, as has been pointed out in previous chapters, without more precise information concerning the costs of educating a medical student, it is at present impossible to establish tuition figures to cover these costs. The low tuition charges of state schools tend to hold all tuition fees down.

There is considerable fear on the part of the administrators of the medical schools that tuition fees, if raised to approximate cost, will automatically bar a great many excellent prospective physicians. It is doubtful, however, whether the high cost of tuition is the only factor which discourages young men and women from entering the study of medicine, especially since tuition increases have not kept pace with increases in the cost of living. The long period with inadequate earnings is probably a stronger deterrent.

Income from Noninstructional Activities

Income from noninstructional activities is generally of little importance. The income from bookstores, dormitories, rentals, and concessions is usually small.

Medical Service to the Community in the Teaching Hospital

The operation of hospitals by medical schools in the past has rarely produced income for the medical schools. In a few instances only have hospital earnings exceeded expenses. A constant effort is being made by medical schools and their teaching hospitals to recover the full costs of the services that they render to their communities. Since most of this hospital care is provided to charity and welfare patients, the medical schools that use their funds to provide free care for patients in their hospitals are serving as charitable as well as educational institutions.

If the welfare of indigent or low-income persons is the responsibility of the community, then the community should pay the full costs of the care of their illnesses. Thereby the drain on the finances of many medical schools and their teaching hospitals would be relieved. Some communities are accepting this responsibility. In other instances, medical school funds amounting to as much as $175,000 per year are being expended on the care of charity patients. The accounts of many medical schools and their teaching hospitals are so intermingled that it is impossible to determine how much—or indeed whether any—of the medical school funds are utilized in maintaining services that might more properly be the responsibility of the hospital or the community. As is described in other chapters, accounting policies and practices must be studied and revised if the financial responsibilities now carried by the medical schools are to be clearly presented.

Indirect Costs of Research Grants

The indirect costs on certain project research grants (which are often designed for the purpose of benefiting the grantor, and not to strengthen the medical schools or improve the quality of medical education) may be said to be a potential source of earned income by the medical schools. Complete defrayment of indirect costs to the medical schools of conducting the research programs supported by grants-in-aid would make unnecessary the expenditure of the schools' own funds that would otherwise support their other activities. Granting agencies are becoming increasingly aware of the financial problem their grants are creating and, as stated in Chapter 3, "Research," it has been suggested that some national organization devise a sliding scale for determining accurately the amount of the indirect costs for grants-in-aid of all sizes. In the meantime, on the basis of an analysis of 91 heterogeneous research programs,[2] it has been recommended that granting agencies defray 90 per cent of the indirect costs to the medical schools. To accomplish this, it has been suggested that they add 46.0 per cent of the total to grants up to $10,000 in amount, and other specific percentages to grants above that sum. Since the grants-in-aid supporting the 91 research programs totaled $3,387,458, and the indirect costs amounted to an additional sum of $1,310,356, it can be seen that the income to the 33 institutions conducting the studies would have been sizable if the indirect costs had been defrayed by the granting agencies.

[2] WEAVER, H. M., A Proposal for Defraying the Cost of Conducting Programs of Research, *Journal of Medical Education*, Vol. 27, p. 316 (September), 1952.

Earnings from the Professional Care of Patients by Clinical Faculty
  Members

Should not be done.

Use of the earnings of clinical faculty members to provide income for
the support of the medical school's activities is a relatively new development. Little accurate data could be obtained during the Survey on the
growth or the magnitude of funds from this source.

Income from clinical practice has always supported the clinical faculties of the medical schools. Before the turn of the century very few
clinical teachers received any salary; they were engaged in the practice
of medicine, and they devoted a portion of their time to teaching. Modi-
fications of this pattern occurred when the "full-time" and "geographic
full-time" concepts were introduced. A faculty member associated with
the medical school on a full-time or a geographic full-time basis spends
all his time in the medical school and the teaching hospitals, but has facilities there for private practice and consultations and may care for private patients admitted to the hospital. The geographic full-time member
is allowed to retain all or a part of his earnings from practice and the
strictly full-time man is not.

A wide range of variations in the methods of handling the earnings
of these men was encountered during the Survey, and the method depended upon the organization of the medical school and the teaching
hospital. In some instances no limit was put on these earnings, which
the faculty member retained. In others, earnings above a certain ceiling
reverted to the department of the medical school in which the man held
his faculty position. In another plan, the total earnings accrued to the
department, and in another these earnings were added to the general
funds of the medical school or the university from which the faculty
member received a full-time salary.

In only one medical school is the entire faculty on a full-time basis.
In this school the university owns a hospital of medium size, and more
than 80 per cent of the patients utilized in teaching are private patients,
paying both for their hospital care and for the professional medical service rendered by the faculty. The income from professional fees totals
more than $800,000 per year and goes into general funds for the sup-
port of the medical school and the hospital. It should be recognized,
however, that this sum does not cover the full cost to the medical school
of the salaries of the faculty members. Because of the university organ-

ization and the accounting practices, it was impossible for the Survey to determine the magnitude of the effect of this policy on the over-all financing of this medical school.

The pattern more commonly encountered is illustrated by a second privately supported medical school. At this school, the major teaching hospital is neither owned nor operated by the university. The medical school has both a nucleus of full-time faculty members, whose professional fees go to the medical school, and a large volunteer clinical faculty on the staff of the teaching hospital who depend upon the practice of medicine for their livelihood. Private patients are not used in student teaching. The earnings of the full-time faculty members have risen rapidly and in 1950 approximated $550,000 per year. These funds are distributed to departmental budgets by the executive faculty, with the clinical departments receiving most of the money. Shortly after the Second World War, the medical school seriously considered expanding its facilities for this type of private practice. Such expansion was strongly opposed by practicing physicians, however, especially by those who served on the faculty on a volunteer basis. The board of trustees of the university failed to approve the new development, and the full-time faculty members, therefore, continued to see private patients only on a referral basis. The chief value to the school of this arrangement is financial, since the private patient plays no part in the medical-students' program.

In a third medical school, again with a nucleus of full-time clinical faculty members, professional fees earned by these faculty members from private patients remain in the respective departments of the medical school. Such earnings have reached a total of $270,000 per year in income for a single department. The private patients are not utilized in student teaching. The clinical departments in this school are strong and rapidly growing, in contrast to the basic science departments, which are relatively small and weak.

Various other methods were encountered, both in tax-supported and in privately supported medical schools, for utilizing fees from private patients. However, it was impossible to obtain exact figures on the earnings from this source. When the fees from private patients became part of the private income of the faculty member, the administrative officers of the medical school had no knowledge of their magnitude.

The Dangers. In the practice of medicine by faculty members, there is a tremendous potential source of income for the medical schools. Nevertheless, there is the danger that the faculty may be selected on the basis of earning ability rather than teaching ability.

Other grave dangers are inherent in some of the plans being used for handling the earnings of the full-time and the geographic full-time faculty. When the faculty member's earnings from the practice of medicine become the property of the school, an undue burden of responsibility for its financial support can be placed upon that faculty member and he may be forced to devote more time to practice and less time to research and teaching; for instance, a school with expanding activities needs more financial support, and the faculty member may be required to increase his earnings. The danger is exemplified by a school visited during the Survey at which the professor of medicine, who became interested in a research problem and began to devote more time to it, was questioned by the financial officer of the school regarding the fall in income from his private practice and was bluntly told that the school was dependent upon this income. The dean of this school stated that he considered the earnings of the geographic full-time faculty to be "the financial savior" of the institution.

When faculty members are permitted to retain the income from practice conducted within the confines of the medical school and hospital, and to use all their facilities, the danger lies in the development of large, independent practices, largely made possible through the use of interns and residents. In one such school with a geographic full-time faculty, individual earnings of faculty members at the time of the Survey's visit had reached sums ranging from $15,000 to $30,000 per year. In order to ensure that faculty members devoted more time to the medical school, an attempt was made to place ceilings on their earnings. After a brief trial period of such control, however, four department heads threatened to resign unless the ceilings were removed. Since the chief administrative officer was himself mainly dependent upon a similar practice for his income, his position in attempting to curb the faculty's practice was considerably weakened.

This situation was not confined to a few schools. The potential danger exists wherever the opportunity is offered to exploit a medical school position as a means of increasing personal earnings. Individual earnings of $25,000 to $30,000 from practices were admitted to the Survey by men in a school which paid small salaries of $3,000 to $5,000 to its clinical faculty members. In no instances were the students allowed to work with the private patients.

When the earnings from the faculty members' practice of medicine become the property of their departments, the danger lies in the financial independence, prestige, and influence that accrue to those departments. Certain of the clinical departments at schools visited during the Survey had budgets two or three times as large as those of other clinical departments, and five to ten times as large as the budgets available to the medical basic science departments. Under such conditions, the wealthy departments become relatively independent of the medical school and much more closely identified with the teaching hospital. Professors of the more affluent departments, when they spoke of the medical school, implied that they referred to the medical basic science departments only; they distinctly gave the impression that they did not feel themselves to be an intimate part of the educational institution. Dissatisfaction and jealousy among departments had become the inevitable result.

Earnings from the practice of medicine of full-time and geographic full-time faculty members are growing. The personal income-tax structure is conducive to such plans. Many faculty members with large earnings from private practice are willing to reduce their practices, and to turn over all their earnings to the school, in return for what they consider an adequate salary and provision for retirement income and sickness insurance. In this way it is possible to avoid the problem of maintaining a private office and of saving for retirement from net earnings after payment of income tax.

In the majority of methods employed for managing the earnings of paid members of the clinical faculties, there is only one advantage over using the same men as volunteer faculty members earning their incomes from private practice outside the medical school. That advantage is the fact that the man with facilities for practice in the medical school or teaching hospital may be more readily available to the school. Ideally, if the faculty members' professional earnings were derived from the same patients who cooperated in the teaching program, great benefit could result to both the medical school and the faculty members. At the majority of medical schools, however, present policies make adoption of any such plan practically impossible. These policies are slanted toward the development of medical centers, with clinical teaching facilities spread over a wide area in hospitals in which patients are classified as private, semiprivate, or ward.

SOME FINANCIAL POLICIES FOR THE FUTURE

The wide variation in the obligations and responsibilities assumed by or thrust upon medical schools makes difficult any general plan for their financial support. The only common denominator of the schools is that they all instruct medical students. In other respects the schools may be quite dissimilar, some of them carrying on such a wide variety of educational, training, and research activities that the institutions assume the proportions and the complexity of structure of universities.

As has been indicated, the activities of the individual schools are of real value to their local communities—city, county, or state. The people benefiting from the activities and service of the schools can decide to pay for them directly at the local level; alternatively, they can decide to pay for them with state or Federal taxes. If the people pay for these services by taxation methods, the funds return to the community for its medical school after passing through government bureaus at several levels, and often in the form of subsidies for those activities which a government agency has determined are of the greatest relative value. Nevertheless, the social trend is toward support of the medical schools by taxation methods. Able medical school and community leadership is needed if greater financial support of the medical schools is to be obtained at the local level.

Many segments of the public today are well aware of the value of the medical research carried on by the medical schools, and of their service activities. The value of a high quality of medical education is, however, more difficult for them to appreciate, since the results are not so immediately apparent or measurable. Persons and agencies who have faith in education and are philanthropically minded should constantly seek new ventures, in concert with the medical schools, in an effort to help those institutions to meet the changes that will constantly occur in a biological field.

All segments of society should contribute to the support of a medical school. A school that is dependent for its support upon only a few sources of income cannot maintain the flexibility and freedom that are so essential to an educational institution, and therein lies the very real danger of present trends. Financial support in which all segments of society participate will result in a well-balanced program for the school. Only in this way can the medical schools remain sensitive to the needs of all segments of society.

CONCLUSIONS

1. Both the expenditures and the income of 59 medical schools more than tripled between the fiscal years 1940–41 and 1950–51.

2. The strongest trend is the use of tax monies for the support of medical schools. In 1950–51 the privately supported schools were receiving nearly forty times the amount of tax monies that they received in 1940–41. In 1950–51 these schools were receiving 30.5 per cent of their income from Federal, state, city, and county tax appropriations; 10 years earlier the proportion was 2.6 per cent.

3. Endowment income increased considerably in the last decade of the half century.

4. Gifts and grants from private sources increased remarkably between 1940–41 and 1950–51, but they were usually restricted by their donors to specific activities such as research.

5. Tuition income, although it doubled in a 10-year period, provided a declining percentage of medical school income because of the great increase in the total income from other sources—much of which was not directly helpful to the education of the medical student.

6. The shifts in emphasis that occurred in the expenditures during the 1940–41 to 1950–51 decade show a trend toward primary emphasis on research and secondary emphasis on instruction. This is a reversal of the generally accepted values in medical education.

7. The shifts in emphasis reflect the value placed upon the activities of the medical schools by their administrative officers and by the public.

8. The medical schools' accounting methods reflect the variations in the schools' policies and objectives.

9. Conclusions can at present be drawn regarding the financial needs of the medical schools only with extreme caution. Until the schools carefully define their objectives and delineate them in terms of desirable magnitude, no such conclusions can be entirely dependable.

10. The variations in the obligations and responsibilities assumed by or

thrust upon medical schools, and the lack of definition, make difficult any general plan for their financial support and have caused government and philanthropic agencies to make their own decisions regarding the activities most in need of support.

RECOMMENDATIONS

1. Concerted action must be taken by the medical schools to define precisely what activities are to be included in medical education.
2. When such definition has been accomplished, accounting practices must be revised so that the expenditures on each activity can be recorded accurately.
3. The policies of the medical schools must be designed to maintain their activities in the balance that will preserve the basic principles of education.
4. When definition of medical education, based on proper principles, has been accomplished, and when the activities of the schools have been placed in proper balance, the financial needs will become plain. The schools should then place their needs before the public.
5. The public, when it has been informed of the value of the activities of the medical schools, should decide whether it will support them directly or through taxation methods.
6. Persons and agencies who have faith in education and are philanthropically minded should constantly seek new ventures, in concert with the medical schools, in an effort to help those institutions to meet the changes that will constantly occur in a biological field such as medicine.

Part IV

THE MEDICAL SCHOOL IN OPERATION

7 ADMINISTRATION

Medical education can be only as good as its leaders. Although in the last analysis it is the governing board and the president of the university who are responsible for the policies and objectives of the university and its medical school, the formulation of these policies and objectives is greatly influenced by the leaders of the medical schools. The leaders of a medical school are the dean or the chief administrative officer, the heads of departments, and the outstanding members of the faculty. Any person serving as a member of one of these three groups may provide the type of leadership that is essential to the progress of a medical school.

The administrative head is responsible for the operation of the institution in the way most effective for the attainment of its objectives. He is, therefore, a key figure in the school. Although the extent of his statutory power may vary greatly, his influence is determined by the force of his personality, the quality of his leadership, and the skill of his executive management.

The administration of a medical school in the latter part of the nineteenth century was relatively simple. The physical facilities of the schools were limited, and income and expenditures were proportionately small. The curriculum covered a two- or three-year period, and instruction was given primarily in the form of lectures by practicing physicians. Most medical schools conducted little if any research. Hospitals were just emerging from the "boardinghouse-for-the-sick" era; they were primarily philanthropic institutions, and their service was simple and inexpensive. The medical schools had little responsibility for their operation. One of the senior members of the faculty, who had the respect of his colleagues and who was willing to devote his spare time to the position,

117

was selected to serve as dean. His responsibilities consisted largely of recruiting students, arranging lecture schedules, persuading local practitioners to give lectures, and managing the simple finances of the school.

Within the last 30 years, however, administration has become enormously more complex and difficult. The deans of half of the four-year medical schools are responsible for the administration of institutions spending more than a million dollars a year exclusive of hospital expenses. With the advancement of knowledge and the social and economic changes that have taken place in the country, important problems have developed in these institutions. The position of dean now usually requires the full time of a highly competent individual with administrative skill.

In studying administration at the 41 medical schools surveyed, extensive interviews were held with the dean of each school, and careful study was made of his written answers to over 100 questions. Interviews were held with the president or the vice-president of the university, with members of the board of trustees, and with the head of each department in the medical school. Opinions on the effectiveness of the administration of the school were recorded, as well as the observations of the Survey teams on the subject. Financial information, supplied by the medical school, was analyzed for the relation between administrative and general expenditures.

OBJECTIVES

Clearly understood objectives are essential to the effective administration of any institution. The objectives of a medical school depend upon the size, age, location, university affiliation, hospital relations, and financial support of the school, as well as upon the vision of its leaders. Thus a certain variation in objectives is to be expected among 41 medical schools.

The dean of each school supplied a brief statement of the objectives of his school with respect to undergraduate, graduate, and postgraduate medical education, research, service, and geographical scope. Statements of published objectives and opinions of boards of trustees and of faculty members were studied. Many deans stated objectives that were simply and clearly directed toward the education of medical students and the training of interns and residents, with research as a by-product and community service and education of students in related fields incidental activities. In only a minority of the schools was it clear that these objectives were understood and accepted by the board of trustees and the faculty.

In many schools, however, the dean's stated objectives were found to vary markedly from those outlined by the university president, the board of trustees, and members of the faculty. For example, in one institution the dean's statement of objectives was clearly directed toward the education of the undergraduate medical student and the continuing education of the physician. But a pamphlet prepared by the faculty and approved by the governing board implied that the primary objective of the medical school was to educate students in many other categories as well as medical students, to offer postgraduate medical education to the medical profession, and to provide numerous community medical services.

In another school, the dean's statement was again directed toward the education of the undergraduate medical student and the continuing education of the physician. But these objectives were at variance with those of the governing board and the faculty. The board had published a statement to the effect that the facilities and the faculty of the university, particularly of the medical school, constitute major resources of the state and are, therefore, dedicated to the service of the people of the state.

In a third school the dean and faculty had prepared, with the approval of the governing board, a sweeping, all-inclusive statement of objectives which covered the full range of medical care, and the school had embarked upon an ambitious and expensive campaign of expanding its influence and services.

These inconsistencies and variations, found to be marked in over half of the schools visited, illustrate two basic weaknesses in the leadership of those schools. One is that communication between the dean and the members of the board and of the faculty has not been adequate to lead to general understanding and agreement on the objectives of the institution. The other is that in too many instances the dean and members of the faculty and of the board fail to distinguish between primary and secondary objectives, or to recognize that although two activities may be parallel and mutually supporting both cannot be considered as primary objectives.

In addition to these variations, in many schools activities are being initiated and expanded without clear formulation of objectives. They are often undertaken by the administration as matters of expediency, either in response to outside pressures or in an effort to obtain additional support for the institution.

The confusion of objectives either on the part of the university or within a medical school produced results that were clearly evident. If the governing board of the university felt that service should be a major function of the medical school, it was common to find that the hospital was well financed but the medical school had a relatively small budget. If the university viewed the medical school as an integral part of the general instructional program, the medical school faculty was frequently found to be floundering under an almost impossible teaching load. If the administration of the university considered that the advancement of knowledge should be the objective, service and teaching were often relegated to positions of secondary importance.

In many schools, although the deans claimed the education of undergraduate and graduate medical students as the major objective, the medical schools had accepted responsibilities for service, research, and nonmedical teaching so large that the major objective was overshadowed. In contrast, in other schools there was general agreement on objectives, and in these schools the teaching of students, research, and the provision of a limited amount of high-quality service were proceeding smoothly and effectively.

It is necessary that the medical school and its parent university agree on objectives. It is also plain that expansion in the scope and magnitude of a medical school's activities should be undertaken only with a clear comprehension of the relation of this expansion to the objectives of the institution. Otherwise the administration of the school, already enormously complex and difficult, lacks focus and direction.

EDUCATION

Profound changes in educational methods have been effected in the medical schools during the last several decades. To a large extent laboratory and small group teaching have replaced didactic lectures in the preclinical subjects. Clerkships and bedside teaching have become dominant pedagogical methods in the clinical subjects. Extensive programs of internship and residency training have been developed in the teaching hospitals. The provision of facilities, equipment, faculty, and patients for these methods of teaching requires planning and leadership. The dean must, therefore, possess broad knowledge of the subjects and the teaching methods involved and ability to promote faculty teamwork. The provision of clinical facilities confronts the administration with the complex and difficult problem of the relations that should exist between the medical school and its teaching hospital.

The advancement and specialization of knowledge have made it necessary for the medical schools to establish additional departments and subdepartments. There is constant pressure for the inclusion of additional subjects in the medical curriculum, and for increasing allotments of time and facilities for other subjects. The faculty should play a prominent role in the solution of these problems, but many of its members are so deeply involved in their own subjects that they find it difficult to appreciate the importance of other subjects to a medical student. The dean, theoretically, is in a position to exert the unbiased leadership that will provide an inclusive, well-balanced program for the medical student.

The administration may have to defend the basic principles of the educational program. In recent years, especially since 1945, there has been tremendous pressure on the medical schools to expand their enrollment. In a few schools the administration resisted this pressure because the school had neither the facilities nor the faculty to provide education of high quality to a large number of students. They defended the principle of close student-faculty contact in education.

Too often, however, administrators followed the line of expediency. They enrolled larger classes on the basis of promises of expanded facilities and appropriations. In a great many instances such schools will graduate many classes of medical students before the new facilities are in operation and faculties enlarged. The pressure of public opinion and state legislature outweighed educational principles.

In many universities the faculties of medical schools are required to provide part or all of the teaching for students in many other categories in addition to medical students. Under such circumstances administration involves attention to many details concerned with class and laboratory scheduling and student records, as well as working contact with divisions of the university in which the nonmedical students are registered. The administrative authority of the institution must solve the problem of how students in so many different categories can be properly taught without interfering with the medical students' program and constituting a serious drain upon the time of the faculty.

SERVICE

The expansion of service activities by the medical school imposes a heavy load upon the administration of the institution. To meet this responsibility, the school must supply a faculty that is willing and competent to provide service at a high level of quality while at the same time conducting the teaching program of the medical school. Much of the responsibility for providing the support for this faculty rests upon the administration.

In organizing a faculty to provide these services, administrative officers are forced to enter one of the most difficult and controversial fields of medicine. Traditionally, in this country, professional service has been rendered by physicians acting as individuals. The carrying out of a modern teaching program and the fulfillment of service obligations require organized teamwork from many able physicians. The problem of how to obtain the advantages of this closer teamwork and yet to preserve, and if possible strengthen, the known advantages of freedom and initiative of physicians is extraordinarily difficult.

It is important for the administration to handle the affairs of this large and growing faculty in such a way as to avoid conflict and undue competition with practicing physicians who are not members of the faculty, and to retain their good will. Not all the present deans and vice-presidents in charge of medical affairs have had enough experience in the practice of medicine, or in efforts to organize medical practice, to have acquired great competence in this area. The evolution of the medical schools and teaching hospitals into medical centers increases this problem to a marked degree.

At this mid-point of the twentieth century, many medical schools find themselves affiliated with hospitals other than their own teaching hospital. For example, one small privately supported medical school owns and operates its own teaching hospital; in addition, it is responsible, through a dean's committee, for all staff appointments at a large Veterans Administration hospital, where some student teaching and house-officer training is carried out. The school is responsible for staff appointments on one service in a city hospital, and sends a few members of its faculty to another hospital of the Veterans Administration and to an Army hospital, both in other cities. It has recently entered into an agreement whereby the interns for all the hospitals in the city will have work in the outpatient department of the university hospital.

In another instance, a small tax-supported medical school has complete responsibility for staff appointments in a county hospital which serves as its teaching hospital. Through a dean's committee it is responsible for all staff appointments at a hospital of the Veterans Administration. It is also responsible for staff appointments at a state tuberculosis sanatorium, and plans are under way for the construction of a hospital owned and operated by the medical school. It sends medical students to still another hospital in the city for a small part of their program. These hospital affiliations require that a considerable amount of time be spent by the dean or his representative in negotiating with the administrations of the hospitals.

RESEARCH

Within the last half century the medical schools have come to be important centers for scientific research. Research programs, now large and constantly growing, are attracting increasing support from many agencies.

Outside agencies giving funds for research are obviously interested in seeing practical results. But the history of science records that the practical applications of today depend upon the advances of knowledge made yesterday, and the business of the university is the advancement of knowledge through teaching and research. Therefore, it is the duty of the dean and the faculty to see that basic or exploratory research is well supported and that the research program of the school is not too heavily weighted toward studies designed for immediate application.

Under present methods of financing research, the administration and the faculty must have a broad acquaintance with philanthropic individuals and agencies. Additional personnel must be employed to cope with the large number of special accounts and to negotiate with the representatives of many different agencies.

Restricted funds have increased more rapidly than the general income of the medical school. The administration must decide what portion of the research expense should be charged to these restricted funds, and what portion to the general medical school funds.

All this research activity requires the use of space and facilities in the medical school or its hospital, a portion of the time of the faculty, and a growing staff of technicians and research associates, all of which should be provided without impairing the teaching activities. The administration must be judicious in deciding salaries and working conditions of research personnel, taking care that they are not out of line with those of the other personnel in the school.

Some schools have a faculty committee to review all research proposals. However, when faculty members have research interests that conflict or overlap, it is the responsibility of the administration to maintain a proper balance in order to avoid excessive duplication of equipment and personnel. No research should be undertaken by the medical school if it is dictated by any other factor than the advancement of knowledge and the strengthening of the school's basic educational program.

FINANCES

One of the major functions of the dean is to prepare and present the budget to the president and governing board of the university and to see that the actual expenditures are in keeping with the approved budget. In a period of rising costs and expanding activities, it is usually necessary for the dean to defend the proposed budget with some vigor. Also in the recent past much effort has been required to maintain expenditures within the budgetary allowances.

In tax-supported medical schools the governing board commonly requests the dean to appear before legislative committees or to present his arguments to individual members of the legislative body. In the privately supported medical schools the governing boards have usually expected the dean to take an active interest in raising additional income, and this requires that he spend time with alumni and influential citizens. The financial difficulties of the teaching hospital make it necessary for him to deal with the management of the hospital and with various community agencies which may provide financial support for the care of the indigent sick.

In order to control the expenditures and plan future budgets effectively and intelligently, it is essential that the dean know of all financial transactions that affect the medical school. In many of the medical schools studied, especially in those in which the business office of the university handled the medical school accounts, the deans were inadequately informed concerning the medical school's finances. Financial statements and reports are often long delayed and incomplete. Many deans were unable to furnish the Survey with accurate information on their school's finances until more than six months after the end of a fiscal year because the business office had not provided the facts. Under such conditions it is almost impossible for the administration of a medical school to plan an intelligent budget for the next year.

RELATIONS WITH THE PUBLIC

Medicine is of great interest to the public, and the need of medical schools for support from their own communities has become increasingly apparent. Helping the public to know and to understand the medical school is another responsibility of the administrative officers of both medical school and university.

The public press is frequently eager to publish news concerning certain patients, research that gives promise of practical benefits, and honors and attainments of the faculty. Such news must be presented accurately and with propriety. Coping with irregular and frequent demands of this sort has led many medical schools to establish a public-relations member of the administrative staff whose special job it is to handle publicity. It remains the dean's responsibility to select this person and to exercise general supervision over his work.

It is to the advantage of the medical school for its representatives to appear at public functions, to accept invitations to speak to large or small groups, to get to know the leaders in the community, and in other ways to bring the medical school to the attention of the public. Although public relations consume a large amount of time and energy, and special abilities are required for their promotion, a successful public-relations program pays large dividends to the school.

NATIONAL AFFAIRS

There are increasing opportunities and many demands for medical school leaders to play an active role in national professional organizations and to supply advice and consultation to those administering state and national programs in the health fields. The Second World War caused a marked increase in these demands, and the trend is still continuing. The affairs of the Association of American Medical Colleges have become increasingly complex and time-consuming; some of the activities of the Council on Medical Education and Hospitals of the American Medical Association require advice and assistance from members of the faculties of the medical schools; the Veterans Administration now seeks advice and consultation from the medical schools at both the national and local levels; grants in support of medical research made by the National Institutes of Health are made on the recommendation of special advisory committees, most of the members of which are drawn from the faculties of medical schools. The deans and the faculty members are also asked to serve on national advisory and study committees, and it has become necessary for them to be away on such missions with increasing frequency and to bring their thoughts to bear on problems far broader and more complex than those which confronted the typical medical school at the turn of the century.

The amount of time that the dean is away from his post varies widely, and the Survey made no effort to determine this precisely. Incidental observations suggest, however, that in some instances the dean is absent a large part of the time. A secretary, who has served under three successive administrative heads, stated that a former dean had conducted one of the busiest practices in the city, yet had managed to be in his office and in the institution more than the present incumbent who devotes full time to his post. In another school the dean had been out of town on national affairs steadily for two months in the middle of the school year, in a period when the school was undergoing extensive changes.

THE DEANS

At the time of the Flexner study in 1910, most of the deanships were part-time assignments which interfered only partially with the individual's activity in his own field of practice, teaching, or research. At the present time this situation has almost completely changed. In most instances the administration of the medical school requires not only the full time of the dean but also enlargement of the administrative staff.

In 12 of the medical schools studied, the dean managed to devote some time to teaching or research in his own field of interest. In six of these schools the dean had the assistance of a competent administrative team; in two the dean worked directly under a vice-president who carried most of the administrative responsibility; while in two others the medical school was small and well knit, and the dean devoted only a very small amount of time to his own professional field. Twenty of the 41 deans found time to carry on a consultative practice in their field of medicine.

In five of the medical schools visited the dean also held the position of head of a major department. Because of exceptional circumstances this seemed to work fairly well in three instances. As a general rule, however, the successful administration of a department is so time-consuming that it is unsound to combine this administrative assignment with the added administrative problems of the medical school.

The deans of the 41 schools studied are, in general, hard-working men who spare no effort to cope with the serious problems that confront the medical schools. In a number of instances all the evidence pointed to the fact that the dean was doing an effective job. He had a clear vision of the educational role of the school and a grasp of the relative values of its various activities. In other instances the multiplicity of current problems and the work load appeared to exceed the capacities and knowledge of the dean and his administrative staff.

In certain schools the dean was frequently engaged with problems outside the school and was unaware of important problems within the school. An example of this situation was the dean who expressed complete satisfaction with the school, its faculty and program, and confidence that he and his faculty would have no difficulty in carrying on their program. However, the students expressed great bitterness toward this school; they were highly critical of its educational methods and said it was virtually impossible for them to see the dean or to get to know the faculty. Several members of this faculty expressed grave concern over the heavy teaching load they were required to carry. The president of the university said that a drastic reduction in appropriations and irresistible pressure to expand the size of the entering class were in immediate prospect.

In some schools the dean and his administrative staff lacked the ability to cope with the problems created by some particular activity of the school. An example of this was the dean who, being administratively responsible for the teaching hospital, had turned over the details of its operation to an inexperienced man. When rising costs threatened to exceed income, the dean and the hospital superintendent authorized the use of reserve funds to such an extent that the board of trustees felt it necessary to dismiss the hospital superintendent and to give a member of the faculty authority to supervise all financial matters pertaining to both school and hospital.

In other instances the administrative staff was so small that neither the staff nor the dean had time for close attention to the progress of the students. In one large and complex school with many assets, including students of high quality, the dean and his administrative staff were so engaged with the activities of a medical center that both students and faculty expressed concern over the fact that most students did not know the dean by sight. They also reported difficulty in getting in to see the officer principally involved in student affairs at any time after their interview for admission, and that cheating among the students was a serious problem and grew more common and flagrant as they proceeded through medical school. The dean appeared to be unaware of these conditions.

In still other schools, the dean's interest in social problems and desire to initiate medical-care programs far exceeded the faculty's capacity to assume additional service responsibilities. An example of this was a medical school with a small, hard-working faculty and meager financial support which had difficulty operating a program of reasonable quality. The dean, however, was actively engaged in promoting a plan whereby the medical school would assume considerable responsibility in a state-wide program to provide medical care in several state institutions.

Study of the medical schools has led to the opinion that the selection of deans does not always result in men with the skill and vision necessary for the future of medical education. Most of the medical schools face challenging problems created by such broad social phenomena as rising costs, expanding population, and changes in the generally accepted philosophy of taxation and social welfare. If true leadership is to be maintained, it is incumbent upon the dean to handle the internal and external affairs of the medical school effectively and to help to adjust its program to social changes so that the school can go forward with its mission.

DIRECTORS OF MEDICAL AFFAIRS

The growth of the medical schools and their evolution into medical centers have accentuated the difficulties of integrating their activities and of financing their expanded responsibilities. The increasing complexity of medical school–hospital relations has been a major factor in the creation of a new university administrative officer, known as "director of medical affairs" or "vice-president in charge of medical affairs."

In recent years when costs have risen so sharply, the incomes of both hospital and medical school have not expanded proportionately. In a number of instances the medical schools have maintained that it was educationally necessary to operate a large number of free beds and that it was the responsibility of the board of governors of the hospital to provide the necessary funds. Hospital administrators have maintained that, except for the cost of large free services, it was possible to keep the hospital in a state of financial equilibrium. With the medical school, the hospital, or both these institutions running large annual deficits, several boards of governors have created an additional administrative position, the incumbent of which is in charge of both hospital and medical school and has as his primary responsibility the solution of this difficult financial problem.

Some of the men holding these positions were drawn from the field of medicine, others were formerly in architecture, mathematics, hospital administration, or public health. Business and administrative ability is more and more being emphasized in the selection of men for these posts.[1] Few if any of these administrative officers carry academic responsibility.

The function of most of these new officers is more accurately described by the title "director of medical affairs" than by the title "vice-president." Usually they have offices in the medical school and closely supervise every policy and administrative act of such officers as the dean and the director of the hospital. In this way they exert tremendous influence upon the activities of both school and hospital. They rarely serve in the simple role of aides in the offices of the presidents.

[1] It is interesting to note that A. A. Abbie, reporting in the *Medical Journal of Australia* (Jan. 13, 1951, p. 69) after his visit to this continent to study American medical education, made this same observation.

Some members of the faculties are gravely worried over this tendency to select men primarily for their competence in administrative and financial matters and to place them in over-all charge of the medical center. They express concern lest this official will come to feel that the size of the budget of each component part of the center indicates its relative importance. It was observed that, where a vice-president was in charge, the dean and the faculty had little or no contact with the president and the board of governors of the university.

Boards of governors, however, find the policy of establishing these university posts justified. The board has a legal responsibility to conserve the resources of the institution and to see that those programs which it authorizes can be operated on the funds available. The boards have the alternatives of giving the dean authority to control both institutions or of creating a new position with that authority.

In at least six universities, the first of these alternatives has been chosen. In three instances the governing board has given the dean additional authority over the institutions making up the medical center, usually signified by an additional title such as "Director of Medical Affairs." At the same time the dean has been given additional assistants to help with the work of his office.

Study of the individual schools has led to the conclusion that, where an administrative head for all the units making up a medical center is needed, the background of experience and long-time interest of the person selected is an important factor in determining the future orientation of the center. An administrator with knowledge and experience in the functions of one of the units may be inclined to strengthen that unit in relation to others. If this unit is the hospital, the center may tend to become primarily a hospital center. If the administrator's interest and experience have been in research, the center may become oriented primarily toward research; if they have been in the teaching of medicine, the center may emphasize medical education. If his interest and experience have been in some field not represented in the medical center, he may be inclined to consider as most important that portion of the center requiring the greatest expenditure of time and money. The choice of man for the post of medical vice-president or director of medical affairs, therefore, may determine in which direction the center will develop its activities in the future.

Regardless of background, however, it is of the greatest importance that the individual who occupies the post of medical vice-president possess vision, judgment, and administrative skill to a high degree. Since the medical vice-president has far greater authority and responsibility than the dean and is more remote from the faculty, he should be skillful at obtaining the cooperation and confidence of the faculty and the dean. He must delegate to the various members of the team authority commensurate with the responsibilities they must carry.

A university is engaged in the field of medicine to advance knowledge through teaching and fundamental research. Therefore, in a university medical center the medical school should be the hub of all medical endeavor. It follows that the educational strength and integrity of the medical school must be protected by close relations with the top administrative officers of the university.

The problem of administering a medical center is illustrated in Figure 11, which shows how complex the chart of organization of such a center

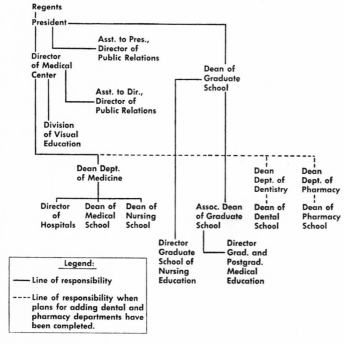

Figure 11. Chart of organization of a modern medical center that is still expanding. The diagram could be extended similarly to the left to include the various business units of the center and the dean of faculties, who is a top-echelon officer at the same level as the director of the medical center and the dean of the graduate school.

can become. This chart shows the relative position of the medical school in such a center. The dean of the medical school is a fourth-echelon administrative officer who has the same rank as the director of hospitals, the dean of the nursing school, and the associate dean of the graduate school. Between him and the president of the university are administrative officers in two higher echelons. He is responsible to the dean of the department of medicine, who has administrative authority for the hospitals, the medical school, and the nursing school. The dean of the department of medicine is responsible to the director of the medical center, who in turn is responsible to the president of the university.

The study of the administration of medical schools has led the Survey to the opinion that, in those institutions which are primarily educational institutions in which training and service are definitely minor activities, the dean should be the administrative head of the institution reporting directly to the president or to the board of trustees when there is no university connection. The director of the teaching hospital should be a member of the administrative team and responsible to the dean.

In those schools developing medical centers in which other activities overshadow education in their magnitude, the dean of the school must play a minor role. The term "dean," meaning the chief or head of a faculty in a university or college, does not apply to the position of director of a medical center. Such a position perhaps corresponds most closely to that of vice-president of a large corporation. Universities have recognized this fact, but have not always clearly explained why they are struggling to support medical centers.

In such a situation the dean of the medical school should at least control the budget of the medical school and speak for the faculty when policies of the center are decided upon which may affect medical education. His position is a difficult one and can be tenable and attractive to able men only if the director of the center believes in education and understands its basic principles. The dean must have his responsibilities and authority clearly defined.

ADMINISTRATIVE STAFF

In most of the medical schools studied, the dean had assistants to aid him in his administrative duties, but their number and caliber varied widely. In those medical schools which have expanded into medical centers, the administrative staff is divided between the office of the dean and the office of medical director. Since the medical center is a relatively new type of organization, the description of the administrative staff which follows refers primarily to the dean's assistants.

In 16 schools the university owned its major teaching hospital, but in only eight of these institutions was the man in charge of the hospital clearly responsible to the dean. In the other eight instances he was responsible to some other officer or board, and it was necessary for the dean to secure his cooperation without any administrative authority.

In the other medical schools, the teaching hospital was owned by a separate corporation and the man in charge of the hospital was responsible to the hospital's governing board and not to the authorities of the medical school. In many instances it had been difficult for the dean to secure the cooperation of the hospital administrator, who often had neither the information nor the background of experience that would be helpful in keeping the hospital well integrated in the teaching program. Since the hospital plays such a vital role in the activities of the medical school, it would seem logical for the dean to have as a member of his administrative staff either the man actually in charge of the hospital or someone with special interest and competence in that field. In most of the schools that was not the case.

The secretary to the dean in many instances serves also as a secretary to the faculty. The competence of this individual may be a very potent factor in the operation of the medical school. In a few instances the registrar, or some other member of the administrative staff, is designated secretary to the faculty, and this device apparently works relatively well.

In two of the schools surveyed, all the postgraduate programs were carried on by separately organized postgraduate schools with their own administrative structure. In the other schools that carried on fairly extensive postgraduate programs, this activity was usually administered by an assistant dean, who devoted part of his time to it. This individual handled all the details, and the dean concerned himself only with broad policies.

The administration of students' affairs including the work of the admissions committee varied considerably. In 28 schools the dean played an active role in student affairs and admissions. In the remaining 13 schools these activities were assigned to a registrar, a dean of students, or to the chairman of the admissions committee. In each case this officer was responsible to the dean.

In general the administrative assistants to the dean (such as the secretary, registrar, business officer, etc.) who were not full members of the faculty devoted their full time to administrative or clerical work; but their training and experience varied, and not all were capable. Administrative assistants who were full members of the faculty were usually able to devote at most one-third of their time to administrative assignments, frequently without additional remuneration. They rarely had an academic rank above assistant professor.

In all but eight of the 41 schools studied, the dean and his assistants were clearly overloaded with the detail work of administration. In the eight medical schools in which this was not the case, four were small, close-knit institutions whose administrations had for some time been in the hands of competent administrative teams.

The administration of a medical school involves activities and responsibilities in several areas in which high-caliber personnel is essential. These areas are accounting and financial control, the administration of the hospital so that it will be educationally sound, student affairs including the functions of the admissions committee, such postgraduate programs as the medical school conducts, and public relations. In addition, in those schools where large numbers of students in many different categories are being taught, the dean's role of educational leadership could be strengthened by assistance from someone with experience and competence in those areas of education not familiar to the dean.

FACULTY RESPONSIBILITIES IN ADMINISTRATION

Members of the faculty have large and varied responsibilities for the administration of the medical school. Legally the responsibility and authority for the conduct of the affairs of the university and its component schools are vested in the governing board. Actually, state laws, charters and by-laws of the university, as well as established custom distribute much of this responsibility and authority to the officers and faculty of the institution. There is considerable variation from school to school as to what member of this large team carries responsibility and authority for specific phases of the total activities of the institution. In general, however, it is the faculty which carries on the actual operation of the institution. The acceptance of responsibility and the exercise of authority at the various administrative levels vary, being determined by a combination of rules, the interplay of strong personalities, and custom.

In each of the schools studied the permanent faculty, especially the heads of departments as a body, had a stated right to some authority and responsibility in the areas of education, research, and service. Often the chairmen of departments were organized as an executive faculty, and both the decisions of the governing board and custom gave to this body great power.

The effectiveness of the dean is determined to a considerable degree by his skill in handling people and by his ability to delegate proper authority to his assistants and members of his faculty. This effectiveness is somewhat independent of the specific rules contained in the by-laws.

For example, in one school the by-laws clearly stated that the dean was a university officer appointed without recourse to the consent of the faculty, and holding his post at the will of the governing board. It was specifically stated that this dean had the authority for decisions in all matters concerning the medical school, subject to the approval of the governing board, and that the faculty was purely advisory. The dean, who occupied this post in a very effective manner, took pains to bring all important problems before the faculty, to delay his decision until the faculty had been consulted, and to follow their decision in all important matters unless he could dissuade the faculty from its viewpoint.

A contrasting situation existed in a second school. In this school the by-laws had for some years delegated all important decisions to the executive faculty, subject to the approval of the governing board, and had called for the dean to be elected by the executive faculty at stated intervals. In the past the executive faculty had voted more than one dean out of office on matters of policy. In the last two decades, however, each dean, once elected, had been reelected annually until his retirement. Throughout this period, the working relationship between the deans and the executive faculty had been good enough to give the school strong, stable, and farsighted leadership. The members of this executive faculty were jealous of their authority, but they had also been willing to play an active role in meeting the problems of the institution as they developed, and to give the deans cooperation sufficient for effective administration.

Other examples of the variation among the 41 schools studied could be recounted. The important principle, however, is that to be effective the dean must have the cooperation, confidence, and understanding of the heads of departments, regardless of the degree of authority vested in either of them by the by-laws. Faculty members must have authority in keeping with their responsibilities, and must accept responsibilities commensurate with their authority.

CONCLUSIONS

1. Effective administration of a medical school requires a clear understanding of the primary purpose of the institution by the faculty, the medical school and university administrative officers, the members of the governing board, and the authorities of the teaching hospitals.

2. The deanship of a medical school has changed in character and expanded in scope within the past 30 years. Medical schools have in some instances outgrown their administrative organization and the background and ability of their administrators. Chief administrators of the schools often fail to grasp the issues when a medical center develops around a medical school. The increasing complexity of the organizations and the large sums of money involved in their support have led to administrative difficulties and confusion.

3. The administration of a modern medical school, and especially of a modern medical center, requires highly effective teamwork.

4. The responsibilities of the deanship have become so great and the rewards are so modest that, in some instances, it is difficult to attract and hold the ablest men.

5. The activities of a modern medical school are of such wide scope and magnitude that their successful management requires keen administrative skill and understanding of financial affairs. Boards of trustees have recognized this and have appointed as directors of medical affairs men whom they have chosen for their administrative ability rather than for their knowledge of medical education.

6. The breadth of the administrator's knowledge and understanding of

medicine and medical education has a decided influence on the policy and educational programs of the school.

7. In centers in which there is a director of medical affairs, the dean and the faculty of the medical school may have little contact with the university president or the board of trustees.

8. The income of the dean is often not commensurate with his responsibilities especially as it is frequently necessary for him to meet from his salary expenses incidental to the office.

9. Administrative costs of a medical school are difficult to determine because of the variation in the methods of medical schools and universities in allocating these costs (see Appendix).

10. The percentage of total expenditures devoted to administration as estimated by the financial officers decreased in the 10-year period 1941 to 1951. This decrease was apparently due to the increase of funds restricted to research which are included in total expenditures (see Appendix II, "Administration").

RECOMMENDATIONS

1. Boards of trustees and administrators of universities and of medical schools should together determine the relative values of the activities of the medical school, keeping clearly in sight the carefully considered objectives of the medical school.

2. The position of chief administrator must be sharply defined in terms of the objectives and activities of the institution concerned.

3. The chief administrative officer of a medical school must have a thorough understanding of the medical school per se, its activities, and the relative importance of each of its activities to its objectives.

4. Each medical school should establish its organization in such a way that the administrative officer has intimate contact with the faculty and easy access to the president and board of trustees of the university.

5. In many medical schools, because of the magnitude and complexity of the school's activities, it is essential that the chief administrator have assistance by competent persons in such fields as finance, hospital administration, public relations, and student affairs.

6. The budget for administration should be adequate to meet the demands placed upon the administrative staff. The salary of the dean or

chief administrator should be commensurate with his ability and his responsibilities.

7. All schools, especially those expending large research grants, should make a careful study of the administrative and operating costs which those grants entail.

8. The expanded activities of the modern medical school call for a new type of leadership and a new type of organization. Both administrative staff and organization must be adjusted to meet the emergent and challenging problems.

8 MEDICAL SCHOOL–HOSPITAL RELATIONS

The teaching hospital is the laboratory in which faculty and students may carefully study patients and through their studies contribute knowledge about disease and develop new methods of therapy to improve the quality of patient care. In addition to providing opportunities for medical students and faculty, the hospital also provides training for interns, residents, postgraduate medical students, and other health personnel. All these people, technical and nonprofessional, contribute to the high quality of patient care which has come to be expected of the teaching hospital.

A hospital not under direct university control, however, can rarely if ever provide ideal conditions for education since it rarely exists for this purpose. Its objective is medical service. Medical schools, striving to obtain ideal conditions for their clinical teaching, are attempting to secure or maintain the necessary degree of control over their major teaching hospitals. Only if the hospital staff is selected by the medical school does the school really control its clinical faculty. If students and professor are not to be unduly hurried in their studies, then the number of patients must be limited. The professor should be able to select an adequate variety of those patients which are of greatest value for teaching and for clinical research. Adequate laboratory facilities are essential, and the highest quality of patient care must be maintained in order to provide the proper educational conditions. These ideal teaching conditions are almost impossible to meet when the hospital must assume the responsibility for the care of too large a number of patients. The patient's needs and demands must always come first even if they encroach upon the study time of the student and professor. Although both men may be

working in a library or laboratory, if a patient for whom they have assumed responsibility suddenly needs attention, they must interrupt their
work in order to meet his needs.

For these reasons the university teaching hospital must guard its staff
and faculty members from unduly large service responsibilities. As the
number of patients increases the faculty must be expanded, or its members will have insufficient time for research and for the instruction of
students. This principle was clearly understood by physicians interested
in medical education and was put into effect in many instances when
funds became available early in the century for the construction of university-owned hospitals. In recent years such institutions have at times
deprecatingly been called "ivory towers" because they did not attempt
to serve all or a large part of the immediate needs of the community.
Actually these institutions have been the leaders of progress in medical
knowledge and in the study of disease. They developed investigation,
bringing the basic sciences to bear directly on the problems of illness.
The residency system of training which has produced the faculties of our
medical schools was born and flourished in such "ivory towers."

Since this is a study of medical education, the discussion of the relations between hospitals and medical schools will deal mainly with the
principles which determine the qualifications of a hospital as a teaching
institution.

THE CATEGORIES OF TEACHING HOSPITALS

For the purpose of this report a teaching hospital is defined as one
utilized by a medical school in the instruction of undergraduate medical
students. Such hospitals can be grouped in three categories. In the first
is the hospital that is owned by the university or medical school; in the
second is the hospital that is not owned by but is closely integrated
physically, administratively, and financially with the medical school,
with which it also shares common objectives; and in the third is the
affiliated hospital that functions as a separate institution but grants
privileges to a variable degree to the medical school. There is another
type which may be described as "associated hospitals." Such hospitals
are related with medical schools primarily for the purpose of internship
and residency training and for the improvement of hospital care, and
carry on little or no instruction of undergraduate medical students.

Thirty-eight four-year medical schools had some relationship with 164 hospitals; 102 were general hospitals, 16 were mental hospitals, 14 were children's hospitals, 11 were for tuberculosis and contagious diseases, and 21 were for other special types of patients. In Table 29 these

Table 29. OWNERSHIP OF 164 TEACHING HOSPITALS

Type of hospital	15 *Tax-supported schools*					23 *Privately supported schools*					Grand total
	Medical school or university	*Private*	Government-owned		*Total*	*Medical school or university*	*Private*	Government-owned		*Total*	
			City, county, or state	*Federal VA*				*City, county, or state*	*Federal VA*		
General........	4	3	16*	5	28	12	41	16	5	74	102
Mental.........	0	0	2	0	2	3	2	7	2	14	16
Pediatrics.......	0	1	0	0	1	0	13	0	0	13	14
Tuberculosis†...	0	0	2	0	2	0	0	9	0	9	11
Special‡........	0	1	1	0	2	1	13	5	0	19	21
Total........	4	5	21	5	35	16	69	37	7	129	164

* Includes hospitals owned by the state but operated as university hospitals.

† May include contagious hospitals.

‡ Includes orthopedic; chronic disease; geriatric; maternity; cancer, woman's; eye, ear, nose, and throat.

figures are divided according to type and ownership of hospital and type of support of related medical school. Of the 164 hospitals, 20 are owned by the university or the medical school.

Twenty-one privately supported and 15 tax-supported schools gave the total number of beds in their related hospitals and the number available for teaching. The private schools reported a total of 66,217 beds of which 66 per cent were available for teaching; the tax-supported schools reported a total of 21,057 beds of which 82 per cent were available for instruction. These data leave much to be desired because many of the reports were incomplete, conveying the impression that the schools did not know how many beds were actually used in instruction. One medical school listed 10 hospitals with a total of more than 5,000 beds but indicated that only approximately 200 beds could be used in teaching.

Of greater importance than the number of beds available for teaching is the faculty control over the care and management of the patient, and the variety of patients available for study. Hospitals for tuberculosis or mental illness may make large numbers of beds available, but these beds are suitable for only one part of a medical student's over-all clinical studies.

The number of yearly hospital admissions and the number of outpatient clinic visits in the related hospitals of 35 medical schools are shown in Table 30. These figures show the magnitude of the service of

Table 30. ADMISSIONS AND OUTPATIENT VISITS IN RELATED HOSPITALS OF 35 MEDICAL SCHOOLS DURING YEAR OF SURVEY

Type of school	Number of schools	Total admissions per year	Outpatient visits per year
Tax-supported.............	15	331,291	2,408,468
Privately supported.........	21	1,298,224	5,365,823*
Total.................	36	1,629,515	7,774,291

* Only 20 schools reporting.

these hospitals, but again they do not indicate the suitability of the patients for teaching. The hospitals related to privately supported medical schools had a larger total number of admissions and outpatient visits than did the hospitals related to tax-supported schools.

Thirty-eight medical schools (15 tax-supported and 23 privately supported) carried out 50 per cent or more of their clinical instruction of

Table 31. THIRTY-EIGHT MEDICAL SCHOOLS, DIVIDED ACCORDING TO TYPE OF HOSPITALS IN WHICH THEY DO 50 PER CENT OR MORE OF THEIR CLINICAL INSTRUCTION, AS ESTIMATED BY THE DEANS

	University hospital	Integrated hospital	Affiliated hospital
15 Tax-supported medical schools...............	8	3	4
23 Privately supported medical schools..........	8	7	8
Total..	16	10	12

medical students in university, integrated, and affiliated hospitals, as shown in Table 31. From this table it can be seen that 16 of the 38 schools carried out 50 per cent or more of their instruction in university hospitals, 10 in integrated hospitals, and 12 in affiliated hospitals.

In many of the affiliated hospitals the staff is not appointed by the medical school, although this method of control is the most important single factor in the relationship between medical schools and hospitals. A medical school does not meet university educational standards if some other authority selects the men who will carry out the clinical teaching. The selection of interns and residents is also extremely important because these young physicians have very intimate contacts with both patients and students. The number of hospitals in which the privately supported and tax-supported medical schools have full, partial, or no control over both senior staff and intern and residency staff appointments is shown in Table 32. In 89 of 149 hospitals, the medical schools had only

Table 32. MEDICAL SCHOOL CONTROL OF APPOINTMENTS IN TEACHING HOSPITALS*

Degree of control of appointments	*15 Tax-supported schools*	*22 Privately supported schools*	*Total*
Attending Staff			
Complete.........	22	38	60
Partial...........	7	34	41
None............	3	45	48
Total..........	32	117	149
House Staff			
Complete.........	22	38	60
Partial...........	6	22	28
None............	4	57	61
Total..........	32	117	149

* Associated hospitals not included.

partial control or no control whatever over the professional and intern and residency staff appointments. One-half of the medical schools reporting had definite and legitimate complaints concerning their hospital relations; the most common was lack of control over staff appointments. Tax-supported schools had control over the staff appointments in a larger portion of their teaching hospitals than did the privately supported schools. Tax-supported schools generally have available to them either a university-owned hospital or a hospital owned by the state which grants to the medical school control over the staff.

UNIVERSITY-OWNED HOSPITALS

In theory, university-owned hospitals offer medical schools maximum teaching opportunities although they do not always fulfill the requirements for ideal clinical instruction. All but three of the medical schools with university-owned hospitals also utilized integrated or affiliated hospitals, or both, in their teaching programs, either because of lack of sufficient teaching beds in the university hospital or because of inadequacy of certain special services that were necessary for the teaching of certain subjects in the curriculum. Frequently beds are set aside for the private patients of the faculty and are not utilized for clerkship teaching. At least one example exists of a university hospital in which all beds are available for teaching whether the patients are private or charity and in which all the clinical instruction is given in the one hospital. At the other extreme is one new university-owned hospital in which only 20 per cent of its beds are available for student instruction, and the remainder are for private patients. This policy has been found necessary in order to finance the hospital.

In some instances the administrator of the university hospital reports directly to the university board of trustees and holds an administrative position equal in importance to that of the dean of the medical school. He may be in a position to make decisions (concerning, for example, the admission of patients, the arrangement or assignment of laboratory space for clinical departments, and the methods of organizing and handling patients' records) which are not to the advantage of the medical school and may be detrimental to its teaching.

Hospitals owned or operated by state universities are, in some instances, considered primarily as service institutions to the state in which education and research are only secondary objectives. The medical school may have difficulty in selecting patients in these hospitals or in controlling their number. In a few instances the budget for such hospitals is included in the over-all budget of the medical school. Unless the value of the hospital service is made clear, this practice may give state legislators the impression that they are supporting a very expensive educational institution. Hospital care of indigent patients is usually assumed by states and counties whether or not there is a state-owned medical school. The costs of such care should not be chargeable to education.

In spite of these handicaps, the university-owned hospital holds the greatest potential for providing for all phases of student instruction.

INTEGRATED HOSPITALS

Of those included in the survey, integrated hospitals such as the Peter Bent Brigham Hospital (Harvard Medical School) in Boston, the Presbyterian Hospital (Columbia University Medical School) in New York City, the Johns Hopkins Hospital (Johns Hopkins Medical School) in Baltimore, and the Cincinnati General Hospital (University of Cincinnati Medical School) may offer opportunities equal to or exceeding those of the university-owned hospitals. The controlling authorities, if they are in accord with the goals of medical education, may greatly strengthen a medical school by their wise counsel, their interest, and their financial support. Administratively, such hospitals and medical schools may collaborate through a joint committee representing both institutions or by having the same individuals serve as members of both boards. However, their weakness lies in the fact that these hospitals are controlled by separate boards of trustees. The hazards of conflicting points of view and objectives are always present, and the medical school cannot exert the same control that is possible when the hospital is under its ownership.

The University of Rochester School of Medicine and Dentistry has a city hospital integrated into its activities on a rather unique basis. The university hospital and the city hospital are united physically, and the university has a contract with the city which gives the medical school complete control of the hospital with the city meeting the costs of patient care. This arrangement has been highly satisfactory from the standpoint of both the university and the city. The citizens of Rochester receive high-quality medical care at relatively low cost, and clinical instruction at the medical school is benefited by the availability of an adequate number of patients.

AFFILIATED HOSPITALS

Affiliated hospitals also can offer excellent teaching opportunities, but in general they are less satisfactory for the medical school's objectives than the two categories already mentioned. The objectives of the affiliated hospitals are less likely to coincide with those of the medical school because the former are primarily dedicated to the care of a large number of patients for the community, and the latter are primarily dedicated to teaching. Although the medical school may have control of professional, internship, and residency appointments, it is frequently very difficult to exert any control over the number and type of patients and the ancillary hospital services. The medical school may be forced to utilize as best it can whatever patients and facilities the hospital provides. If the hospital assumes a large service load, the medical school must attract and appoint a sufficiently large professional staff to carry out this service and still allow adequate time for the study of patients by faculty and students. Only infrequently do such hospitals contribute financially to the medical school.

Although the precedent has been well established of giving to medical schools authority for staff appointments in both city and county hospitals, certain large city and county owned and supported hospitals continue to refuse to grant such authority, mainly for political reasons. These hospitals are essential to several medical schools for clinical instruction. In 1910 Flexner,[1] describing the situation in many of these same hospitals, pointed out their educational weaknesses and suggested that the medical schools should have control over staff appointments. The situation is essentially the same today in several of these hospitals as it was in 1910. To a considerable degree, their reputation for quality of service has depended upon the work carried on in them by the medical school faculties. Because of the difficulties of carrying out instruction in these institutions, some of the medical schools that have other teaching facilities available have discontinued work in these hospitals. In such instances the hospitals generally encounter difficulty in obtaining an intern and resident staff.

In many of these tax-supported hospitals the patient load and the quality of ancillary services leave much to be desired and make clinical teaching difficult. In one of the largest of them seen during the Survey, student laboratories for the examination of urine and blood consisted of boards along the windows of wards already crowded with patients beyond their capacity. In another, the isolation of contagious diseases was

---

[1] FLEXNER, ABRAHAM, "Medical Education in the United States and Canada, A Report to the Carnegie Foundation for the Advancement of Teaching," New York, 1910.

so inadequate that children admitted for an operation frequently contracted contagious diseases during their stay in the hospital. Although this was the major teaching hospital for a medical school, the faculty was unable to improve the conditions and the local health officers had been totally inadequate in dealing with the situation.

The best quality of medical care and clinical instruction can never be carried out in such institutions, and the education of young physicians will suffer accordingly. It is apparent that such hospitals do not fulfill what should be minimum requirements for a teaching hospital. Public pressure can bring about a decided improvement both in the facilities for patient care and in the teaching opportunities for the schools. Until these hospitals fulfill the requirements for a teaching hospital, the medical schools should abandon them.

The value of teaching in improving patient care in such hospitals has long been proved and recognized. An interesting example of this fact was encountered during the Survey. A member of the Survey team, while sharing a taxicab with other members of the team, was describing to them a city-owned hospital at which he had spent the day. The medical school had recently agreed to assume the responsibility for appointing the staff and had initiated a new teaching program at that hospital. The taxi driver, joining in the conversation, praised the care that patients were receiving in the city hospital, saying that his father had been a patient there on three occasions. The first time had been several years previously, and the care had been wretched. A year or two later it had become necessary for the father to enter a hospital again. The family had tried to raise funds for his admittance to a private hospital but had failed, and he had returned to the city hospital. This time care had improved somewhat but still left much to be desired. Within the last year his father had been admitted again. The driver said that this time the hospital was entirely different. The doctors were better and often saw his father twice a day. In fact the care was so excellent that if his wife were to become ill he planned to take her to the same doctors in the city hospital. Although this man was unaware that the medical school had entered the scene, he did have accurate observations that proved to him beyond a doubt that the hospital had improved.

In the past such hospitals have considered that they were granting the medical school a favor by allowing teaching to be carried out in their wards. In very few instances did the city or the county contribute financially in any way to the professional staff responsible for providing service to their patients. In some instances, however, a new philosophy concerning the value of a medical school to a hospital of this type is being adopted. For example one city hospital, in order to improve its staff and the care of its patients, has offered the medical school in the city complete control over professional, intern, and residency staff appointments, and has also agreed to pay the full salaries of certain full-time staff members who will be appointed to the faculty of the medical school and who will instruct medical students in the city hospital. In addition this hospital is making research laboratories and budgets available to these members of the staff at considerable expense.

COSTS OF PATIENT CARE

The cost of patient care in all categories of teaching hospitals is very difficult to determine, although it is claimed to be high. Sixteen of the medical schools were able to supply data on the patient-day costs in 33 of their teaching hospitals computed upon the government reimbursable cost formula. These costs ranged from $11.38 to $24.69 per patient per day with a median of about $17.00. The university-owned, the integrated, and the affiliated hospitals were all included in arriving at these figures. Many factors contribute to this wide variation in costs. In the Northeastern part of the country, costs were found to be definitely higher than in the South. A second factor is that, in those large public hospitals whose primary obligation is caring for large numbers of indigent patients, the costs are substantially lower than in hospitals which care for an appreciable number of part-pay patients or private patients.

It has generally been assumed that the cost of patient care in teaching hospitals is considerably higher than in nonteaching institutions. The director of one large privately owned hospital stated that he estimated the cost in the teaching hospital to be 25 per cent higher than that in a nonteaching institution. However, when he attempted to review the figures available on the costs in other hospitals in the same city, he was forced to admit that the cost in the teaching hospital was exceeded by some other private hospitals. In another instance, an able hospital administrator stated that he felt certain that the cost in his teaching hospital must be higher than in other hospitals. However, his statistics showed that the costs in the teaching hospital were only slightly above the median figure for other hospitals in the state. The information on this problem seems to be so inadequate and confused that it certainly deserves further study. The impression gained in the Survey was that the teaching hospital costs were no higher, and in some instances were lower, than those in private hospitals offering a quality of medical care similar to that of the teaching hospital.

Information was also supplied by 26 teaching hospitals on the costs per outpatient visit. These costs range from $1.34 per patient visit to $6.10, the median being about $3.00. It was apparent that there was considerable variation in the methods used in determining these figures. Nevertheless, when it is considered that professional fees are practically never included in these costs, one may question the efficiency of the management of the outpatient departments. Ordinarily these costs include the maintenance of outpatient facilities, the salaries of ancillary personnel such as secretaries and nurses, and occasionally the cost of drugs, x-rays, and laboratory tests. Some of these figures exceed the charge for an office visit made by the average practicing physician. Community and welfare agencies usually refuse to pay the full cost per visit for patients on welfare rolls. Many medical schools operate outpatient facilities at a loss of a few thousand to $150,000 per year. The charge to the patient for a visit to the outpatient clinic varies from nothing to $2.50 per visit, but income from this source covers only a fraction of the cost.

ASSOCIATED HOSPITALS

The affiliation between medical schools and "associated" hospitals marks a notable and important development in the role played by medical schools in hospital care and house-staff training. Such hospitals may be said to be units in a system of coordinated hospital and medical-care plans. Rarely are these hospitals used in undergraduate medical-student teaching. Their general purpose has been to provide more clinical facilities for expanded residency training programs, to improve hospital services in areas at considerable distances from the teaching centers, and to provide postgraduate instruction by the faculty of the medical school for staff physicians of such hospitals. The hospitals benefit markedly from such an association by the greater ease in obtaining interns and residents and also by the consultative services of the medical school faculty. These advantages are so real that many hospitals are willing to pay honoraria and the travel expenses of the faculty members assigned by the medical schools to visit them.

Six of the medical schools visited had established programs of hospital affiliations of this sort. The number of hospitals associated with one medical school may vary from 2 to more than 15. The hospitals may be located several hundred miles from the medical school. Some members of the faculty travel 5,000 to 25,000 miles per year in order to meet their commitments to these hospitals. Residents from the hospitals usually rotate back to the medical school for periods of a few months or more in order to take courses in the medical basic sciences.

In one medical school with such a program, several professors stated that the school had overextended itself. They found it necessary to be absent from the school more frequently, even though the size of the medical school classes had been increased. They were having to restrict their own research, and they had discontinued some methods of medical-student instruction which they thought were effective in order to have time to meet all their commitments outside the medical school.

VETERANS ADMINISTRATION HOSPITALS

Veterans Administration hospitals, of which, in 1951, 69 were related to medical schools through dean's committees, may be affiliated or associated hospitals. The majority of these hospitals train residents, and in a few of them some undergraduate medical-student instruction is also given. The medical schools have not only the privilege but also the responsibility of nominating the professional staff, including interns and residents, and they must see to it that the professional care of patients in these hospitals is maintained at a high level. This responsibility requires considerable time and energy of the dean and the faculty. The chairman of a department in one medical school surveyed had just completed a trip of several thousand miles for the purpose of interviewing men for positions on the staff of the associated veterans hospital.

Since the number of patients in these hospitals is increasing, the schools have assumed a huge obligation. The 1950 annual report of the Administrator of Veterans Affairs stated that "the best medical talent, including men of professorial rank in the country's leading medical schools, was serving in the VA programs as consultants, supervising patient care, directing research, and participating in the education of

residents and interns." A number of hospitals of the Veterans Administration designed to be associated with medical schools are under construction at the present time, and their impact on the medical schools is
not yet apparent.

Six hospitals of the Veterans Administration associated with medical
schools were visited; four of these were being used for some undergraduate medical-student instruction. In two instances, because of the
inadequacy of the facilities in the medical school's teaching hospital, the
Veterans Administration hospital offered better opportunities for clinical instruction. In one hospital, however, the manager was opposed to
undergraduate students' working with veterans, and in that hospital the
facility was of little or no value to the medical school. In one instance a
large part of the clinical faculty of the medical school spent almost one-
third of its time at the Veterans Administration hospital because the
university hospital could not afford to maintain comparable teaching
opportunities. In other instances only intern and residency training were
carried on at the hospitals of the Veterans Administration. The fact that
these hospitals normally have only male patients makes it necessary for
the medical schools to utilize either their own hospital or other affiliated
hospitals if the interns and residents in the Veterans Administration
hospital are to have any experience in the care of women or children.
Sixty-five to 80 per cent of the patients in hospitals of the Veterans Administration have non-service-connected disabilities; therefore, these
hospitals are providing hospital care which often competes with that
offered by private hospitals and by the teaching hospitals of the medical
schools. The situation has created problems for some of the medical
schools.

THE MEDICAL CENTER

The medical school's method of studying and caring for patients has
proved its value to both affiliated and associated hospitals. The development of the medical center built around a medical school has been due
in part to the development of these related hospital programs. Such a
center may have the university-owned or integrated hospital as its nucleus, with some affiliated hospitals and institutes for special services
and research in close geographic and administrative relationship to the
central hospital. In addition, several associated hospitals may be located
at considerable distances from the center. This type of organization gives

rise to many challenges and difficulties for the medical school. In one of these centers the activities are so diffuse and so complex that the board of trustees of the university has difficulty deciding what areas and what activities require their attention and support. The administrative officers of the medical school cannot always keep in touch with the multiple departments and institutes. Some faculty members are barely acquainted with the dean and the administrative officers. Each unit of the center—and each unit may include a department of the medical school—tends to be independent and self-sufficient, each with its own clinics and its own laboratory facilities such as are required in bacteriology, pathology, and x-ray, for example. The number of interns, residents, and fellows receiving special training, plus the graduate students, exceeds the total enrollment of undergraduate medical students.

In a medical center, the integration of the educational program becomes particularly difficult. There are many evident weaknesses. For example, certain phases of a subject may be taught by at least three different departments with each of the departments knowing little about the instruction the other departments are giving to the students. In one of the medical centers visited during the Survey, one of the medical basic science departments feels that its mission is to give the student the clinical applications of all other sciences. Certain clinical and pathological material has become so fragmentized among the units of the center that departments responsible for teaching certain subjects must obtain material from outside the medical center or send the students away for some instruction. Although this medical center has a large number of beds, the majority are devoted to private patients or to patients with special diseases, and only a fraction of the total number are available for the instruction of undergraduate medical students. For clinical teaching the students are, therefore, sent to distant hospitals in which patient care is inferior to that offered at the medical center. The patient service load is so large in some of its clinics that even this large center has difficulty in staffing them with qualified personnel. In fact the medical school—the school for the education of undergraduate medical students—is being lost in the maze of complex medical service, specialized training, and research units. This same phenomenon is occurring to a greater or lesser degree in other medical schools as they expand their activities.

The expansion of a medical school into a medical center may be compared to the vertical expansion of departments in other disciplines which has constituted a serious problem to large universities for the past three decades, and which led to reorganization of the undergraduate liberal arts college at the University of Chicago in 1930. Before reorganization, the departments of that university were designed as independent or semi-independent units primarily for research and graduate education. The situation that existed after the First World War was described by C. S. Boucher, when he was dean of the college, as follows:[2] "Undergraduate work was grossly neglected; even worse, the College came to be regarded by some members of the university family as an unwanted, ill-begotten brat that should be disinherited." The report of the president of this institution in 1920–21 showed that, "one group defended the College because (1) it provided the departments with an opportunity to select promising research students; (2) it brought revenue which helped pay for research and graduate instruction; and (3) it attracted contributions from college alumni—since it was this group, rather than graduate school alumni, which had greater wealth.[3] The University of Chicago finally decided to develop the college with its own dean and faculty who would be responsible for designing a curriculum for the undergraduate college student.

Although no medical school can be said to be in such an inferior position as described at the undergraduate college of the University of Chicago, nevertheless, several medical schools are facing similar situations in rapidly growing hospital medical centers with relatively autonomous clinical departments.

COORDINATED HOSPITAL PLANS

In some areas a coordinated hospital plan has been developed which involves the coordination of associated hospitals with teaching hospitals. The plan is that the associated hospital will refer difficult and complicated cases to the teaching hospital, and the teaching hospital will supply certain complex laboratory services, consultants, and postgraduate teachers. Similar plans are being discussed for many other areas.

These coordinated hospital plans have been designed primarily to im-

---

[2] FRODIN, R., "Very Simple but Thoroughgoing," a chapter in "The Idea and Practice of General Education" (by present and former members of the faculty of the University of Chicago), Chicago, University of Chicago Press, 1950.

[3] *Ibid.*

prove hospital service; they have not been designed for the improvement of the education of undergraduate medical students. The plans have proved their value in terms of medical service, but they constitute a definite challenge to medical education. Is the provision and maintenance of high-quality hospital care for large segments of the population the responsibility of the medical schools or of the hospitals? Although service to a community, to the state, or to the nation is of the utmost importance, no good purpose can be served by confusing service and education. It is of the utmost importance to a medical school to decide whether the provision of medical service and postgraduate medical education is its primary objective, or whether service through education of the medical student for the future is its primary objective with the provision of a limited amount of the highest quality of medical service an essential and desirable by-product.

The medical schools have so many weak links in their major teaching hospitals that are urgently in need of careful study and improvement that it would seem the better part of wisdom for them to spend their time and energy correcting these faults before dissipating their educational energies on widespread public-service programs. The great difficulty lies in the fact that the public can readily appreciate the value of direct services rendered day by day, but the service rendered through the education and the training of physicians for the future is not so easily discernible. Financial support is, therefore, more easily obtained and public relations are more easily improved by catering to the current desire for service than on the basis of building for the future. Some medical educators have become so involved in the mechanics of all the complicated plans for expanding medical centers and medical service that many of the real problems of medical education are receiving little attention.

CONCLUSIONS

1. Creation of a suitable educational environment in a teaching hospital requires control of professional, intern, and resident appointments, control of the quantity and quality of hospital services, and control of the type and number of patients admitted.
2. The medical schools control the professional staff appointments in less than half of their teaching hospitals.
3. Approximately half of the medical schools studied have inadequate

control of the other factors vital to an educational environment in their teaching hospitals.

4. University-owned hospitals offer the greatest promise for clinical instruction. Frequently, however, the medical schools are handicapped in their teaching activities by certain details of the hospital's administrative organization and by the number of beds devoted to patients who are not available for teaching.

5. The costs of both inpatient and outpatient care in teaching hospitals are said to be higher than in nonteaching hospitals, but there is little evidence to support this contention.

6. Medical schools, through the examples set in their teaching hospitals, have largely set standards of quality for hospital medical care.

7. The expansion of medical service to an extent that it unduly absorbs the resources and energies of the school is a serious threat to the medical school.

8. The provision of a high quality of hospital medical care is not in itself a justification for medical schools to develop an association with other hospitals.

RECOMMENDATIONS

1. Medical schools should control the appointments of the staff, including interns and residents, in their major teaching hospitals. Inasmuch as medical care and research are dependent upon teamwork, medical schools should have authority to establish standards of quality and quantity for ancillary hospital services.

2. The ideal teaching hospital should be designed so that all patients are available for teaching and actively cooperate in the teaching program. Such a design would eliminate some of the existing confusion and complexity of medical school–hospital relations and in some cases permit a desirable reduction in the number of hospital affiliations.

3. When full-pay, part-pay, and non-pay patients enter teaching hospitals, they should expect to cooperate fully in the study of disease and in the teaching program for undergraduate medical students, and to be provided with the highest quality of medical care.

4. Hospital costs for indigent patients should be borne by appropriate private and governmental agencies, not by the medical schools from funds provided for the education of the medical student.

5. Teaching should be discontinued in those hospitals which do not afford good opportunities for teaching and for a high quality of hospital care.
6. Certain broad policy decisions should be reached as to what costs should be charged to hospital care and what to medical school instruction, as a guide to determining the costs to the medical school of inpatient and outpatient service in teaching hospitals.
7. Medical schools should be completely clear, as regards their activities, between those justified as contributing to medical education and those which are medical service.
8. Extensive medical service should not be undertaken by medical schools under the guise of medical education.

9 MEDICAL SCHOOL DEPARTMENTS

Departments of a medical school serve as administrative, educational, research, and service units of the institution. They fall into two general categories—medical basic science (or preclinical) departments and clinical departments. Such activities as the library, medical art, animal care, research, and graduate and postgraduate education are assigned departmental or subdepartmental status according to their size and importance in the school.

Terminology varies. In some schools the word "division" describes a major unit of the school which may include departments and subdepartments. In other instances the term is used to designate a unit of a department, more commonly called a subdepartment. In still other instances, it is used to describe such units or activities as the library, medical art, and legal medicine. For the purposes of this discussion the term "department" will be used to define a major teaching unit devoted to a particular medical science or field of medicine. A subdepartment is a division of the major unit or department devoted to a specialized branch of the broader field.

ORGANIZATION

Medical Basic Science Departments

The medical basic science departments are generally the departments of anatomy, biochemistry, physiology, pharmacology, bacteriology (microbiology), and pathology. They are usually staffed by full-time faculty members.

In the 41 schools studied, the departments were organized in several ways (Table 33); physiology was in some instances combined with

157

pharmacology, and bacteriology with preventive medicine or pathology. These departments, although frequently known as basic science departments, do not cover the fields of the truly basic sciences, but have as their roots the basic sciences of biology, chemistry, physics, and mathematics. They really represent those portions of the true basic sciences from which have developed certain organized bodies of knowledge of definite

Table 33. MEDICAL BASIC SCIENCE DEPARTMENTS AS ORGANIZED IN 41 MEDICAL SCHOOLS

Anatomy	41
Biochemistry (physiological chemistry)	37
Biochemistry and nutrition	3
Biochemistry and toxicology	1
Pathology	39
Pathology and bacteriology	2
Physiology	33
Physiology and pharmacology	7
Physiology and biophysics	1
Pharmacology	33
Pharmacology and radiation biology	1
Pharmacology and physiology	7
Bacteriology (microbiology)	32
Bacteriology and preventive medicine	6
Bacteriology and experimental pathology	1
Bacteriology and pathology	2

value to medicine, and they might be called "medical science" departments. In discussing the relation of the basic sciences to medicine, Flexner[1] wrote that "in so far as they figure in medical education, they cannot be allowed to be indifferent to this definite function."

In its development, anatomy, the oldest of these departments, utilized the biological methods of accurate observation, description, comparison, and classification, and made use of mathematics for measurement in its study of the structure of the human body. More widespread use of the microscope during the nineteenth century gave rise to histology, or the

[1] FLEXNER, ABRAHAM, "Medical Education in the United States and Canada, A Report to the Carnegie Foundation for the Advancement of Teaching," New York, 1910, p. 59.

study of the cellular structure of tissues, as a subdivision of anatomy. Embryology as another subdivision of anatomy owed its origin to biological studies in reproduction.

Physiology, the study of function, made use of biological and physical methods in studying the human body and its organ systems. As an organized body of knowledge with its own discipline it is less than 100 years old.

Biochemistry is a comparatively recent offspring of physiology. The physiologist found chemistry useful in the examination and analysis of body tissues and fluids. As the value of chemical knowledge about the human body became apparent, departments of biochemistry were established.

Pathology was a natural outgrowth of anatomy. Anatomists in the course of studying the structure of the body encountered the variations produced by disease. Men primarily interested in disease soon adopted the anatomical methods of study, and the microscope as a tool, and established departments of pathology.

When it was discovered that bacteria caused disease, these organisms became of interest to pathologists, who rapidly explored the role of bacteria in producing structural changes in the human body. Men specializing in this field proved the value to medicine of the study of bacteria and separated their work from that of pathology with the result that bacteriology was recognized as a separate department.

Modern pharmacology was the result of the application of physiological methods to the study of the action of drugs.

Clinical Departments

The basis on which the clinical departments of a medical school are organized is different from that of the medical basic science departments. The former are founded upon special fields of interest, techniques of examination, and methods of therapy rather than upon organized bodies of basic scientific knowledge. In the clinical departments, medicine and surgery differ primarily in their methods of therapy while medicine and pediatrics differ in the age group of the patients each is interested in. Radiology is based upon its special techniques in diagnosis and therapy. There is more variation in the organization of the clinical departments (Table 34) from school to school than is found in the medical basic sciences.

Within clinical departments numerous subdepartments may be established for the teaching in special fields; or these specialties may be taught at the undergraduate medical-student level without formal subdepartmental organization. The more common subdepartments of the department of medicine are those of neurology (or neuropsychiatry) and dermatology; other medical specialties are seldom organized as sub-

Table 34. CLINICAL DEPARTMENTS AS ORGANIZED IN 38 FOUR-YEAR MEDICAL SCHOOLS

	Major department	Subdepartment	Total
Medicine.....................................	38	0	38
Surgery......................................	38	0	38
Pediatrics....................................	37	1	38
Obstetrics....................................	6	0	6
Obstetrics and gynecology.....................	32	0	32
Gynecology...................................	4	2	6
Psychiatry....................................	17	4	21
Neuropsychiatry..............................	13	4	17
Neurology*...................................	8	11	19
Preventive medicine and/or public health.........	30	4	34
Radiology....................................	31	3	34
Physical medicine............................	12	5	17
Ophthalmology...............................	19	14	33
Otolaryngology and ophthalmology.............	2	2	4
Otolaryngology...............................	17	16	33
Urology......................................	7	30	37
Orthopedic surgery...........................	8	27	35
Neurosurgery*................................	3	28	31
Dermatology.................................	17	12	29
Anesthesiology...............................	6	21	27
Oncology....................................	4	8	12

* Neurology and neurosurgery are a joint department in two schools.

departments. Departments of surgery frequently have a larger number of subdepartments within their framework, including orthopedics, ophthalmology, otolaryngology, neurosurgery, surgical pathology, plastic surgery, and chest surgery, each of which may be headed by a faculty member with one or more assistants.

In some medical schools certain specialties are organized as major departments (Table 34), although in such departments the instruction of a medical student is frequently only a minor function. The prime reason for the separate organization of these departments is the uniqueness of the diagnostic and therapeutic techniques of the specialty. Other reasons are the service functions of these departments and the facilities that are necessary for the training of medical school graduates at the residency and postgraduate levels.

FUNCTIONS

Specific differences exist between the functions of the medical basic science departments and those of the clinical departments, although in general the functions of the two groups are similar.

Medical Basic Science Departments

The head of a medical basic science department, who, in the administrative pattern, is responsible to the dean of the medical school, must organize his faculty and the teaching program of the department; he must prepare his budget and present it to the dean; he is in charge of the office for the handling of routine business of the department.

He must supervise the research activities, and usually he must approve the positions and salaries of technical assistants. He may serve as a member of the school's executive faculty, which is primarily concerned with educational policies, appointments, curriculum, and the promotion and graduation of students. He may also serve on several special committees, such as the admissions committee, library committee, and research committee. Frequently, he is asked to sit on local or national committees dealing with research or with the application of his field of knowledge to various aspects of human welfare.

In their educational activities, the medical basic science departments are usually responsible for the instruction of only one class of medical students for a portion of one academic year. They may also be responsible for graduate students working toward a Master's or a Doctor of Philosophy degree, and often they participate in a course for resident physicians or for postgraduate medical students. Depending upon university and hospital relations, these departments may also give instruction to nurses, technicians, dental students, and pharmacy students; in many instances, they give courses for students in the college of the university.

Most of the medical basic science departments carry on active research programs. Individual members of a department may carry out research work in special areas of the broad field covered by the department or may participate in a phase of an over-all research program which is designed by the head of the department. In these departments the faculty members' time available for research ranges from at least 25 per cent in most instances to more than 50 per cent in others.

Service, meaning service to patients or to a community, is not usually an important activity of medical basic science departments. In several medical schools, however, departments of biochemistry and bacteriology are responsible for the routine laboratory work in teaching hospitals and occasionally for the laboratory work of city or state health departments. Departments of pathology differ from other medical basic science departments in one important respect: almost invariably their routine functions include the provision of pathological services to hospitals and of diagnostic services to the clinical departments. The following two examples may illustrate this point and at the same time give some idea of the activities encompassed by a medical basic science department.

A typical department of pathology of a tax-supported medical school received from the medical school a budget of $40,500, and from outside sources, $14,500 in special funds for investigative purposes. Six full-time members made up the faculty. The department's teaching of medical students included a second-year course in general pathology, a third-year course in surgical pathology, and a fourth-year clinical pathological conference. Thus, with approximately 60 medical students in each class, the department instructed 180 medical students each year. In addition, 51 nurses, 3 residents, 2 fellows, and 2 technicians received instruction. Research on cancer of the liver and genitourinary tract, on parasitic diseases, and on immunity reactions was being carried on in the department. In its service functions the department performed 300 autopsies and examined 17,000 pathological specimens for affiliated hospitals in the year in which the department was surveyed.

A second example is that of a typical department of microbiology (bacteriology) in a large privately owned medical school. This department had a medical school budget of $40,000 and $58,000 in special funds. The staff consisted of eight faculty members. Eighty-five medical students received instruction for one semester of their second year; seven other students took the same course. Courses were also given for 60 dental students, 10 technicians, and 20 graduate students. The research program was of considerable magnitude. The chief of the department estimated that, in addition to the special funds, 30 per cent of the medical school budget was utilized for research. Problems under investigation included studies of the metabolism of bacteria, sites of antibody formation, and the effects of enzymes on bacteria. As part of the school's service activity, the department was responsible for supervising the routine bacteriological laboratory of the teaching hospital, but no provision was made for this activity in the departmental budget of the medical school.

Clinical Departments

The professor or chief of a clinical department has administrative duties and responsibilities for education and research similar to those described for the medical basic science departments. In addition, however, he must organize the staff for the care of patients. He must serve on hospital committees as well as on medical school committees. His staff will normally range from 10 or 15 men to more than 100 who serve on a full-time, part-time, or volunteer basis. The department may be responsible for supervising the training of as many as 50 or more young physicians as interns and residents.

The functions of the clinical departments differ from the medical basic science departments in three ways: The clinical departments are responsible for the professional care of both ambulatory and hospital patients; the instruction given to the medical student by the major departments extends through two or more years of the four-year course and includes work with patients and bedside instruction; the instruction offered to nonmedical students is usually a very minor fraction of that generally given by the medical basic science departments. The activities of clinical departments and their financial support may be illustrated by the following examples.

The department of internal medicine in one of the relatively small privately owned medical schools had a budget of $19,850 and received $1,000 from outside sources which was used to support a research project. The faculty was composed of 66 members. Of this number eight received some salary from the medical school, six of them receiving less than $1,200 per year for part-time work. The department was responsible for instructing medical students in the second, third, and fourth years; approximately 150 medical students received instruction each year. In addition 250 nurses received some instruction, and 75 to 100 physicians were registered in postgraduate medical courses. The department was responsible for the training of 12 interns and residents. In the field of service, the faculty gave professional medical care to 1,384 ambulatory patients and to an unknown number of patients on the medical wards. The department had practically no laboratory facilities, and research was a very minor activity.

A department of pediatrics in one of the tax-supported schools received $78,000 as a budget from the medical school and $13,000 in special funds. There were eight full-time members of the department of whom one was a chemist and one a bacteriologist. The department gave instruction to medical students throughout the third and fourth years of medical school with 250 students receiving instruction each year. In addition some instruction was given to 40 nurses and 110 postgraduate medical students. The faculty members were responsible for the training of 21 interns and residents. The staff gave free professional care to all the patients admitted to 84 beds in the hospital and to outpatients totaling 9,000 visits per year. The research programs were carried out in several large laboratories, and problems in nutrition and infectious disease were under study.

In another privately supported medical school, the department of surgery, with seven subdepartments, had a budget of $122,000. Fifty thousand dollars was added to this budget by the professional earnings of the salaried faculty members. Special funds totaled $76,000. There were 53 faculty members in the department, 11 of whom received full-time salaries. Instruction was given to two classes of 90 medical students each, or to a total of 180 medical students each academic year. Fifty nurses, 30 dental students, and 30 postgraduate medical students received some instruction. The department was also responsible for the training of 37 interns and residents and 17 fellows. The research program was large and involved laboratories for chemical, physiological, endocrinological, and pathological studies. The staff of the department gave free professional care to more than 2,000 patients in the major teaching hospital and to outpatients totaling 18,000 visits per year. In addition it was responsible for the surgical care of patients in a city hospital with 250 surgical beds. The department received no compensation for this work.

These three examples give a representative idea of the range and magnitude of the activities of clinical departments and of their financial support.

DEPARTMENTAL BUDGETS

Information concerning the budgets of departments of medical schools for the years 1940–41 and 1948–49 was obtained by the Surgeon General's Committee on Medical School Grants and Finances. Similar information for the year 1949–50 or 1950–51 for 41 medical schools was obtained by the Survey. For various reasons it was impossible to compare the departmental budgets of certain schools over this nine-year period. Of 23 four-year private medical schools, three had submitted no departmental budgets for the year 1941, one school was founded after 1941, and one school did not submit budgets of its major departments to the Survey. Of 15 four-year tax-supported schools, three gave no reports for the year 1941, one was not organized as a four-year school until after 1941, and one gave incomplete reports. Thus 10 of the 38 four-year medical schools could not be used in studying the growth of departmental budgets over a nine-year period.

The budgets of the medical basic science departments followed a fairly consistent pattern. Because of various factors, however, it is almost impossible to deal with the finances of the clinical departments in any uniform way. The variation in the organization of the clinical departments has been mentioned earlier. Another factor is the circumstance that in several medical schools the teaching hospitals contributed to the salaries of faculty members and maintained offices and laboratories for their work, and that such expenditures were not reflected in the medical school budgets of these departments. In a few schools the professional earnings of full-time or geographic full-time faculty members appeared in the departmental budgets, while in the majority of schools this was not the case. None of the departmental budgets indicated the value of the time contributed by the volunteer faculty members. Thus two clinical departments, with almost identical activities and approximately the same number of faculty members, were found to have budgets so disparate that one was several times the size of the other.

During the nine-year period from 1940–41 to 1949–50, the medical school budgets of the medical basic science departments increased notably

(Table 35). In the tax-supported schools the budgets of these departments almost tripled in the nine-year period, while in the privately supported schools the budgets nearly doubled. In general, departments of anatomy had the largest budgets of any of the medical basic science departments, and departments of pharmacology the smallest.

Table 35. BUDGETS OF MEDICAL BASIC SCIENCE DEPARTMENTS FOR 1940–41, 1948–49, AND YEAR OF SURVEY, AND PER CENT INCREASE IN NINE-YEAR PERIOD

	*Number report- ing**	1940–41†	1948–49†	*Year of survey* (1949–50 *or* 1950–51)	*Per cent increase*
Anatomy					
Tax-supported schools.......	10	$ 324,000	$ 612,000	$ 717,000	121
Privately supported schools...	18	576,000	897,000	1,018,000	77
Biochemistry					
Tax-supported schools.......	9	144,000	357,000	452,000	214
Privately supported schools...	17	356,000	608,000	736,000	107
Physiology					
Tax-supported schools.......	10	232,000	490,000	583,000	151
Privately supported schools...	18	466,000	701,000	829,000	78
Pharmacology					
Tax-supported schools.......	11	154 000	292 000	402,000	161
Privately supported schools...	18	286,000	515,000	548,000	92
Bacteriology					
Tax-supported schools.......	10	182,000	468,000	571,000	214
Privately supported schools...	18	407,000	638,000	760,000	87
Pathology					
Tax-supported schools.......	9	206,000	446,000	589,000	186
Privately supported schools...	17	507,000	766,000	870,000	72
Totals					
Tax-supported schools.....	..	$1,242,000	$2,665,000	$3,314,000	167
Privately supported schools.	..	2,598,000	4,125,000	4,761,000	83

* Budgets were not obtained from all the schools or all the departments studied.

† Figures obtained from the Surgeon General's Committee on Medical School Grants and Finances.

Of the 15 tax-supported schools represented, one was not founded until after 1941; three gave no department budgets for 1940–41; and one reported budgets for 1940–41 and 1948–49 only for pharmacology and pathology.

Of the 23 privately supported schools represented, one was not founded until after 1941; three gave no department budgets for 1940–41, and one gave no department budgets for the year of the Survey.

According to the budgets submitted, the five major clinical departments (medicine, surgery, pediatrics, obstetrics and gynecology, psychiatry or neuropsychiatry) in the tax-supported schools in general trebled their expenditures. Departments of psychiatry showed the greatest increase, while departments of obstetrics and gynecology showed the

Table 36. BUDGETS OF CLINICAL DEPARTMENTS FOR 1940–41, 1948–49, AND YEAR OF SURVEY, AND PER CENT INCREASE IN NINE-YEAR PERIOD

	Number of schools*	1940–41†	1948–49†	*Year of survey* (1949–50 or 1950–51)	*Per cent increase*
Medicine					
Tax-supported schools.......	10	$ 369,000	$ 908,000	$1,004,000	172
Privately supported schools...	16	982,000	1,565,000	1,804,000	84
Surgery					
Tax-supported schools.......	10	320,000	836,000	904,000	183
Privately supported schools...	18	731,000	1,196,000	1,177,000	61
Pediatrics					
Tax-supported schools.......	8	96,000	343,000	352,000	267
Privately supported schools...	18	348,000	598,000	631,000	81
Obstetrics and Gynecology					
Tax-supported schools.......	10	151,000	328,000	314,000	108
Privately supported schools...	16	326,000	465,000	541,000	66
Psychiatry or Neuropsychiatry					
Tax-supported schools.......	6	58,000	260,000	328,000	466
Privately supported schools...	13	141,000	372,000	428,000	204
Totals					
Tax-supported schools.....	..	$ 994,000	$2,675,000	$2,902,000	192
Privately supported schools.	..	2,528,000	4,196,000	4,581,000	81

* Budgets were not obtained from all of the medical schools and departments studied.
† Figures obtained from the Surgeon General's Committee on Medical School Grants and Finances.

least. The clinical departments in the privately supported schools did not quite double their budgets with the exception of psychiatry or neuropsychiatry which trebled its budget (Table 36).

The degree to which both tax- and privately-supported schools have been able to increase their departmental budgets during this nine-year period is remarkable. However, budgets do not in themselves reveal increased costs of goods and services purchased, the growth of the activities of the departments, or the improvements that have occurred. For example, the Consumers Price Index increased 86 per cent in approximately this same period and, if medical school costs had risen proportionately during the nine years—and it is logical to suppose that they did so—the departments would have had to approximately double their budgets by 1949–50 in order to maintain only those activities which existed in 1940–41. However, according to the Council on Medical Education and Hospitals, during the same nine years medical student enrollments increased countrywide from 21,379 to 25,103, and during the last three of these years the number of nonmedical students receiving instruction

Table 37. MEDICAL BASIC SCIENCE DEPARTMENTS WITH BUDGETS OF LESS THAN $25,000 OR MORE THAN $100,000, IN 36 MEDICAL SCHOOLS, DURING YEAR OF SURVEY (1949–50 OR 1950–51)

	Less than $25,000			More than $100,000		
	15 Tax-supported schools	22 Privately supported schools	Total	15 Tax-supported schools	22 Privately supported schools	Total
Anatomy	0	3	3	1	1	2
Biochemistry	2	4	6	0	1	1
Physiology	0	5	5	2	1	3
Pharmacology	4	9	13	0	0	0
Bacteriology	1	7	8	1	1	2
Pathology	0	4	4	3	1	4
Total	7	32	39	7	5	12

in the medical schools almost doubled.[2] These and other factors complicate the figures and obscure their meaning. However, it is doubtful whether the over-all educational activities of many departments were as adequately financed in 1950 as they were in 1941.

The wide variations in the financial support of departments are demonstrated in Tables 37 and 38. In Table 37, which shows the number of medical basic science departments with budgets of less than $25,000 and the number with budgets of more than $100,000 in both

[2] ANDERSON, D. G., and ANNE TIPNER, Medical Education in the United States and Canada, *Journal of the American Medical Association,* Vol. 144, p. 109 (Sept. 9), 1950.

tax-supported schools and privately supported schools, the figure of $25,000 was selected as a minimum because it seems unlikely that any department can be maintained adequately on less than this amount. Departmental budgets of privately supported schools are seen to vary more widely than those of tax-supported schools; more of the former have departments with budgets of less than $25,000 than is true of the latter.

Table 38. MAJOR CLINICAL DEPARTMENTS WITH BUDGETS OF LESS THAN $25,000 OR MORE THAN $100,000 IN 36 MEDICAL SCHOOLS, DURING YEAR OF SURVEY (1949–50 OR 1950–51)

	Less than $25,000			More than $100,000		
	15 Tax-supported schools	21 Privately supported schools	Total	15 Tax-supported schools	21 Privately supported schools	Total
Medicine	2	5	7	7	7	14
Surgery	1	7	8	7	5	12
Pediatrics*	6	10	16	0	3	3
Obstetrics and gynecology	6	10	16	0	1	1
Neuropsychiatry	4	8	12	1	0	1
Total	19	40	59	15	16	31

* Three of these departments of pediatrics have very large funds from other sources.

Table 38 shows similar data for five major clinical departments. Again a larger number of the major clinical departments in private schools than in tax-supported schools had budgets of less than $25,000. Both types of schools had departments with budgets in excess of $100,000, but the 15 tax-supported schools had a proportionately greater number than the 21 privately supported schools.

SPECIAL FUNDS

The departmental budgets derived from the medical school do not reflect all the funds expended, since they do not include additional, or so-called "special" funds, which are almost entirely for research purposes. Of the 41 schools, the medical basic science departments in 37 schools, and the clinical departments in 36 schools, supplied data in 1940 and 1950 which could be utilized.

The medical basic science departments in 37 medical schools had regular medical school budgets totaling approximately $10,800,000 and special funds totaling approximately $6,000,000 (Table 39). In the tax-supported schools, special funds were equal to about 50 per cent of the regular departmental budgets. In the 22 privately supported schools, special funds amounted to approximately 60 per cent of the regular medical school budgets.

Table 39. DEPARTMENTAL FUNDS AND THEIR SOURCES IN FOUR-YEAR MEDI-
CAL SCHOOLS, 1949–50

| | Funds and their sources | |
	Medical school	Special funds
Medical Basic Science Departments		
15 Tax-supported schools............	$ 4,920,000	$2,450,000
22 Privately supported schools........	5,840,000	3,680,000
Total..........................	$10,760,000	$6,130,000
*Five of the Major Clinical Departments**		
15 Tax-supported schools............	3,990,000	3,050,000
21 Privately supported schools........	5,590,000	6,900,000
Total..........................	$ 9,580,000	$9,950,000

* Medicine, surgery, obstetrics and gynecology, pediatrics, psychiatry (or neuro-psychiatry), selected because of the consistency of their organization from school to school.

Although the clinical departments differ widely in their organization, 36 schools supplied usable data on the five major departments already mentioned. The medical school budgets of these departments totaled approximately $9,600,000 and their special funds $9,950,000. The special funds for these departments in the privately supported schools, as a whole, exceeded their regular medical school budgets by 20 per cent, while in the tax-supported schools they were only about 75 per cent of the regular budgets. Two privately supported schools surveyed, whose medical school budgets, combined, exceeded four million dollars, and whose special funds amounted to more than $2\frac{1}{4}$ million dollars, were not included in these statistics because of lack of dependable data on their clinical department budgets.

From these comparisons it is apparent that the medical basic science departments had special funds available primarily for research equal to more than half of their regular medical school budgets, and that the privately supported schools had larger proportions of such funds than tax-supported schools. Five clinical departments of 36 schools had special funds approximately equal to their regular budgets; the privately supported schools had a much larger amount of such funds in proportion to their regular budgets than did the tax-supported schools. Although accurate factual information was not available, it was the impression of the Survey that with the establishment of more full-time positions in the tax-supported schools the special funds for research are steadily increasing.

FORCES INFLUENCING DEPARTMENTAL ORGANIZATION

Minor changes are continually taking place within departments, and new subdepartments are occasionally established. Social forces and advancements in knowledge, mentioned earlier, are not the only factors which produce these changes. Certain other factors are at work. On the one hand are forces which tend to perpetuate the present organizational pattern; on the other hand are forces which challenge it.

For a department to maintain full status it must constantly prove its value and importance to medicine and medical education relative to the values offered by other departments or by new bodies of knowledge and new technical and scientific methods. The development that has taken place in departments of anatomy is an illustration of this point. Anatomy, because of its proved value to medicine, has maintained full departmental status in spite of steady reduction of its teaching time during more than half a century while the whole curriculum has expanded from two to four years. The field of otorhinolaryngology (diseases of the ear, nose, and throat) is another example. This specialty had full departmental status in approximately half of the medical schools surveyed, even though its teaching requirements have been greatly curtailed by the introduction of chemotherapy and antibiotic therapy, which has made many surgical procedures in this field—formerly a major activity— far less common. New therapeutic agents are bringing about similar changes in the field of syphilology, which has frequently held subdepartmental status. With new knowledge and methods of combating disease, the departments or subdepartments representing such fields of activity must either develop new knowledge and techniques or lose their positions of importance in medical schools.

Tradition is a force which inhibits change in the organization of departments. Men heading and staffing departments have usually received their education and training in similar fields or departments. They have been indoctrinated in the tradition of continuing established patterns of departmental organization.

Vested interest of the faculty members also acts to maintain the status quo. A professor given responsibility and authority as head of a department strives to maintain the prestige of the department, and will generally, therefore, resist attempts to reduce the facilities or the teaching time of the department. To reduce the status of a major department to that of a subdepartment, or to combine it with another department, may produce a major upheaval within a medical school.

On the other hand, forces exist today which challenge the structure and functions of departments. There are at least five of these forces. The first is the tremendous growth and importance of chemical knowledge to medicine. The contributions of chemistry have tended to cut across the boundaries of presently organized bodies of knowledge. Chemistry has given both the medical basic science departments and the clinical departments knowledge and tools which allow them to explore and understand phenomena to a degree never before possible. As understanding of basic phenomena increases, the dividing lines between the fields of individual departments become less apparent. Thus it is practically impossible to teach the physiology of the liver without leaning heavily on biochemistry. The same is true for the physiology of digestion and to a large extent for the physiology of the endocrine system. Pharmacology must also rely upon biochemical reactions and enzyme chemistry for the explanations of the actions of certain drugs and biological products used in therapy. This interdependence often leads to some confusion as to the scope of the teaching of various departments and to duplication of coverage.

Physics and biophysics are beginning to have an impact on the medical basic sciences similar to that of chemistry. At present such instruction as is offered in this field may be given in the departments of biochemistry, physiology, and radiology, or in a few instances, in new subdepartments of biophysics. It is apparent that this field has not yet found its proper place in the existing departmental organization of medical schools.

A second force exerting an influence on departmental structure is the demand by a more highly complex society for the help of science and medicine in dealing with some of its social problems. With an aging population there is evident need for study of the ailments of older people and for instruction in that field. Industrial medicine, preventive medicine, social and environmental medicine, rehabilitation, military medicine, medical economics, psychiatry, and family medical-care programs are all seeking more prominence in the medical school curricula. In so doing, they reflect the desires of society to apply scientific methods and medical knowledge to social and environmental problems on a mass scale rather than on an entirely individual basis. Many of these interests are being incorporated into existing departments. They will continue to seek their proper positions in medical schools as their relative values to medicine as a whole becomes more clearly established. Some may be expected to reach full departmental status.

A third force affecting departmental organization, especially at the medical basic science level, is the increase in the instruction of nonmedical students by the medical basic science departments. Medical centers, and indeed everyone engaged in the practice of medicine, have come to rely on teamwork of a highly complex type. The team includes many groups of persons active in the health field: nurses, technicians, medical social workers, psychologists, sociologists, and geneticists as well as dentists and pharmacists, all of whom may contribute to work in the health field. As students these individuals need proper instruction. Universities, seeing the need for educating health personnel, have made use of the departments of the medical schools for this purpose. Thus, medical schools, although they were originally designed for the education of medical students alone, have found themselves carrying increasing teaching responsibilities for nonmedical students. Although separate schools have been established for nurses, dentists, and pharmacists, nevertheless it has seemed economical and reasonable to the universities to ask the medical basic science departments of the medical schools to give courses for students in those schools. Following this line of expediency has given rise to educational practices which are of questionable validity in promoting a high quality of education. A faculty selected primarily for the purposes of instructing medical students and graduate students finds itself asked to design courses for other students with markedly different educational backgrounds, motivations, objectives, and abilities. Not only do these students require instruction for very dissimilar fields, but they have been selected by the colleges of the university for training in those fields and not by the medical school for training in medicine. Requirements for admission and methods of selection of students for those colleges may differ markedly from those of the medical school.

A typical example is that of a tax-supported medical school, located on the same campus as the rest of the university, in which the faculty participates in the teaching of many groups of students in the health field as well as of students enrolled in the college. Nursing, pharmacy, and liberal-arts students are admitted to their respective schools with a high-school education; dental students are required to have two years of college education; medical students and graduate students must have college degrees. The department of physiology in the medical school, staffed by a professor, two associate professors, and five research assistant professors, offers more than 15 courses. Two courses are designed for nurses, one for students of physical education, one for dental students, one for pharmacy students, and the others for medical and graduate students.

Another typical example is that of a privately supported medical school in which the department of physiological chemistry gives separate courses for students of physical education, medical technologists, medical bacteriologists, graduate students, and medical students.

The pattern of education illustrated by these two examples was found by the Survey to be fairly common; more than one-third of the medical schools surveyed had extensive programs of this type. This practice may jeopardize high standards of instruction. Faculty members of the departments must design and teach courses for students with not more than a high-school or one year of college education, as well as give courses in a graduate school to students with Bachelor's or Master's degrees. Thus the functions of the medical basic science departments are being confused with those of the basic science departments of the university. The system emphasizes the teaching of subject matter, not the teaching of students. With instruction covering such a range of student preparation, it is natural that the faculty should emphasize the instruction of certain groups. Basic changes will be needed in departmental organization, in personnel, in finances, and in concepts of education, if medical schools are to include the teaching of health personnel, dental and pharmacy students, and regular college students in addition to medical students, whose education is at present their prime responsibility. Otherwise it is doubtful if teaching can be carried on at a high level of quality for all the groups of students now receiving instruction.

The fourth and perhaps the most immediately effective pressure on departmental organization is the development of clinical departments with full-time faculty members and laboratory facilities for routine and research work. At the turn of the century many forces were brought to bear upon medical schools to establish adequate laboratories for the teaching of the sciences and for the employment of full-time faculty members in these departments. Flexner[3] described the "wretched" laboratories found in a majority of the medical schools in 1910. The clinical departments were staffed almost entirely by volunteer or a few part-time faculty members. Of the 155 medical schools he surveyed, Flexner mentioned only 14 or 15 with any laboratory facilities definitely designated for the clinical departments. Of the schools mentioned, often only one clinical laboratory existed for the use of all the clinical departments. Within a period of 40 years since Flexner's report, not only have laboratories been provided for medical basic science departments, but there has been a very rapid development in the appointment of full-time or geographic full-time men in the clinical departments and in the establishment of research laboratories for their work, so that "clinical research" has become a common term.

It has already been shown (Table 39) that five clinical departments in the medical schools surveyed were expending 50 per cent more on research, from special funds, than were the six regularly organized medical basic science departments. Several of the medical schools and teaching hospitals surveyed were constructing research laboratories for the use of the clinical departments at costs ranging from several hundred thousand to $2\frac{1}{2}$ million dollars. Departments of medicine usually have the largest sums of money for research and the largest research facilities. One such department in a private medical school received a budget from the medical school of $145,000 and had available $385,000 of special funds. Seventeen members of the faculty of this department were on a full salary basis and 24 were on part-time salary. There were 16 large laboratories equipped for dealing with physiological, pharmacological,

[3] FLEXNER, ABRAHAM, "Medical Education in the United States and Canada, A Report to the Carnegie Foundation for the Advancement of Teaching," New York, 1910.

chemical, and bacteriological research programs. These laboratories were staffed with 85 technicians, research fellows, and faculty members. Several members of the faculty had refused offers of full professorships in medical basic science departments. Many problems under study in such clinical departments are as fundamental as those under investigation by medical basic science departments.

The pattern described is developing rapidly in the majority of medical schools visited during the Survey as full-time men are added to the clinical departments. In less than 40 years these departments have adopted the scientific method and the laboratories and techniques of the medical basic science departments in order to bring scientific knowledge and methods to bear directly upon the problems faced in clinical medicine. They are competing for manpower with the medical basic sciences and are attracting not only able young physicians but also able men with Ph.D. degrees in the basic sciences. Clinical instruction in several areas is being introduced into the second and even the first year of medical school and is encroaching on the teaching time of the medical basic sciences.

This trend is undoubtedly part of the long-range trend to bring science to the bedside. While it has obvious advantages, it poses certain problems since, in the present pattern of teaching, the clinical departments are neither prepared nor willing to undertake the teaching of medical students in the elementary aspects of medical science. It is important that all departments of the medical school be sound and their several activities well integrated into the whole field of medicine in order to provide a well-balanced educational opportunity for medical students. Furthermore, it is obviously of the utmost importance that there be a reasonable amount of research designed primarily for the advancement of knowledge, as well as an adequate amount designed to apply knowledge to the pressing problems of the patient. As the research activities of the clinical departments grow stronger in facilities, financial support, and well-trained workers, they carry on reasonable amounts of fundamental research.

Another feature of the clinical departments which gives them unusual influence in a medical school is their ability to partially finance themselves. Those clinical departments in which the professional earnings of the salaried faculty members become a part of the budget of the department have a source of financial support not available to the medical basic science departments. The professor of one of these clinical departments in a school studied during the Survey paid the salaries of some of the faculty members, secretaries, and nurses, and supplemented the stipends paid by the teaching hospital to his intern and resident staff. In a second instance a clinical department donated $100,000 of its earnings for the support of the medical basic science departments. The administration of the school and the medical basic science departments were made clearly aware of the source of these funds.

In the two examples cited, neither the university nor the medical school administration had any control over the funds derived from professional earnings, nor did such sums appear in the regular departmental budgets. In a few schools, however, the professional fees from all clinical departments were pooled, and the funds were allocated by a committee composed of clinical faculty members. The advice of the dean or chief administrator was available to these committees, but in their allocations they were in no way bound by his advice.

The faculty members of many large clinical departments have greater allegiance to the hospital than to the medical school. In at least two instances the heads of clinical departments, although receiving their salaries from the medical school, used the term "medical school" to refer to the medical basic science departments and indicated that they considered themselves a part of the teaching hospital. This trend leads to the development of hospital medical schools with sharp lines of division between the medical basic science and clinical departments. In such circumstances the task of administering a medical school as a unit becomes most difficult, and it is almost impossible to maintain any balance between the departments of the school.

A fifth factor bearing upon departmental organization in clinical fields has been the influence of the American Boards, which certify to the competence of physicians in the many highly specialized areas of medicine. A clinical faculty member may engage in teaching not only undergraduate medical students but also medical school graduates who limit their studies to a single special field such as anesthesiology or urology. The importance of the field of study at the medical graduate level tends to lend prestige and importance to the special field out of proportion to the significance of the field in undergraduate medical education. Consequently, demands are made for independent departmental status for the many special fields, to meet the real or fancied needs of graduate education, often at the cost of a less effective organization for the instruction of undergraduate medical students.

CONCLUSIONS

1. Departments of a medical school function as administrative, teaching, research, and service units of the institution.
2. Teaching departments in medical schools fall into two categories: (a) medical basic science (or preclinical) departments, established on the basis of certain organized bodies of knowledge of special value to medicine and derived from the truly basic sciences; (b) clinical departments, established on the basis of fields of interest and special diagnostic and therapeutic techniques.
3. There is greater variation in the organization of the clinical departments from school to school than there is in the medical basic science departments.
4. In their functions the medical basic science departments differ in several respects from the clinical departments. The former are frequently responsible for the instruction of a greater variety of students than are the clinical departments, and their instruction of medical students is usually given in only one year of the curriculum. Major clinical departments give instruction to medical students in two or more years of the curriculum and are responsible for patient care and the training of young physicians at the intern and residency levels.
5. The medical basic science departments and five major clinical departments in 37 medical schools slightly more than doubled their medical school budgets in the nine-year period 1940–41 to 1949–50. These departments in tax-supported schools generally tripled their budgets; those in privately supported schools failed to double their budgets. Thirty-two medical basic science departments in 22 privately supported schools and only seven in 15 tax-supported schools had budgets of less than $25,000.
6. It is doubtful whether the over-all educational activities of many departments are as well financed in the 1950's as they were in 1941. The budgets have approximately kept pace with the increased cost of goods and services, but they do not reflect the additional educational responsibilities the departments have assumed.

7. Special funds received from outside agencies, chiefly for the support of research, in 37 schools were equal to four-fifths of the regular medical school budgets. Privately supported schools surpass tax-supported schools in the amount of such funds, and clinical departments receive larger sums than do the medical basic science departments.

8. Departments tend to be perpetuated in their present pattern of organization by their proved value to medicine, by tradition, and by the vested interests of their faculty members.

9. Departments must constantly prove their value to medicine and medical teaching relative to the values offered by other departments or by new bodies of knowledge, scientific techniques, and methods of therapy.

10. Five major forces are challenging departmental organization. They are the growth and importance of chemical knowledge to medicine; the demands of an increasingly complex social order for the application of science and medicine to group health problems; the increasing responsibilities for the instruction of various groups of students by departments primarily designed for the education of medical students; the application of medical basic science knowledge and methods by the clinical departments in investigation and patient care; and the influence of the American Boards in the medical specialties.

RECOMMENDATIONS

1. Medical schools must assume full responsibility for the education of medical students, for the teaching in the medical basic sciences of graduate students working for a Master's or a Doctor of Philosophy degree, and for the training of those interns and residents working in the teaching hospitals under clinical faculty members.

2. Other teaching activities should be provided by medical school departments only within the limits of their resources.

3. Departments of the medical schools must be critically examined and, if necessary, reorganized on the basis of
    a. The total scope of the school's educational responsibilities.
    b. New developments of scientific knowledge and their value to medicine.
    c. Social movements which place new demands on medicine.

    d. The relative values of existing departments to medical teaching and to medicine.

4. The medical basic science departments of the medical schools should not be required to carry the teaching responsibilities of basic science departments of universities.

5. Multiplicity of clinical departments should be avoided for the purpose of promoting continuity in the design and supervision of the medical student's education. Departments whose chief responsibility is for residency training and postgraduate medical education should not function as major departments of a medical school.

6. In view of extensive additions to scientific knowledge, the medical basic science departments must be redesigned. They must be better staffed and better financed if they are to give the student a fundamental grasp of their fields of knowledge.

7. Medical schools should experiment with various new departmental organizations.

8. The clinical departments should not be allowed to become independent units and completely self-supporting.

9. Universities, dental, pharmacy, and nursing schools, and hospitals should examine their educational and training programs for the purpose of improving the opportunities of their students.

10. Schools of nursing, dentistry, and pharmacy should assume full responsibility for the education and training of their students.

11. Delegation of teaching responsibility by one school to another school should be avoided. The practice frequently leads to discontinuity in the student's program and to lack of interest and inferior instruction by the faculty of the school to which such responsibility is delegated.

10 THE LIBRARY

Throughout the long history of man's struggle against disease, countless observations and a vast amount of knowledge have been recorded. These records are stored in libraries—chiefly in the libraries of medical schools and universities but also in the libraries of medical societies, hospitals, and other scientific institutions—where they can be made available to seekers of knowledge. The faculty and the students of a medical school need ready access to these archives, for, to paraphrase Osler, to study medicine without books is to go to sea without a compass.

For many years, most of the medical writing was contained in text-books. When medicine entered its "scientific era," however, another type of literature became an increasingly important means of communicating knowledge, and several thousand periodicals are now published regularly in which current observations and experiments are recorded long before they find their way into textbooks. Textbooks are still of importance, but the periodicals, which are published weekly, monthly, or quarterly, offer the scientist and the student a more immediate means of communication than books, which can be published in new editions only at relatively long intervals.

Medical libraries maintain complete catalogues of all their bound volumes and monographs by means of a highly efficient card-index system. Few libraries, however, can employ sufficient personnel to prepare cross indexes of individual articles in the current literature and to maintain them as permanent records in the library catalogues. To fill these detailed needs, the libraries depend upon published indexes.

An index of all the medical writing that has been published is also essential, and to fill this need, the American Medical Association prepares the *Quarterly Cumulative Index Medicus,* which is available at a price far below the cost of publication. Difficulties caused by the Second World War delayed publication for a period, and the fact that the Index is still more than a year from being current is immensely handicapping its users. The Survey heard librarians complain that the Index, which is an important part of every medical library, was still not current. It found no evidence, however, of offers by the schools to aid the Index, which is published as a service, and upon which not only medical school libraries but research institutions and other scientific libraries depend, as a guide to the current literature in medicine and related fields. To fill the gap, the *Current List of Medical Literature,* prepared by the Army Medical Library under the direction of the Surgeon General, is available in most medical schools. The list is cumbersome and unfamiliar, however, to most students and faculty members. A third and newer index, *Excerpta Medica,* published in the Netherlands, contains abstracts of the literature prepared by an international board of editors, and is becoming an important asset to every medical school library.[1]

As a storehouse containing both the seedcorn and the harvest of medical education and of medical research, the library is an integral part of a medical school, and it was in this role that the libraries were studied by the Survey. Data were collected from the librarians, the department heads, and the deans of the medical schools regarding the adequacies of the library's facilities and budgets to perform its functions in the medical school, as well as the adequacy of the assistance given to the medical student in the use of the library as a tool to sound methods of study. Opinions were sought on the greatest needs of the library in relation to the needs of the school, but no attempt was made to explore their operation and organization in detail. In addition, the wider services of the library in the medical community at large were examined.

The Survey found many points of excellence in the libraries of medical schools, both individually and collectively. However, a study such as this is valuable only if it calls attention to deficiencies and describes ways in which the needs are being met.

THE LIBRARY AS AN AID TO THE STUDENT'S LEARNING

A great many students enter medical schools today apparently without ever having had experience or training in the use of a library, and with

[1] Distributed in the United States by The Williams & Wilkins Company, Baltimore.

little incentive to explore for themselves the advantages of a specialized library. They need instruction in the use of medical literature as an aid to learning and to the sound methods of study that must become their habit during their medical school years and that will help them to remain effective students during the rest of their career. It is essential, therefore, that the medical schools weave into their curriculum instruction and practice in the use of the medical library.

According to the statements of librarians, faculty members, and students, instruction in the use of the library is neglected in the majority of medical schools, and students make far from optimal use of the literature throughout their medical school years. In over half of the schools studied, no planned effort was made to instruct the students in the use of this most important tool or to stimulate methods of study that require library research. In the remaining schools, the librarian gave one or two didactic lectures, sometimes supplemented by a conducted tour through the library. In a few schools, the librarian also assigned to each student the problem of looking up a reference in one of the standard indexes or catalogues. Only in exceptional instances, however, did the faculty of the medical school cooperate with the librarian in this instruction, or supplement his efforts, by including in its courses assignments that would develop skill in the use of the library's sources of information.

Frequently, students use the library little, if at all, in their first and second years in medical school. According to one librarian, the use of the library had declined steadily since 1946, and it was now used more by graduate and postgraduate students than by medical students. Medical students, she asserted, began to make more use of the library when they were in their third and fourth years; only one department had so organized its instruction that students were required to look up references in the literature. At another school, the librarian stated that no effort whatever was made to interest the students in the use of the library until their second year, and in that year not one department cooperated in her efforts to introduce the students to the literature. In the third year, she reported, two departments made it necessary for the students to look up specific topics in the literature. In that school, with about 400 medical students enrolled, not more than 10 or 20 made use of the library in the evenings. In some of the other schools, it was common in the evenings for students to bring their own textbooks and notebooks to the library and to use it as a study hall without using the library's literature. In some schools even the students in their fourth year were apparently unable to use the library catalogue and indexes effectively.

Access to the Stacks

The policy of giving medical students free access to the library's stacks is an incentive to the student to finding for himself the literature he is seeking. It enables him to glance briefly at a large amount of literature and to learn where he can find it in the future, and at the same time it conserves the valuable time of the trained librarian. In 35 of the 41 schools visited, the medical students, faculty members, and other users of the library were all permitted free access to the stacks. Of the six remaining schools, in which access to the stacks was not permitted, in two instances the medical library was a physical part of the general university library located at some distance from the medical school; and in three instances the library and its budget were small and its literature was so poorly organized that the librarian's assistance was required before any piece of literature could be found when it was wanted.

LIBRARY NEEDS OF THE FACULTY

Although the specialized literature needed by the faculty members, and used almost daily, is a part of the medical school library, and is catalogued as such, in most schools it is kept in the departments using it the most. There are advantages and disadvantages to this policy, which encourages each department to accumulate a sizable library of its own but removes some of the medical school's literature from a central location. While the more ready access of this reference material enables the members of the department to make better and more frequent use of it, other departments find it less easily accessible and medical students find it practically inaccessible. It is necessary that all the literature be recorded in the catalogue of the main library, but such cataloguing is made difficult when the material is housed in many different departments.

In small schools in which the physical facilities are compact and the library is conveniently close to most of the departments, the question of departmental libraries is not an important problem. In the medical centers, however, in which the departments are remote from the main libraries, departmental libraries are the only means of easy access by the faculty to the literature they need in their work.

Policies imposing limits on the size of the departmental libraries have been adopted by the faculties of some medical schools. In a few schools, however, the only limit is the amount of the department's funds.

The arrangement that apparently works the most satisfactorily is that of encouraging and assisting each department to keep on hand the literature that its members refer to almost daily, as well as literature so specialized that students and members of other departments have little use for it. The main library keeps the material catalogued, and its staff assists with renewals of subscriptions, binding of volumes, planning of shelf space, and other such matters.

Research

The tremendous expansion of the research activity, described in earlier chapters, has placed increasingly greater demands on the libraries of the medical schools. Each research worker usually is investigating a problem so highly specialized that the literature concerning it, which he must have available, may be of little or no immediate interest to medical students or to other members of the faculty. These research workers require also the services of highly trained librarians who are skilled in searching all the published literature for material of value to specific research problems, and are able to judge what material to purchase, what to borrow and where it can be obtained, and how to spend the limited funds that are available.

LIBRARY FACILITIES IN A MEDICAL CENTER

Medical libraries are becoming more departmentalized as medical schools expand into medical centers and their facilities become spread over a wide area. Careful administrative planning is needed to avoid fragmentation of the library. When departmental libraries become separated from the medical school and housed in special institutes, these separate libraries may need to be expanded further to meet the needs of the faculties and students working in the institutes. Ideally, to make the literature accessible to all its users, the literature in these special libraries should also be on the shelves of the library of the medical school.

Expanding hospital affiliations have placed additional loads on the libraries of the medical schools. Although many hospitals have their own libraries, they usually contain little more than current periodicals bought with hospital funds, and they rarely have adequate files of the older literature. In most instances, they are inadequate for the needs of house staffs with active programs and for the research being carried on in the hospitals. To a great and increasing extent, therefore, the libraries of the medical schools are serving these needs.

The growing number of hospitals of the Veterans Administration affiliated with medical schools poses administrative and financial problems for the medical school libraries which must be recognized and met with realistic and careful planning to avoid reduction of the library's effectiveness to the faculty and students. One hospital of the Veterans Administration even sends a truck to the medical school several times a week to transport back and forth the literature needed for an active residency program and the research that is under way. The supply of current periodicals acquired under the supervision of a dean's committee since the time of the hospital's affiliation with the medical school could not possibly be adequate for the purposes of research workers.

PRACTICING PHYSICIANS

Access to a medical library is essential to practicing physicians, and they are increasingly making use of the libraries of the medical schools, and in a few instances contributing to their financial support. In some areas, the only medical library available to practicing physicians is that of the nearest medical school, but in a few cities medical societies have built fine libraries of their own and have made them available to medical students and faculty as well as to their members.

A few medical school libraries operate a lending service by mail for the benefit of physicians throughout the region or the state who would otherwise have little access to the medical literature. Only those libraries with strong financial support are able to adopt such a policy, however, since it requires duplication of much of the literature and a relatively large library staff.

In a few cities, the physicians in practice have cooperated with the medical school in building up a library that meets the needs of both the school and the practicing physicians. This arrangement has had excellent results. In one school, a newly built library contains a special reading room for practicing physicians, and the library houses a book collection turned over to it by the medical society. The physicians contribute to the support of the library from their annual society dues. A valuable feature is a service whereby literature requested by telephone is dispatched by messenger to the physician's office. Similar arrangements exist at only a few other schools. This type of joint effort might well be more widely adopted.

LIBRARY FACILITIES AND EXPENDITURES IN 1950–51

According to figures supplied by the librarians in 37 medical schools, the libraries employed 1 to 21 staff workers (mostly on a full-time basis), had 7,000 to 160,000 bound volumes on their shelves, and subscribed to 105 to 1,061 journals. Seating capacity ranged from 18 to 250; 21 schools had seating capacity under 100. The lowest salary budget was $2,880, and the highest $46,380. According to figures supplied by the deans, 1950–51 expenditures on libraries in these 37 schools ranged from $5,734 to $67,954. These figures, however, represented the medical schools' total expenditures on libraries, commonly including the medical school's share of the expenses of the general university library. In some of the libraries, it was almost impossible to consider the finances and personnel separately from those of the general university library, of which the medical library was an integral part.

In some instances, the university library was not conveniently available to the medical school, the two being several blocks apart. In a few cases, in which the library of the medical school is small, some other excellent medical library is readily available and meets the needs of both students and faculty. In other instances the medical school library, although fairly large and with a relatively large budget in comparison with other libraries, must meet the needs of a large number of students in many other fields besides medicine, and of a large faculty, so that in reality it is barely adequate. The value of these statistics for comparison is, therefore, limited.

In 27 of the 41 schools visited, the librarians stated that their most urgent need was for space, both for the storage and processing of literature and for the use of the students and the faculty. This opinion is supported by the fact that 21 of these libraries had no space for expansion, although they were acquiring at least 500 new volumes per year. In most instances the statements of the heads of departments also supported the opinion. In 12 of these schools the dean listed space for the library as one of the major needs of the school. Seating capacity alone was entirely inadequate for the needs of those dependent upon the library.

Several factors have led to this need for enlarged library space. One factor is an increase in the number of periodicals the library should make available. The libraries receive between 200 and 1,500 periodicals each year.[2] It is imperative that these periodicals be bound and kept available because they are referred to for many years after they are published. In addition, each library purchases a number of monographs and textbooks each year for which space must be available. A few libraries are exploring the possibilities of putting their older literature on microfilm in order to conserve storage space, but this process is expensive and inconvenient and is not yet widely used. Some less expensive and more practical method will be urgently needed if the trend to expansion into a medical center continues and the library becomes a storehouse of literature to serve the scattered institutions affiliated with the center and all their personnel.

Other factors have been the marked increase in the number of medical students, interns and residents, graduate students, and students in other health fields, and in the size of the faculties, as well as the number of research projects carried on in the schools.

Ten of the libraries are housed in buildings completed before 1914, and 13 others in buildings completed before 1930. These buildings were not designed to meet the unforeseen growth in the number of periodicals and monographs that has accompanied the expansion of research. In one school the building housing the library had been condemned because of lack of structural strength to carry the increased weight of the library, and volumes were being stored in another building. In another instance, filing space was so inadequate that volumes had to be stored in the basement, without shelving, and were almost inaccessible.

In 35 of the medical schools visited, the library was an integral part of the medical school and housed in its building. In these schools the librarian was administratively responsible to the dean and had the advice of a committee of the faculty on the procuring of books and periodicals. In the remaining six schools, the library was separated from

[2] Includes periodicals received gratuitously.

the school either by distance or by its position under the administration of the university library, or by both factors. Separation was only a moderate disadvantage in the four instances in which the library was near the school. In two instances, however, the two were a mile apart. In both of the latter instances, the medical library was part of the general university library, which was so inconveniently located that its use by medical students and faculty was considerably impaired. In these six schools the librarian had the advice of a faculty committee on the procurement of books and periodicals, but when the committee was drawn from all parts of the university, the needs of the medical school were not well represented. In the selection and purchase of books and periodicals for use by the medical school, it is essential that the librarian have the advice of a medical school committee.

FINANCIAL SUPPORT OF THE MEDICAL LIBRARY

In the 59 schools whose finances for the years 1940–41, 1947–48, and 1950–51 are described in an earlier chapter, expenditures of general operating funds—including sums spent on libraries but not including funds restricted to research—more than doubled in the 10-year period, increasing from $24,192,000 in 1940–41 to $57,862,000 in 1950–51 (Table 40). Library expenditures also more than doubled, increasing

Table 40. TEN-YEAR TREND IN LIBRARY EXPENDITURES, GENERAL OPERATING EXPENSES, AND FUNDS RESTRICTED TO RESEARCH, OF 59 MEDICAL SCHOOLS

	1940–41*	1947–48*	1950–51
Libraries..............................	$ 522,000	$ 1,084,000	$ 1,377,000
General operating expenses (including libraries, but not including funds restricted to research and expenses for hospitals and clinics)............................	24,192,000	49,603,000	57,862,000
Funds restricted to research..............	3,162,000	14,313,000	27,881,000

* Figures for 1940–41 and 1947–48 computed from those of the Surgeon General's Committee on Medical School Grants and Finances.

from $522,000 to $1,377,000. The expenditures of funds restricted to research in these schools, however, increased more than eightfold in the same period, rising from $3,162,000 to $27,881,000.

With an eightfold increase in expenditures on research, and the indirect costs of that research being absorbed largely by the instructional budget of the school and charged to administration and maintenance, it would seem that the libraries have not been provided with sufficient funds to meet the demands placed upon them by the research expansion. When knowledge is sought increasingly, the libraries will be used increasingly. Every research worker must have available the records of the present knowledge in the field of his problem, and of what progress other workers are making in that field. While it would be impossible to estimate what the ratio should be of library expenditures to research expenditures, it would seem that an eightfold increase in research expenditures should be accompanied by much more than a doubling of the library expenditures. Not only is expansion in research inevitably accompanied by increased use of the library, but it is usually accompanied by a need for subscription to periodicals that have not previously been required, by a need for additional copies of volumes already on the shelves, and by a greater need for the services of trained librarians.

The demands placed upon the libraries by research projects have not been recognized by the administrative officers of medical schools or by agencies granting funds to support such projects. It is estimated that, in 1950–51, the allocation to the libraries of 2 per cent of the funds restricted to research would have resulted in an average increase of approximately 40 per cent in the total funds available for the libraries in the 59 schools.

Little evidence was found by the Survey of attempts to meet the libraries' increased needs during a period of tremendous expansion in the research and other activities of the schools. Faculty members, research workers, and students will be severely handicapped unless the new demands placed upon the libraries are met by careful administrative and budgetary planning. In a nation dependent upon medical research to a greater degree than ever before, surprisingly little is being expended on the housing of the reports of that research and on making those reports available.

CONCLUSIONS

1. The libraries of medical schools are important in their role as indispensable aids to study and learning and as storehouses for the accumulated medical literature of the past and of the present.

2. Good libraries are essential to the development of sound methods of study in the medical student, and to the stimulation of the habits of continual study that he will need throughout his career.

3. Good libraries are essential for the academic and research purposes of all members of the faculty of a medical school.

4. Good libraries are essential also in the continuing study of the practicing physician.

5. Few schools give the students instruction in the use of the library based on the proper educational principles that are at the root of instruction in other departments of the medical school. In only approximately half of the libraries of the medical schools visited during the Survey was any planned effort made to introduce the medical student to the efficient and practical use of the library and its literature.

6. More than half of the libraries are inadequately housed for the demands placed upon them.

7. Expanding research activities have increased the demands upon medical libraries for both general and highly specialized material as well as for the services of highly trained librarians.

8. The trend toward expansion of medical schools into medical centers spread over a wide area may create a need for expansion of departmental libraries housed in separate institutes in the center, as well as expansion of the libraries housed in the medical schools.

9. The trend toward additional affiliations with hospitals in which there are active residency and research programs is also placing increasing demands upon the libraries of medical schools.

10. The financial support for libraries and for the medical schools' general operating expenses have both doubled in amount over a 10-year period. This increase has not, however, been adequate to meet the additional load placed upon the libraries by the expansion of research, support of which—with restricted funds—increased eightfold during the same 10 years.

RECOMMENDATIONS

1. Librarians and faculties should give as serious thought to methods of effectively introducing the student to the use of the library as they give to instruction in other courses in the curriculum.

2. Remodeling and building programs to ensure adequate physical facilities for the libraries should be given high priority in plans of the medical schools for the future.

3. Both the medical schools and the agencies that grant them funds restricted to research should take cognizance of the fact that access to and proper use of medical literature is an indispensable part of research programs. They should make every effort to improve the quality of the research under way by providing that some adequate portion of the funds restricted to research is made available for the strengthening of the library.

4. Hospitals related to medical schools and finding it necessary to use the library should pay their share of the cost of the library.

5. Medical societies in the communities where there are medical schools without adequate libraries should give serious consideration to improving the educational opportunities of their members by strengthening the financial support of the medical school library.

6. When a departmental library develops into a special library in a separate institute in the medical center, the librarian and the faculty of the medical school should increase the collection of literature in the central location in order to make it readily accessible to all the students and faculty members.

11 THE FACULTY

The faculty of a medical school, which determines the quality of teaching, is its most important asset. To a large extent its members determine the educational policies of the school, the content and organization of curriculum, the selection of students and of teaching and research personnel, and the teaching methods. Their research contributes to medical knowledge, and they play an important role in the administration and public relations of the school. Together with the graduates of the school, the faculty determines its reputation.

FACULTY CLASSIFICATIONS

Faculty members are classified according to academic rank and also according to the methods by which they are compensated. Although the terms vary, the common classification of rank includes the titles of professor, associate professor, assistant professor, instructor, and assistant. If the title is preceded by the adjective "clinical," the faculty member is usually serving on a volunteer or a part-time basis. In the lower categories, a variety of terms are used, such as fellow, research fellow, teaching fellow, and graduate assistant. These terms usually indicate that the younger man is still a graduate student but assists in the instructional program to some degree for either medical students or other students.

The designation "full-time" has several meanings. The earned income of a strictly full-time faculty member is derived wholly from the medical school; any income from practice reverts to the medical school. The "geographic full-time" man is allowed to supplement his medical school salary with fees from private practice, which he conducts in an office provided for him at the medical school or the teaching hospital.

Often the school attempts to set limits upon the amounts these men may retain from practice; in some instances amounts above certain limits must revert to the medical school for the strengthening of the budget of the faculty member's department.

The number of members holding the rank of professor or associate professor in a department varies among the medical schools. It is common in clinical departments to find many men with the title of clinical professor.

The catalogues of medical schools list large numbers of faculty members. Many of them, however, serve in limited teaching capacities. Most of them are volunteer faculty members who are perhaps able to devote a few hours per week to the actual work of the medical school or to give only a few lectures each year. A few devote very large amounts of time to teaching. The number of names on the faculty list is, therefore, misleading. Many schools have difficulty in manning the teaching programs and service functions in spite of a large faculty roster.

Volunteer clinical faculty members may expend much time and energy in teaching and even in research at the sacrifice of their opportunities in private practice. On the other hand, these volunteer teachers may be selected because of their influential position in practice, in the community, or on the hospital staff, or because of their importance in residency training, without any real degree of certainty as to their interest and ability in the teaching of the undergraduate medical student.

Residents in the teaching hospitals are commonly utilized in the instruction of medical students, nurses, and other personnel. By some medical schools they are given an academic title, such as instructor, assistant, or teaching fellow.

GROWTH OF THE FACULTIES

The number of paid faculty members has been increasing (Table 41). The trend is to employ more men on a full-time or a geographic full-time basis. This is especially true in the clinical departments. In the *clinical departments* the privately supported schools increased their full-time faculty by 65 per cent between 1940–41 and 1949–50, while the tax-supported schools increased theirs 160 per cent. In both privately and tax-supported schools, the ratio of part-time to full-time faculty members decreased. The *medical basic science departments* of 19 pri-

Table 41. INCREASE IN PART-TIME AND FULL-TIME FACULTY MEMBERS OF
THE RANK OF INSTRUCTOR OR ABOVE BETWEEN FISCAL YEARS 1940–41
AND 1949–50, AT 32 FOUR-YEAR MEDICAL SCHOOLS

	1940–41	1949–50	Per cent increase
Part-time Faculty			
Medical basic science departments			
13 Tax-supported schools.............	35	79	126
19 Privately supported schools........	86	101	17
Clinical departments			
13 Tax-supported schools.............	324	466	44
19 Privately supported schools........	701	912	30
Total.........................	1,146	1,558	36
Full-time Faculty			
Medical basic science departments			
13 Tax-supported schools.............	295	416	41
19 Privately supported schools........	518	645	25
Clinical departments			
13 Tax-supported schools.............	192	499	160
19 Privately supported schools........	437	722	65
Total.........................	1,442	2,182	51

vately supported schools increased their full-time faculty 25 per cent
during the nine-year period, while 13 tax-supported schools increased
theirs 41 per cent. The increase in the part-time paid faculty members in
these departments was approximately 17 per cent in the privately supported schools and 126 per cent in the tax-supported schools, but the
ratio of part-time to full-time men remained approximately the same in
the nine-year period.

The rapidity of growth of the full-time faculties is evidence
of the growth in size and prestige of the clinical departments. The medical basic science departments historically were the first to be organized
with full-time faculty members. The clinical departments have followed
the same pattern and by 1949–50 had surpassed the medical basic science departments in the number of full-time faculty members.

The need for full-time men who can devote all their time and energy
to the work of a medical school and its teaching hospital is clear. In
their present magnitude, the activities of large medical schools and
medical centers can no longer be properly organized and carried out
without at least a nucleus of full-time faculty members. In spite of the

increase in the number of full-time men, the full-time faculties of a large percentage of medical schools are still too small.

FACULTY FINANCES

A majority of young men who seek a true academic life do not expect financial reward equal to that of private practice. Theoretically, the basis for entering an academic career is idealism. Teaching and research are creative activities requiring imagination, critical thinking, energy, and some sacrifice of personal ease. The individual entering such a career should be able to look forward to an opportunity for study and thought, to intellectual stimulation from his coworkers and students, and to sufficient economic stability and security to permit the devotion of his energy to his professional duties. Many faculty members are fortunate enough to have private incomes with which they are able and willing to help finance their academic careers.

In actuality, however, idealistic reasons do not always provide the motivation for seeking faculty appointments, nor do they always enter into the selection of faculty members. Some men move from university science departments to the medical schools because of the attraction of a higher salary scale, because money and facilities for research are greater, or because of an opportunity for more rapid advancement in rank. Some men seek full-time clinical positions because of the prestige, the regular hours, or a dislike of assuming all the responsibilities inherent in private practice. A few faculty members were encountered who remained in medical schools because of personality or physical defects which they recognized would be a handicap in the practice of medicine.

Medical schools find it extremely difficult to finance the salaries of strictly full-time members, especially those in clinical departments, since the men whom they would like to appoint on a full-time basis in those departments have opportunities in the practice of medicine that are not available to men in the medical basic science departments.

The salaries of the clinical faculties, as reported by the deans, are extremely variable. This wide range is not solely the result of differing salary scales, however; it is due to the fact that some of the salaries are derived from a number of sources. Many of the faculty members have additional income from private practice.

The average of the maximum salaries paid to faculty members in each

Table 42. COMPARISON OF AVERAGE MAXIMUM SALARIES PAID TO FULL-TIME FACULTY MEMBERS OF THE RANK OF INSTRUCTOR OR ABOVE IN 34 FOUR-YEAR MEDICAL SCHOOLS FOR FISCAL YEARS 1940–41 AND 1949–50

	Medical basic science faculty, 34 *schools*				*Clinical faculty,* 32 *schools*			
	Number of schools	1940–41	1949–50	*Per cent increase*	*Number of schools*	1940–41	1949–50	*Per cent increase*
Professor								
Tax-supported schools.......	13	$ 6,042	$10,035		13	$ 7,520	$11,785	
Privately supported schools..	21	8,528	11,067		19	11,125	15,632	
Average...................	34	7,578	10,702	41	32	9,580	14,069	47
Associate Professor								
Tax-supported schools.......	13	4,268	6,747		13	5,333	8,627	
Privately supported schools..	21	4,756	7,217		19	7,020	9,010	
Average...................	34	4,579	7,037	54	32	6,378	8,862	39
Assistant Professor								
Tax-supported schools.......	13	3,565	6,007		13	3,914	6,811	
Privately supported schools..	21	3,631	5,953		19	4,574	7,801	
Average...................	34	3,606	5,974	66	32	4,274	7,372	72
Instructor								
Tax-supported schools.......	13	2,408	4,014		13	2,735	4,810	
Privately supported schools..	21	2,597	4,210		19	3,008	5,925	
Average...................	34	2,526	4,133	64	32	2,918	5,527	89

Note: The figures given for average salaries of full-time faculty members of the teaching staffs of the medical schools represent very roughly that amount which is paid by the medical school itself. In many institutions the so-called "full-time" faculty member is allowed to supplement his income by consultations, either private or in government or industry. In other institutions full-time faculty members receive a part of their stipend from hospitals or from university teaching appointments outside the medical school. In the past this has been especially true of the clinical years, with some institutions relying entirely on volunteer or part-time instruction in these years.

Of these 34 schools one had no full-time clinical faculty members and one had only one instructor. These schools are therefore not included in figures for clinical faculty.

of the ranks has been increasing (Table 42). The average maximum salary of a professor increased 41 per cent between 1940–41 and 1949–50 in the medical basic science departments and 47 per cent in the clinical departments; for associate professors it rose 54 per cent in the medical basic science and 39 per cent in the clinical departments; for assistant professors it rose 66 per cent in the medical basic science and 72 per cent in the clinical departments; and for instructors it rose 64 per cent in the medical basic science and 89 per cent in the clinical departments. These increases should be viewed against the 86 per cent increase in the cost of living during the same period.

The average maximum salary of instructors, especially in the clinical departments, has met the increase in the cost of living more adequately then the increases in the other ranks.

In both the clinical and the medical basic science departments, the older professors and associate professors whose salaries approximated or approached the average maximum were forced to reduce their standard of living considerably during the nine-year period and to do without many of the amenities that had been part of their way of life.

The salaries of the instructors in the medical basic science departments are low for men with Ph.D. or M.D. degrees who have spent three to five years in graduate education and training. Even the average maximum salary in this category is approximately the same as the average earnings of carpenters and bricklayers in the year 1948 as reported by the Bureau of Labor Statistics of the U.S. Department of Commerce. Men entering the faculties of medical schools at the instructor level are usually twenty-five to twenty-eight years of age. They look ahead to a professorship if they are successful in their fields, and they are keenly aware of the average maximum salary of $8,000 to $11,000 which, if they are fortunate, they may some day attain. It is little wonder that young physicians enter the clinical fields or the fields of research and industry instead of the medical basic sciences. To bolster the opportunities in academic medicine, the John and Mary R. Markle Foundation has established a limited number of five-year scholarships of $30,000 which are available to medical schools for the support of young men entering either a medical basic science or a clinical field. There is a great need for additional programs of this general type.

The clinical departments offer to young men a much greater range of opportunity than do the medical basic sciences. In the clinical areas a man may teach, carry on research, and keep in touch with clinical medicine. If he is not successful in obtaining a full-time position on the faculty, he may work on a part-time basis, or he can enter the practice of medicine and work for the medical school on a volunteer basis. All this constitutes stiff competition for the medical basic science fields.

The advantage of the geographic full-time concept is that it increases the number of men who spend their entire day in the hospital and medical school, and often, at the same time, allows them to earn a large portion of their income from the practice of medicine. It is a more efficient method of utilizing such faculty members than by having them serve on a volunteer faculty basis and maintain offices outside the medical school. There are, however, several potentially serious disadvantages, which have already been discussed in Chapter 5. First there is the danger that, when a portion of the faculty member's earnings become the property of the school, the administration may find it convenient to bring pressure to bear upon him to increase his earnings in order to help to finance the over-all activities of the institution, as was the case in some of the schools included in the Survey. The other handicap is the opportunity offered to individual faculty members, if no limit is placed on their earnings by the school, to enhance their personal incomes through the development of large practices by making use of the hospital and medical school facilities. For this reason, many schools have attempted to establish ceilings on the earnings of such men. This device tends to limit the time and energy faculty members devote to practice, but many individuals in a department are willing to earn sums considerably in excess of their ceiling if they can employ additional residents and secretaries and purchase equipment which the medical school could not ordinarily afford. Schools which encourage this practice frequently develop dissatisfied younger instructors who soon realize that their earnings from practice exceed the ceiling placed upon them, and see no reason why they should not leave the medical school and enter the practice of medicine so that they may retain all their earnings.

Another unfortunate consequence of the geographic full-time principle is the tendency, on the one hand, to fix an established faculty member at a given institution because much of his income derives from the community. He may be loath to accept an educational post at another school, even though he may have opportunities for more important contributions to education and research, because he does not relish the attendant necessity for establishing a new or less profitable practice. On the other hand, a younger faculty member may be influenced to move to a new institution by the prospect of a more remunerative practice, regardless of educational or academic considerations.

SELECTION AND PROMOTION

The nomination of men for professorships, chairmanships of departments, and often for associate professorships is usually made by a committee of the faculty working with the dean. The nominations are transmitted by this committee to the president of the university and to the board of trustees. Nominations of faculty members of lower rank are usually recommended to the dean by the head of the department.

In the policy pronouncements of most schools, it was generally stated that faculty members were to be selected on the basis of ability in teaching, scholarship, research, leadership, and capacity for growth, but the statements did not always list all these qualities or place them in the same order of importance, nor were the policies always followed in practice. The dean of one strong medical school wrote, in reply to the Survey's question: "Selections and promotions up to assistant professor are based upon ability in a specialty or in productive research; promotions above the rank of assistant professor are based upon demonstrated proficiency in original productive research. These are policies, not written rules." Teaching ability and scholarship were not mentioned in this statement.

In a majority of schools visited, the chief consideration in the selection of full-time faculty members was proved research ability. For instance, in one well-financed, privately supported school, a young man has just been added to the faculty in a research capacity at a salary of $8,000 a year, while another faculty member, who was an excellent teacher whom the students, interns, and residents followed about the halls, was receiving a salary of $5,000. The dean described that teacher as "an excellent wheel horse for the school." In another school, a new head of a department had just been selected who had not been in a medical school for five years and had had little or no previous teaching experience. The students' comment that he "seemed to be learning rapidly how to teach" was not surprising.

The impact of such policies on young men was also observed. A typical example is the young research fellow in one medical school who had been offered by another medical school a position with increased responsibilities that involved teaching and some administrative work. He had refused the offer because he had published only one research paper and if he remained one more year as a research fellow he could turn out three more. He was aware that this demonstration of his research productivity would greatly improve his opportunities for obtaining advancement in academic rank in the future.

The concern regarding the balance between education and research was well stated by the dean of a privately supported school when he commented to the Survey:

Research is vitalizing but teaching is vitalizing too. There is overemphasis on research. It is trite to say this because it has been reiterated ad nauseam, but the fact still remains that we do not place enough emphasis on teaching, nor do we compensate adequately for the capacity to teach. We give lip service constantly to the importance of teaching, but when the chips are down, research always tips the balance.

It is not unusual for faculty promotions to be made on the basis of research productivity. Many of the best faculty members are in agreement with the statement made to the Survey by an associate professor, who said that in his opinion "more bold and imaginative research would be produced in our medical schools if promotion were not based so largely on the number of publications, but rather on their quality."

RESIDENTS

The use of residents as instructors in the teaching hospital is widespread. All members of the resident staff may be given important teaching responsibilities in the clinical departments. They most commonly participate in the instruction of the medical student in the courses in physical diagnosis, and in outpatient department teaching. Both of these areas are apt to be less attractive to the full-time or part-time paid faculty members. These young residents are men in training and are usually selected not because of their teaching ability or experience, but because of their intellectual capacities and their desire for specialty training or research. Nevertheless, in the opinion of the department heads, residents often constitute some of the better teachers in the medical schools.

INBREEDING

Policies with respect to the selection of faculty members also frequently lead to "inbreeding." In one tax-supported school, all students admitted to the medical school must be residents of the state. Upon graduation from this school 75 to 80 per cent of those students obtain internships in hospitals in the state, and almost two-thirds of the faculty members are graduates of the medical school. Only a few of the members of this faculty were aware of teaching methods and experiments being carried on in other schools in the United States. Some of the larger schools, both tax and privately supported, have faculties composed of 60 to 70 per cent of their own graduates.

At what level inbreeding may be said to occur and to be detrimental cannot be accurately defined. It is certainly more dangerous at the level of the professorship and the department head, because these men carry most of the responsibility for organizing and orienting the point of view of the faculty of the department.

EXCHANGE AND DEBATE OF IDEAS

There was little evidence of any planned exchange of ideas among the schools concerning the teaching methods and organization of instruction. Although faculty members of all medical schools have many opportunities to meet one another at scientific meetings, similar conferences for the discussion of educational problems and experiments are held much less frequently. The literature on the subject is meager. Only one journal, the *Journal of Medical Education,* is devoted entirely to medical education, and only a few medical journals publish articles on the subject. It was unusual to find a faculty member of one school who had visited another school for the specific purpose of studying its organization and methods of instruction. Men within a few hundred miles of one another were only vaguely aware of the type of teaching being carried on in the sister institution. A few medical schools make it their policy to invite visiting professors to participate for short periods in their educational program, but the practice was rarely found during the Survey.

Perhaps the greatest exchange of personnel between medical schools occurs at the level of the internship and residency periods of training, with much less occurring after a man has once obtained an instructorship. It was at this level of faculty rank that the Survey found the greatest interest and willingness to debate problems of education. However, it was in the same area that the greatest amount of ignorance and lack of information was to be found. These young men did not have the stimulation, the opportunity, or the financial means to take a lively interest in the educational process and to study it in action at other institutions.

There is recently an increasing interest in teaching and in experiments in medical education. This interest has been predominantly in limited fields such as in psychiatry, preventive medicine, and public health, with a few experiments in major curricular redesign. The Survey found little experimentation in teaching methods, and none in the form of carefully controlled experiments.

Even within institutions there was often found a lack of knowledge and information by various faculty members concerning the policies or programs within the institution. This lack is understandable in view of the size of some of the medical schools and medical centers. In some schools volunteer or part-time men hold the positions of heads of clinical departments and compose the majority of the executive faculty which is responsible for the educational policies of the school. In many of these departments there are full-time faculty members of less than professional rank who carry on the daily work of the department but have little or no voice in medical school affairs. A very few schools hold occasional meetings—one to three a year—to which the full faculty or teaching staff is invited.

Faculty morale or interest tends to be departmental. Schools on the whole have not done a very satisfactory job in keeping their faculty members informed and in arousing their interest in the impact of the full medical school program on the medical student. The focus is still on the subject and the department, and not on the student and his four-year program.

With the increasing numbers of faculty members, the increasing size of departments, and the tendency toward isolation of departments into units relatively independent from the medical school and widely spread, opportunities for general exchange of information by the faculties decrease and new means need to be created. In a few schools, circulation of a school bulletin helps to accomplish the purpose. In other schools, general faculty meetings held at stated intervals, and to which admissions, curriculum, executive, and other committees make reports and the dean and sometimes the president present new problems and plans, furnish opportunity for general exchange of information by the faculty. Some schools have a faculty club or a medical school or hospital dining room in which faculty members from the various disciplines can meet at mealtimes. Often residents and students can meet informally in the dining rooms—occasionally with members of the faculty—and participate in discussion of some of the larger problems of the school.

THE QUALITY OF EDUCATION

The faculty determines the quality of the education offered by an institution. The effectiveness of the faculty is limited by the objectives and responsibilities of the medical school and the vagueness of definition of medical education. It is limited also by an overload of teaching, research, or administrative responsibility. Some faculty members are almost overwhelmed by a great multiplicity of duties—including administration, large teaching responsibilities for increasing numbers of medical students and nonmedical students, professional service, and consultations—and by the struggle to maintain some research activity by constantly bidding for grants of short duration. Many such men have become frustrated and resigned; they are unwilling to think imaginatively because new ideas might bring increased responsibilities. Another group of men are alert and using considerable imagination, chiefly applied to research. Much of the energy of the faculty, and of these men especially, is expended on fellows and graduate students engaged in research projects rather than on medical students.

Certainly in not more than eight or ten medical schools did the Survey encounter the spirit described by a dean who served as a staff member in the survey of one school. He wrote:

> Here one experiences the sense of common purpose in the faculty which is frequently missing in many of the large and elaborately organized university hospital groups. There is spirit, there is gentleness, and finally one is aware of that intangible quality which Whitehead has insisted is essential to any true teaching institution—the habitual vision of greatness.

CONCLUSIONS

1. The faculty of a medical school is its most important asset. It determines the quality of teaching, the selection of students and teaching and research personnel, the form of the curriculum, and the educational policies; and it plays an important role in administration and public relations.
2. The medical basic science departments are staffed predominately by full-time paid teachers, and the clinical departments are staffed predominately by volunteer staff members.
3. The number of full-time and geographic full-time faculty members has been increasing, especially in the clinical departments.
4. The number of paid faculty members who can devote the major part of their time and energy to the medical schools is too small for the present magnitude of the schools' activities.
5. Salaries of professors and associate professors have not increased

so rapidly as those of assistant professors and instructors, and have not kept pace with the increased cost of living.

6. Geographic full-time clinical faculty positions, in which the faculty members have private offices in the teaching hospital, are increasing in number.

7. Residents in teaching hospitals are commonly utilized as instructors, although they are not usually selected on the basis of teaching experience or ability.

8. Research ability is now the prime consideration in the selection and promotion of faculty members in most medical schools. Teaching ability is being given secondary importance.

9. There is a need for greater exchange of educational ideas and discussion of teaching methods among the faculties of medical schools.

10. Faculties of medical schools are often overwhelmed by responsibilities and activities not directly related to medical education.

RECOMMENDATIONS

1. The faculty of a medical school should be composed of men who have faith in the value of education, a deep interest in students, and a continuing curiosity and desire to add to their own knowledge.

2. The medical schools should employ a greater number of faculty members on a full-time paid basis to meet the growing responsibilities and expanding activities of the medical schools.

3. The geographic full-time system of employing clinical faculty members should be so designed that the patients seen by such men participate in the teaching programs.

4. Residents should not be given major teaching responsibilities as part of their routine duties unless they have demonstrated an interest in students and ability in teaching.

5. The faculty of a medical school should devote its major time and energy to teaching and research. It should not be exploited by the university in a wide variety of training and educational programs for other students, or by the medical school to carry on large medical service and welfare functions.

12 ADMISSIONS

The medical student is the key figure in medical education. The quality of the young men and women who seek to enter medical school and the wisdom and care with which they are selected are of vital importance to the public. The school should offer to its students the best possible instruction and training, but the education of a medical student requires an expenditure of human and material resources so great that it can be justified only if the highest possible percentage of those admitted complete its work successfully and become competent physicians.

A good physician must have more than medical knowledge and technical skills. He must possess a sense of responsibility, human understanding, social sensitivity, and moral courage. His intellectual capacity will determine to a large extent the future quality of medical practice and the advances in medical knowledge.

Forty years ago the policies and procedures for selecting medical students were of little interest to the public. In the interval, however, all phases of American higher education have been expanded and medical education has moved from trade-school standing to recognition as a university discipline (Table 43). Rapid advances in medical science and the prospect of even greater discoveries in the prevention and cure of disease have fired the interest of the American public. As a result of these developments, the public is today deeply interested in medical education and the selection of medical students.

The admissions problem of the medical schools has changed steadily in the past 40 years. In 1910, at the time of the Flexner study of medical education, 156,000 students graduated from high school and 37,000 from college. At that time, there was some doubt that medical school

Table 43. GROWTH OF SECONDARY-SCHOOL, COLLEGE, AND MEDICAL SCHOOL GRADUATING CLASSES IN THE UNITED STATES, 1889–90 TO 1949–50

Year	Secondary-school graduates*	College graduates (Bachelor's and first professional)	Medical school graduates (M.D. only)†
1889–90	43,731	15,539‡	
1909–10	156,429	37,199‡	3,165
1919–20	311,266	48,622	2,680
1929–30	666,904	123,484	4,565
1939–40	1,221,475	186,500	5,097
1943–44	1,019,233	125,863	5,134
1947–48	1,189,909	272,144	5,543
1949–50	1,200,000§	433,734	5,553

* From "Biennial Survey of Education in the United States, 1946–48" (FSA, Office of Education, Statistical Summary of Education, 1947–48), Chap. 1, p. 27, Table XIII.

† From Anderson, D. G., and Anne Tipner: Medical Education in the United States and Canada, *Journal of the American Medical Association*, Vol. 144, p. 115 (Sept. 9), 1950.

‡ Cited by the "World Almanac and Book of Facts for 1951," p. 581, as not including graduates of teachers colleges and normal schools; credited source is the United States Office of Education. The remaining statistics in this column (except for the last item) are from "Biennial Survey of Education in the United States, 1946–48" (FSA, Office of Education, Statistics of Higher Education, 1947–48) Chap. 4, p. 26, Table XVII. The college graduates figure for 1949–50 comes from, "Earned Degrees Conferred by Higher Education Institutions, 1949–50" (FSA Office of Education Circular 282, December, 1950) p. VII, Table A.

§ Since the Office of Education has not yet compiled statistics on secondary-school graduates for 1949–50, the figure 1,200,000 is only an estimate based upon trends noted in the current literature of education.

classes could be filled if a high-school education were required for admission. Nevertheless requirements were increased, and by 1918 all approved medical schools required two years of college work. Concurrently, there was a nationwide movement toward higher education (Table 43). The number of high-school graduates rose to 666,000 in 1930 and 1,156,000 in 1947. College graduates increased in number to 123,000 in 1930 and 271,000 in 1947. In 1910, a few of the better known medical schools had more applicants than they could accept. The number of schools in this position steadily increased until 1924, when there were more applicants in the nation than there were places in the entering classes. By 1939 all medical schools in the United States had more applicants than they could accept (Table 44). Thus the problem of selective admissions became a common problem for all medical schools. This is the background against which the various aspects of present-day admissions must be considered.

Table 44. COMPARISON OF THE NUMBER OF APPLICATIONS, APPLICANTS, APPLICANTS ACCEPTED, AND APPLICANTS ENROLLED, 1929–30 TO 1950–51

Year	Number of applications	Number of applicants	Number of applicants accepted	Per cent of applicants accepted	Number of applicants enrolled*
1929–30	31,749	13,655	7,035	51.5	6,457
1930–31		(Statistics unavailable)			6,456
1931–32		(Statistics unavailable)			6,260
1932–33	31,429	12,280	7,357	59.9	6,426
1933–34	29,705	12,128	7,543	62.2	6,457
1934–35	32,321	12,779	7,419	58.0	5,356
1935–36	34,427	12,740	6,900	54.2	6,605
1936–37	35,439	12,192	6,465	53.0	5,910
1937–38	34,416	12,207	6,410	52.5	5,791
1938–39	36,268	12,131	6,223	51.3	5,764
1939–40	34,871	11,800	6,211	52.6	5,794
1940–41	34,434	11,854	6,328	53.4	5,837
1941–42	34,665	11,940	6,822	57.1	6,218
1942–43	39,111	14,043	6,835	48.7	6,425
1943–44		(Statistics unavailable)			6,561
1944		(Statistics unavailable)			6,648
1944–45		(Statistics unavailable)			6,523
1945–46		(Statistics unavailable)			6,060
1946–47		(Statistics unavailable)			6,564
1947–48	56,553	(Statistics unavailable)			6,487
1948–49	81,662	24,242	6,973	28.8	6,688
1949–50	88,244	24,434	(Statistics unavailable)		7,042
1950–51	81,931	22,280	7,254	32.5	7,187

Source: Except for the last column, these statistics are from the office of the Association of American Medical Colleges.

* Statistics in this column compiled by the Council on Medical Education and Hospitals of the American Medical Association.

The methods utilized in studying the problems of admission at each medical school were to interview the administrative officers of the medical school and university, the registrar, members of the admissions committee, groups of students, and representatives of local medical organizations. At each school the records, grades, and Medical College Admission Test scores of students were reviewed. Full use was also made of information published by the Association of American Medical

Colleges and by the Council on Medical Education of the American Medical Association.

ADMISSIONS POLICIES

The admissions policies of the medical schools are determined by the purpose for which the medical school was founded, the ownership, the rulings of the trustees or legislators who have legal responsibility for the school, the president of the university, the sources of financial support, and public opinion. Within certain established policies the dean, the medical school faculty, and the admissions committee are the most important forces in shaping actual admissions procedure.

The relative importance of these factors varies from school to school. In institutions founded for a specific purpose, such as special preference on the basis of race, sex, or religion, this is the major factor in the selection of candidates. Legislatures, in whom is vested final legal authority for state universities, in most cases emphatically support policies favorable to residents of the state.

REQUIREMENTS FOR ADMISSION

The Association of American Medical Colleges and the Council on Medical Education and Hospitals of the American Medical Association recommend as minimum two full years of college work, including courses in English, theoretical and practical physics, biology, and general and organic chemistry. Although these two organizations do not specify the number of credit hours in these subjects, many individual schools make their requirements in these and other subjects much more detailed, and a number of them require the possession of a Bachelor's degree. Most medical schools require a stated number of hours of chemistry, biology, physics, English, mathematics, and a foreign language. Most schools recommend additional courses in both science and liberal arts. A few carefully point out that they do not suggest added scientific courses, and note that they are willing to leave to the student and his college the problem of his general education.

More than half of the students questioned in the Survey stated that, by the time they had completed the courses required by the college and met the medical school requirements, little time remained for them to select subjects of interest to them as individuals. If they made application to several medical schools, the problem became more difficult because of the varying requirements of the different schools. The intense competition for admission to medical school has also led many college students to accept as mandatory the recommendations of the medical school and to attempt many of the suggested courses. Students reported that their favorite courses in college were highly regarded because of their content or because they were taught by excellent teachers. Many of the required courses were poorly taught and uninteresting.

ADMISSIONS COMMITTEES

The admissions committee is usually appointed by the dean from members of the faculty of the medical school. The number may vary from 3 to 20. In many schools the admissions committee is composed of the dean and two or three members of the basic science departments. In some universities a member of the college faculty may sit with the admissions committee of the medical school. It is the committee's responsibility to carry out the policies of the board of trustees and of the faculty concerning admissions.

Because of the vast amount of work involved in screening the large number of applicants to medical schools, many of the more able faculty members refuse or attempt to avoid service on admissions committees. Hard-working, conscientious teachers who accept such committee appointments may be required to devote to these duties four to eight hours a week for a period of two to three months. A considerable number of deans appoint members to admissions committees for a limited period of time, varying from two to four years. External pressures from racial groups, alumni, physicians, legislators, and friends also make membership on the admissions committee unattractive.

An increasing number of deans regard the work of this committee as an important part of administration. In schools which have had extensive experience in selective admissions there is clear evidence that faculty members with the greatest experience and wisdom have served on the admissions committees. In such schools it is also evident that the admissions committees receive effective administrative support and adequate clerical help, and that in each instance the entire university organization makes an effort to protect the committee from undue pressure for the admission of individual students.

In other schools less satisfactory provisions have been made for the work of the admissions committee. The chairman may carry most of the burden of admissions alone, frequently with an inadequate staff. Members of the committee may lack the training and experience necessary to evaluate students or may be unwilling or unable to give to the work of the committee the attention that it deserves. It seems clear that the design and organization of many of these committees, originally intended to consider a relatively small number of applicants, are not adequate for the increased numbers and changed conditions of recent years.

The cost of processing large numbers of applicants and assembling full information about them is great; it is probably not fully covered by the application fee of $3 to $10 charged by some of the schools. An adequate clerical staff is basic to the functioning of an effective admissions committee.

ADMISSIONS PRACTICES: GAINING INFORMATION ABOUT THE APPLICANT

The sources and types of information now being used by the medical schools in the selection of the student are as follows: (1) application forms filled out by the student himself giving such information as his name, age, place of birth, etc.; (2) a transcript of the student's secondary and college scholastic record; (3) his score on the Medical College Admission Test; (4) letters of information which may come from his premedical advisor, teachers, personal and family acquaintances, or from local representatives of the medical school who interview him or are acquainted with his family and place of residence; (5) personal interviews with the student by one or more members of the medical school faculty, which may include an interview with a psychiatrist; and (6) the scholastic record in medical school of students from each college in the country. These records have been assembled by the Association of American Medical Colleges and are available to the admissions committees of medical schools.

Personal Information

The application of the student usually gives factual information such as his name, age, sex, race, place and date of birth, father's and mother's name, and religion. Because of charges of discriminatory practices on the part of the schools, two states have passed laws making it illegal to request information about the race or religion of the candidate. In some instances it has been suggested that even a photograph of the applicant should not be requested.

Grades

In a majority of the schools visited, admissions officers stated that the most important single factor in their evaluation of an applicant was undergraduate college grades and especially grades in premedical science courses. Two or three schools indicated that grades were their only criteria for admission. A majority of the schools visited said they considered only those applicants who had attained a certain minimum grade average.

This procedure probably represents a combination of educational conviction and deference to expediency. Many medical admissions officers stated that undergraduate scholastic performance was the best single criterion for success in medical school. But emphasis upon grades is also the easy refuge of admissions committees forced to cope with applicants in such numbers as to make any close individual personal investigation difficult or impossible. A second, and again questionable, advantage of emphasis upon grades has recently developed. The grade is one of the simplest forms of evidence with which an admissions committee can defend itself against the criticisms of disappointed applicants, their friends, and pressure groups who charge the school with unfair decisions.

In more than half of the schools visited, grade point averages were appraised at their face value by the admissions committee. In nine schools, critical consideration was given to the college in which the premedical student was enrolled, with a significant weighting of grades. One state school has established a factor for the purpose of weighting students' college grades. The factor is determined by dividing the college grade point average of the group of students from a given institution by the grade point average achieved by the same group in medical school. They have found this factor to range from .57 to .97, a 40 per cent spread in the grade value of the group of colleges. The Association of American Medical Colleges has followed the accomplishments of the graduates of all colleges whose students have been admitted to medical schools, and has made this material available to the admissions committees of medical schools. Some committees were unaware that this information was available. Only five or six admissions committees interviewed had kept a long-time, systematic record of the accomplishments of medical students, classified according to the various colleges from which they came. Other schools depended upon the judgment of an older member of the admissions committee long familiar with the grading practices and instructional quality of certain colleges.

Criticism of the heavy emphasis on grades, especially in times of keen competition for admission, came from elements in medical faculties and from medical students. The younger teachers in one school, which admits on grades alone, stated that such a procedure enrolls some students not fitted to be physicians. In nine of the schools in which students were consulted, some students freely admitted cheating in undergraduate college in order to obtain better grades to offer for admission to medical school. For the same purpose, others, when they could, chose courses in which high grades came easily. These attitudes, which cannot be defended, raise important questions as to what caused them and how they may be changed.

Perhaps a more valid student criticism of emphasis on grades, and particularly on examination grades, was that, in pursuit of grades, students failed to master the material of the course, and trained only their memories. These comments are familiar to the experienced educator, but their prevalence among carefully selected groups of medical students is disconcerting.

Medical College Admission Test

The Medical College Admission Test was developed by the Educational Testing Service of Princeton, New Jersey, for the Association of American Medical Colleges. It consists of four objective tests designed to measure certain abilities of the candidate. The average of the scores made on all tests given each year is set at 500, and candidates are graded on that basis; scores are being recorded in intervals of 10 units. The middle two-thirds of the group tested receive scores between 400 and 600. There is no passing grade, and each medical school may make whatever use it wishes of the test results. The test was first given in 1947, and its authors and sponsors emphasize that it is still in the experimental stage.

At the time of the Survey, 59 medical schools required this test, another 18 recommended it, and only 2 appeared to make no use of it.

Students making a low score are considered poor candidates for the study of medicine; good scores work in favor of the applicant, particularly if they corroborate a good academic record. The test, therefore, is thought to be of value in establishing a cutoff line, in aiding in the appraisal of students with doubtful credentials, and in helping the committee to decide between candidates whose qualifications appear equal in other respects. The scores made by applicants from various colleges have also been used as a method of evaluating the academic standards of these colleges.

This test is the only test at present available to medical schools admissions committees which can be applied to all candidates. The test, as its sponsors indicate, is still in the experimental stage, although information available to the Survey indicated that it had been given to some 100,000 students, about 25,000 of whom had been admitted to medical school and 5,000 or 6,000 had already been graduated. Though this should constitute a sufficiently large sample for evaluation of the test, the Survey was unable to find that any well-controlled experiment was under way in a medical school for determining its predictive value. It is nevertheless true that many members of admissions committees interviewed assumed the complete predictive validity of the test and considered the applicant's MCAT score a very important factor in evaluating his credentials.

Letters of Information and Premedical Advisers

In general, the members of the admissions committees interviewed were of the opinion that the majority of the letters of recommendation from sources other than premedical advisers were of little or questionable value. They stated that such letters frequently contained vague generalities concerning the student, and were rarely based on accurate observations.

Most undergraduate colleges appoint one or more members of their staff to serve as advisers to premedical students. Such advisers should serve a dual purpose. They should inform the candidate about medical education and entrance requirements, and they should aid the medical school admissions committee in obtaining pertinent information about the scholastic ability and personal attributes of the applicant.

These premedical advisers apparently vary greatly in the interest they have in their advisory work, in the support they receive from the college officers, in their value to the premedical student, and in their service to medical admissions committees. A few medical schools effectively encourage and support the advisory system; one at least develops closer liaison with undergraduate colleges by sending each year several members of its staff to visit colleges and discuss medical education and admissions requirements. Others invite college deans and premedical advisers to visit the medical school for the same purpose. Most medical schools sincerely desire closer relations with undergraduate colleges, but few of them find or make time for their effective cultivation.

Though the medical students consulted were generally critical of premedical advisers, some reported that certain specific advisers had been very helpful. Most of them were emphatic in stating that the premedical advisory system should not be abolished, but improved. Students suggested that such advisers be more carefully selected for both interest and knowledge; that they make themselves better informed about variant medical school requirements and about the content of medical education; that more time be allowed them for effective premedical advising; and that they be invited to visit medical schools and to observe them in operation.

About four-fifths of the medical students interviewed, however, thought that their own premedical adviser had not known them sufficiently well to write a proper recommendation. More than half stated that their premedical advisers had been of small value to them, knew little of medical education and medical schools, and gave insufficient time or interest to their advisory assignment. Students also said that many of the premedical advisers in college science departments merely urged added science courses upon them.

To meet the difficulty of providing adequate information about these students, several undergraduate colleges have established special committees to formulate a composite evaluation of each premedical student. Medical schools are watching this effort with hopeful sympathy. It is apparent that really effective systems of premedical advising and student evaluation require much of the time of unusually interested and able college teachers.

Interviews

In the medical schools visited, innumerable hours were spent by busy faculty members interviewing applicants. In a few schools there was clear evidence that the objectives of the interview had been clearly formulated, the methods for attaining these objectives carefully worked out, and a program developed for comparing the results of the interview with the subsequent performance of the student in medical school. Rarely did the staff find any written record of the interview.

The methods of interviewing students varied widely. In some schools the applicant was interviewed individually by two or three faculty members. In another method, committee members as a group interviewed one student. In a third method, one or two faculty members interviewed two or three students as a group. One school followed a program of having two preclinical teachers and one clinician interview each applicant. The interviewers might or might not be members of the committee, but their opinions were recorded and filed with the student's record. In some schools a psychiatrist sat with the group or held an individual interview.

Each member of one admissions committee of three made a field trip to colleges each fall, interviewing students and advisers in an effort to give orientation and advice and to recruit well-qualified applicants. Unhampered by provincialism, this school has established liaison with some of the better colleges of the country.

The opinions of admissions committee members concerning interviews were extremely variable. A few felt that the interview was one of the most important methods of gaining a specific type of information about a student. Others felt that the interview simply gave them an opportunity to visualize the student and to appraise his personality and use of language.

At least half of the students consulted believed the interview to be of real value, provided it was adequate in length and conducted by a skilled interviewer. They regarded 15 minutes as an absolute time minimum and felt that the applicant should be interviewed by more than one person.

MECHANICS OF ADMISSIONS

Multiple Admissions

One of the problems which have been greatly augmented as the total number of applicants to medical schools has come to exceed the number of places available is that created by the student who makes multiple applications. In order to be sure of admission somewhere, many applicants apply simultaneously to several medical schools and, if accepted by more than one, may switch to their favorite at the last moment. This practice increases the work and the uncertainties of admissions committees.

Time of Notification

Competition for outstanding students was most noticeable among the privately supported medical schools of high reputation. Schools less favorably regarded expected that some of their best applicants would

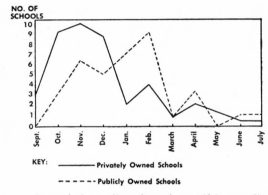

KEY: ——————— Privately Owned Schools

— — — — — Publicly Owned Schools

Figure 12. A comparison of the earliest dates for notifying applicants of their acceptance in 40 privately owned and 35 publicly owned medical schools. Three tax-supported and one privately supported school were not included in this study because of insufficient information.

leave them, even after acceptance. Privately supported medical schools inform most of their candidates before January of the year of matriculation; in state schools the peak of notifications does not come until February (Figure 12). Some state schools delay notifications in order that as many state residents as possible will have an opportunity to gain admission to out-of-state schools. Thus more residents of that state are provided the opportunity to study medicine. The month in which applicants are officially notified of their acceptance is a compromise between the desire to have plenty of time for the orderly processing and consideration of applications and the fear that good students may drift to another school which offers the attraction of an earlier acceptance.

SPECIAL PROBLEMS OF ADMISSION

Questions of both policy and public relations confront medical schools as a result of increased numbers of applicants and of the need to acquire personal information about them. The marked excess of applicants has made some form of selection inevitable. It has for the first time enabled many schools to practice selective admissions, it has awakened public interest in medical school admissions practices, and it has both raised the question of discrimination and created confusion concerning it.

In the past the word "discrimination" possessed affirmative virtues; in recent years it has come to have a largely negative connotation, partly because of its wide use by groups who feel they have received unfair treatment. For purposes of clarity in this report, we shall defer to the current connotation of the word and use it only as limited to unfair racial or religious action. The term "selective admissions" appropriately defines the actions of admitting officers who are primarily motivated by a desire to recruit the young men and women best qualified to become custodians of the science and art of medicine. The term "geographical restriction of admissions" will be used to describe the exclusion of nonresidents from medical schools, usually state owned, and the term "preferential admissions" to describe the action of those schools which give special preference to certain groups on the basis of sex, race, or religion.

Altogether about half of the medical schools of the nation and about half of their admitted applicants are subject to some definite form of restriction, of which geographical restriction is the most prevalent. Doubtless there are restrictions and preferences not explicitly stated which cannot be measured.

Restrictions and Special Preferences

Twenty-eight tax-supported schools and three privately supported schools drew at least 90 per cent of their students from within the borders of their own states. For purposes of the study the Survey considered that these 31 schools practiced geographical restriction. Thirty-nine schools—31 privately supported and 8 tax-supported—did not practice geographical restriction in this sense of the term, although some of these schools stated in their catalogues that preference was given to residents of a state, a section, or to sons and daughters of alumni.

Eleven of the 48 states have no medical school and must depend for medical education upon the schools which do not select their students upon the basis of residence. Five states have only two-year schools and are dependent upon other schools for the latter years. If all schools practiced geographical restriction, medical education would be behind state barriers. This type of restriction, however, has the firm support of legislators and public opinion.

Religious restriction as a declared policy is much less extensive. Six medical schools are controlled and at least in part maintained by religious denominations. These appeared to give preference to members of their respective sects, though others were admitted. The right of any religious group to provide and maintain educational facilities for its own members is an approved American concept. But it cannot be assumed that membership in any particular religious group is in itself qualification for the study or practice of medicine. And as the need for the best possible physicians becomes more apparent, it can be questioned whether national and human welfare should not have primacy over any group interests.

Two schools established to offer medical education to Negroes, though not so restricted by their charters, virtually limit their enrollment to members of that race. Together they admit some 140 students each year. One medical school limits its entering class of 50 to women.

Do these various restrictions, and any others possibly covertly applied, lower the general average of the students selected by the schools which practice them? The Survey can offer no conclusive proof, but some facts are indicative. Table 45 shows that the 31 schools which, in 1950–51, restricted admissions 90 per cent or more on the basis of residence and the 9 schools that appeared to give preference on the basis of race, religion, or sex received little more than one-third as many (22,986) applications as received by the 39 medical schools (63,082) whose restrictive practices are negligible.

The average of Medical College Admission Test scores for students admitted to those 39 medical schools which apparently practiced little or no restriction was significantly higher than the comparable average for students admitted to 40 schools which did restrict. Those 40 schools in-

Table 45. A COMPARISON OF THE 1950–51 APPLICATION AND ADMISSION STATISTICS OF 40 SCHOOLS WHICH RESTRICT (90%) OR GIVE SPECIAL PREFERENCE WITH 39 SCHOOLS WHOSE ADMISSION PRACTICES ARE LESS RESTRICTIVE

Geographical restriction, 90% or more					Geographical restriction, less than 90%			
Medical school	*Type of support*	*No. of applications* *	*No. of students admitted* *	*Per cent restriction*	*Medical school*	*Type of support*	*No. of applications* *	*No. of students admitted* *
Alabama	T	277	56	100	Albany	P	2,000	50
Arkansas	T	150	90	100	Boston	P	1,875	72
Baylor	P	704	91	94	Bowman Gray	P	1,180	56
California	T	800	72	97	Buffalo	P	1,500	70
Georgia	T	259	80	100	Chicago Medical	P	1,700	72
Illinois	T	633	166	100	Cincinnati	T	1,500	90
Indiana	T	906	150	95	Colorado	T	197	80
Iowa	T	211	120	96	Columbia	P	2,800	120
Kansas	T	300	101	90 .	Cornell	P	2,950	80
Louisville	T	400	96	92	Dartmouth†	P	624	24
Louisiana	T	615	125	100	Duke	P	1,093	76
Michigan	T	850	160	90	Emory	P	523	72
Minnesota	T	450	124	93	George Washington	P	2,400	94
Mississippi†	T	350	56	100	Hahnemann	P	2,000	105
Missouri†	T	280	44	100	Harvard	P	996	110
Nebraska	T	286	86	90	Jefferson	P	3,028	166
North Carolina†	T	335	58	91	Johns Hopkins	P	650	75
North Dakota†	T	89	30	93	Long Island			
Ohio	T	580	150	100	(St. N.Y.–N.Y.C.)	P-T	3,500	150
Oklahoma	T	213	80	100	Maryland	T	450	100
Pittsburgh	P	1,045	100	99	New York Medical	P	3,153	124
So. California	P	1,200	69	94	New York Univ	P	2,500	125
South Carolina	T	280	60	100	Northwestern	P	2,103	128
South Dakota†	T	264	36	96	Oregon	T	429	75
Southwestern	T	406	100	94	Pennsylvania	P	2,850	125
Tennessee	T	212	140	100	Rochester	P	2,100	70
Texas	T	500	162	100	Stanford	P	928	62
Utah	T	213	52	92	Syracuse			
Wayne	T	500	68	100	(St. N.Y.–Syr.)	P-T	2,600	76
West Virginia†	T	170	31	100	Temple	P	3,089	125
Wisconsin	T	167	80	100	Tufts	P	834	112
Special Preference					Tulane	P	2,000	128
Creighton	P	747	75		Univ. of Chicago	P	1,700	72
Georgetown	P	1,471	120		Univ. of Washington	T	412	75
Howard	P	1,000	75	100	Univ. of Virginia	T	970	72
Loyola	P	1,210	88		Vanderbilt	P	1,415	52
Marquette	P	1,433	100		Vermont	T	288	45
Medical Evangelists	P	275	97		Virginia Med. Col.	T	520	84
Meharry	P	400	65	100	Washington Univ.	P	1,024	86
St. Louis	P	2,500	125		Western Reserve	P	1,800	80
Woman's Medical	P	305	50	100	Yale	P	1,401	65
Total		22,986	3,628		Total		63,082	3,443

T—tax-supported; P—privately supported.

* From Stalnaker, J. M., and R. A. Dykman, "Admission Requirements of American Medical Colleges," Chicago, Association of American Medical Colleges, 1950.

† Two-year school.

cluded 31 in which 90 per cent of the students came from within a restricted geographical area and the 9 medical schools giving preference to students on the basis of sex, race, or religion (Table 46). Any con-

Table 46. AVERAGE MCAT SCORES FOR MEDICAL STUDENTS ENTERING 1950–51 CLASS—79 MEDICAL SCHOOLS

	Number of schools in group	Average score
Less than 90% geographical restriction................	39	550
Geographical restriction 90% or more and special preference...	40	509

clusions drawn are dependent upon one's opinion of the validity of the test. It must also be assumed that the quality of premedical education available to the student is essentially the same for both groups.

The urbanization of American society has urbanized medical education and brought an uneven distribution of physicians in terms of medical need. Some recent state legislation has tried to improve the balance between city and country as regards medical care, through provision for rural hospital facilities, for subsidies in terms of part-time salaries to practitioners with public-health appointments, and for scholarship loans to medical students who agree to return to a needy area to practice for a stated number of years. Medical schools which have become especially sensitive to public needs, local challenges, and public opinion have shaped their admissions practices accordingly.

For example, one state-owned medical school, in a city which contains half the state's population, until recently accepted about two-thirds of its entering classes from its own urban area. At the time of the Survey, by intention, it accepted about 50 per cent from the balance of the state. Moreover, the admissions committee of this school had an agreement with the state medical society and the state agricultural association to give special consideration to applicants from rural areas who met the minimum requirements and were recommended by those organizations, and who would sign contracts to practice for at least five years in medically needy areas of the state. One state is seriously considering establishing a new state medical school, at an initial cost of some 12 million dollars, so that more residents of the state may have a chance to study medicine. In that state there is currently one practicing physician to every 650 people.

It has not been conclusively demonstrated that these restrictive practices have strengthened the quality or even the number of physicians within a given region. Through the cooperation of the Bureau of Medical Economic Research of the American Medical Association, the Survey was able to obtain exact information on the number of graduates of all approved four-year medical schools practicing in each state, the number of practicing physicians who were graduates of each school, and the state in which each of these physicians was practicing in 1949. Although figures varied widely from school to school in both groups, a slightly higher percentage of graduates of schools which practiced geographical restriction remained to practice in the state in which they received their education. The difference, although not large, is probably significant (Table 47). It is difficult, however, to interpret these figures, or with accuracy to assess geographical restriction as a factor in the decision of graduates to remain in any particular locality. The population growth of the state, the number of physicians already in practice, the opportunity for professional advancement in these or neighboring states, access to hospitals or medical centers, climate, and many other intangibles play an important part.

There are one or more four-year approved medical schools in 32 states and three in the District of Columbia. Table 48 shows the distribution of graduates of these schools according to the states in which they were residing in 1949 and the number in each state educated locally. It is interesting to observe that California had less than 40 per cent of locally educated physicians although a very high percentage of graduates of all the local schools remained there to practice. In contrast, almost 70 per cent of Vermont's physicians received their medical education at the University of Vermont although only 27 per cent of that school's graduates remained in Vermont to practice. These figures bear out the impression that factors other than restriction of admissions influence the physician in his choice of a place to practice. Rapidly growing communities may be unable to educate enough physicians to take care of their needs. Older communities with stable populations may educate more physicians than they can support. In the latter case, restriction of admissions on a geographical basis can serve no useful purpose.

Table 47. GRADUATES OF FOUR-YEAR APPROVED MEDICAL SCHOOLS PRACTICING IN 1949 IN STATE IN WHICH THEY RECEIVED THEIR EDUCATION

	Geographical restriction, 90% or more					Geographical restriction, less than 90%				
Medical school	Type of support	Total graduates of each school	Graduates in state No.	%	Date of organization	Medical school	Type of support	Total graduates of each school	Graduates in state No.	%	Date of organization
Alabama	T	356	258	72	1943	Albany	P	1,179	923	78	1838
Arkansas	T	1,332	602	45	1879	Boston	P	1,444	657	45	1873
Baylor	P	1,480	1,095	74	1900	Bowman Gray	P	224	117	52	1941
California	T	1,733	1,541	89	1864	Buffalo	P	2,149	1,720	80	1846
Georgia	T	1,195	740	62	1828	Chicago Medical	P	220	187	85	1912
Illinois	T	4,677	2,501	53	1882	Cincinnati	T	1,876	1,053	56	1896
Indiana	T	2,786	1,875	67	1907	Colorado	T	1,226	594	48	1885
Iowa	T	2,323	1,099	47	1870	Columbia	P	4,094	2,404	59	1767
Kansas	T	1,584	662	42	1905	Cornell	P	2,181	1,318	60	1898
Louisville	T	2,894	1,068	37	1837	Duke	P	817	221	27	1930
Louisiana	T	945	575	61	1931	Emory	P	1,699	748	44	1854
Michigan	T	3,864	1,812	47	1850	George Washington	P	1,804	557	31	1825
Minnesota	T	3,509	2,005	57	1883	Hahnemann	P	2,886	1,463	51	1848
Nebraska	T	1,971	664	34	1882	Harvard	P	4,539	1,710	38	1782
Ohio	T	2,211	1,642	74	1907	Jefferson	P	5,227	2,498	48	1825
Oklahoma	T	1,241	690	56	1910	Johns Hopkins	P	2,851	517	18	1893
Pittsburgh	P	2,142	1,674	78	1886	Long Island					
So. California	P	775	690	89	1895	(St. N.Y.–N.Y.C.)	P-T	3,171	2,375	75	1858
South Carolina	T	1,222	815	67	1823	Maryland	T	3,137	1,152	37	1807
Southwestern	T	213	163	77	1943	New York Medical	P	2,100	1,450	69	1858
Tennessee	T	2,537	898	35	1876	New York Univ.	P	3,890	2,669	69	1841
Texas	T	2,294	1,850	81	1892	Northwestern	P	4,543	1,466	32	1859
Utah	T	144	72	50	1943	Oregon	T	1,419	708	50	1887
Wayne	T	2,030	1,619	80	1885	Pennsylvania	P	5,174	2,464	48	1765
Wisconsin	T	1,001	517	52	1925	Rochester	P	804	382	48	1925
Average	..	....	....	61		Stanford	P	1,276	1,092	86	1908
Special Preference						Syracuse					
Creighton	P	1,677	329	20	1892	(St. N.Y.–Syr.)	P-T	1,376	1,038	75	1872
Georgetown	P	2,053	339	17	1851	Temple	P	2,296	1,355	59	1904
Howard	P	1,296	215	17	1869	Tufts	P	3,369	1,916	57	1893
Loyola	P	2,324	1,261	54	1915	Tulane	P	3,689	1,247	34	1834
Marquette	P	1,716	954	56	1912	Univ. of Chicago	P	716	254	35	1924
Medical Evangelists	P	1,852	1,240	67	1909	Univ. of Virginia	T	1,508	521	35	1827
Meharry	P	1,660	167	10	1876	Vanderbilt	P	1,833	543	30	1874
St. Louis	P	3,236	922	28	1901	Vermont	T	1,241	340	27	1822
Woman's Medical	P	922	353	38	1850	Virginia Med. Col.	T	2,311	987	43	1838
						Washington Univ.	T	2,625	989	38	1842
						Western Reserve	P	1,879	1,203	64	1843
						Yale	P	1,360	471	35	1812
						Average	...	....	....	50	

T—tax-supported; P—privately supported.

The University of Washington (Seattle) is not a restricted school but was organized too recently for figures to be significant.

Source: Compiled from data supplied by the Bureau of Medical and Economic Research of the American Medical Association.

Table 48. PERCENTAGE OF PHYSICIANS FROM APPROVED FOUR-YEAR SCHOOLS
WHO RECEIVED THEIR EDUCATION IN THE STATE
IN WHICH THEY PRACTICE (1949)

State	Physicians from approved schools		
	Total in each state	Educated in same state	Per cent who obtained education in state
Alabama	1,729	258	First class graduated 1947
Arizona*	623		
Arkansas	1,101	602	55
California (4 schools)	12,664	4,563	36
Colorado	1,541	594	39
Connecticut	2,687	471	18
Delaware*	366		
Florida*	2,425		
Georgia	2,383	1,488	62
Idaho*	401		
Illinois (5 schools)	8,071	5,669	70
Indiana	3,270	1,875	57
Iowa	2,218	1,099	50
Kansas	1,479	662	45
Kentucky	1,887	1,068	57
Louisiana (2 schools)	2,510	1,822	73
Maine*	600		
Maryland (2 schools)	2,772	1,669	60
Massachusetts (3 schools)	6,203	4,283	69
Michigan (2 schools)	5,783	3,431	59
Minnesota	3,521	2,005	57
Mississippi†	1,032		
Missouri (2 schools)	3,536	1,911	54
Montana*	457		
Nebraska (2 schools)	1,289	993	77
Nevada*	151		
New Hampshire†	543		
New Jersey*	5,063		
New Mexico*	369		
New York (9 schools)	21,561	14,279	66
North Carolina (2 schools)	2,716	338	12
North Dakota†	343		
Ohio (3 schools)	7,483	3,898	52
Oklahoma	1,575	690	44
Oregon	1,473	708	48
Pennsylvania (6 schools)	12,254	9,807	80
Rhode Island*	804		
South Carolina	1,342	815	61
South Dakota†	374		
Tennessee (3 schools)	2,390	1,608	67
Texas (3 schools)	6,025	3,108	52
Utah	662	72	First class graduated 1947
Vermont	500	340	68
Virginia (2 schools)	2,561	1,508	59
Washington	2,105		First class graduated 1950
West Virginia†	1,291		
Wisconsin (2 schools)	2,879	1,471	51
Wyoming*	198		
District of Columbia (3 schools)	2,118	1,111	52

* No medical school.
† No four-year medical school.

Source: Compiled from data supplied by the Bureau of Medical and Economic Research of the American Medical Association.

Discrimination

The experience of the past half century has strengthened the conviction of medical educators that the good physician must be a man of character, dependability, emotional balance, and sound orientation, as well as scholastic attainment. It follows that medical schools must seek to find, identify, and admit applicants who possess these desired qualities.

The medical schools studied indicated that they strongly favored a careful evaluation of the character and personality traits of the candidate. Such an evaluation requires the collection of personal and confidential information about each applicant as well as a resumé of his academic career. In the collection, analysis, and use of such information many admissions committees have made forward strides in recent years though much remains to be done to clarify policies and improve techniques of testing, judging, and recording.

There has been racial and religious discrimination in schools and colleges of the country, including medical schools; where that kind of discrimination exists today, it is without legitimate defense. The customary absence of women students from two medical schools also suggests discrimination on the basis of sex. The Survey believes that the prevalence of such discrimination in medical education has been exaggerated, and the motives, problems, and procedures of medical admissions committees have often been misunderstood or distorted. Liberal and responsible medical educators who are firmly opposed to all racial and religious discrimination are also concerned lest some of the methods used to force the elimination of discriminatory practices result in new limitations upon a school's freedom to select those students who will most advance the quality of medical education. It is as unsound to compel an admissions committee to select medical students without adequate consideration of personal qualifications as it would be to compel patients to select their own personal physicians in such a manner.

The trend toward more careful selection of applicants by going beyond paper records and college grades is handicapped by pressures upon admissions committees to limit the personal information they request of an applicant. A desire for such facts as an applicant's sex, race, nationality, and preference in religion is not necessarily indicative of a desire to discriminate, and can be a legitimate wish to secure a complete personal picture of each applicant. Yet in two states at least, to ask such questions is to risk charges of discrimination and even to hazard legal penalties. Whatever good has been accomplished by recent "antidiscrimination" campaigns must be measured against the public suspicion they have created, the handicaps they have brought to the work of admissions committees, and the fundamental dangers of challenging the right of an educational institution to request and to use any facts it wishes about any prospective student.

At the turn of the past century it was possible for any person with a high-school education to gain admission to some medical school. The practice of selective admissions as we know it today was virtually unknown. The large number of technically qualified applicants now seeking admission to medical schools has forced admissions committees to develop new policies. Restrictive practices have become more rigid. These restrictions may justly be criticized if it is shown that they either prevent the admission of better qualified men to the study of medicine or allow poorer candidates to enter medical school.

Medical schools generally face the problem of clarifying the principles on which their admissions policies and practices are established so that admissions committees may act intelligently within established policy. The Survey has found that the 41 schools visited were in various stages of progress on this point. The current variety of opinions and practices among medical educators and the pressure of public opinion justify the continued attention of medical schools to this problem.

CONCLUSIONS

1. Granted competent medical school faculties, with adequate facilities and financial support, the future quality of medical education, research, and service will depend primarily upon the quality of students selected by the medical schools.
2. Admissions policies, in the last analysis, are the responsibilities of the governing boards of medical schools.
3. The faculties of medical schools, experienced in both the teaching and practice of medicine, are the most competent agencies for the final selection of medical students. Other members of the university such as preprofessional advisers are of great assistance in this selection.

4. The admissions committees of medical schools are composed of men of integrity, who, in general, carry on their work intelligently and conscientiously within the framework of established admissions policies.

5. Admissions committees are charged with the responsibility of selecting applicants who will not only be successful as medical students, but will also develop into physicians acceptable to the people on a uniquely personal basis. Therefore, the students must possess academic ability plus those qualities of character and personality most people desire in their physician.

6. Medical schools, therefore, continually face the problem of reexamining and clarifying the principles which underlie their admissions practices, so that admissions committees may function more effectively.

7. With modern teaching methods, the number of students who can be admitted to medical school is necessarily limited by the available facilities, faculty, and financial support.

8. Selective admissions is a process of choosing those applicants who show the greatest promise of developing into high-quality physicians. The fact that the choice must be made is not evidence that it is made unfairly. The applicants not chosen may have ability, but if more promising applicants are available the latter should be admitted.

9. In the evaluation of an applicant for medical school, it is extremely important to evaluate carefully the sources and types of information about the applicant.

10. College grades remain the major determining factor in medical school admissions. Too few schools effectively weight an applicant's grades according to the academic standards of the undergraduate college or the accomplishments of its graduates in medical school, but many schools are developing methods of doing this.

11. Since the content of courses and quality of instruction in preprofessional curricula are of great importance, efforts to ensure an applicant's sound preparation simply by specifying the title and number of credit hours in required arts college courses is inadequate to the purpose.

12. Competition for admission to medical school is so keen that courses recommended by a medical school, but not required for admission, are assumed by the applicant to be virtually mandatory.

13. Medical schools generally are showing an increased interest in and emphasis on a broad educational background for admission to medical school.

14. The results of the Medical College Admission Test are being used by many schools as additional information about the applicants and as an aid in establishing a level of minimum acceptability. This test is still in its experimental stage, and its validity has not been demonstrated.

15. Many medical schools are finding letters of recommendation generally inadequate and are improving their methods for obtaining more accurate information concerning the character and personality of applicants.

16. Personal information concerning various aspects of an applicant's background is extremely useful for the intelligent discharge of the duties of an admissions committee.

17. Restrictive or preferential admissions practices have been established by the governing board of certain medical schools for the purpose of giving an educational advantage to specific groups of individuals. Membership in these specific groups is determined by residence in the state supporting the school in most instances. A secondary objective of this policy of preference is that of providing a greater number of doctors to a given geographic area. A few schools give such preferences to groups whose membership is determined by sex or race. The very few schools which give such preference to members of religious groups are maintained by those groups.

18. Restrictive admissions practices are an advantage to relatively small segments of the population and make it impossible for a school to consider a candidate entirely on the basis of his positive qualifications.

19. The future welfare of medicine clearly depends upon making the selective process of admissions an affirmative search for quality wherever it can be found.

RECOMMENDATIONS

1. Medical school faculties and governing boards should continue to review and further clarify their admissions policies.

2. Great care should be exercised to appoint competent and willing

admissions committee members. Continuity of membership and adequate clerical and technical help should be recognized as basic to the work of the committee. Financial provision should be made for this procedure.

3. Individual admissions committees should constantly strive to develop more efficient techniques for the evaluation of applicants.

4. Medical schools and undergraduate colleges should cooperate closely in an effort to secure for the medical school a more accurate appraisal of the student and his personal qualifications.

5. The significance of the various admissions' criteria including the MCAT should be determined by appropriate studies.

6. Medical schools should incorporate in their student personnel files continuing records of faculty reports that illuminate the character and personality of individual students.

7. Medical schools should announce their acceptances at the same time of year in the interest of conserving the time and energy of applicants, their advisers, and admissions committees.

8. Medical schools and licensing boards should continue to require collegiate work in the sciences basic to medicine, but they should abandon the requirement of specific course titles or hours in those fields. Medical schools and colleges should collaborate in studying ways of improving students' college preparation.

9. Medical schools should eliminate suggestion and publication of "recommended courses."

10. State authorities, civic groups, private citizens, and educational institutions should recognize that the intelligent discharge of the admissions function is hampered, not aided, by laws and regulations designed to limit the nature and extent of personal information available regarding each applicant.

11. Selection of medical students should be made on the basis of the individual's qualifications for the study and practice of medicine, and these should transcend regard for residence, creed, color, or sex. Where restrictive requirements now prevail, legislatures, trustees, medical school officials, and admissions committees should modify their policies so as to permit selection on the proper basis.

Part V

THE CURRICULUM AND TEACHING METHODS

13 THE CURRICULUM

The curriculum of the medical school is the loom on which the cloth of medical education is woven. During his four years in medical school the student weaves his own fabric, guided, stimulated, and taught by the faculty, which is responsible for the design.

The curriculum should help the student to acquire basic knowledge of man, his physiological functions, the ills to which he is subject, and the most effective preventive and therapeutic measures available.

No formal curriculum, however long or crowded, could include all the medical knowledge that would profit the student. Teaching methods are of even greater importance than curriculum design in helping the student to develop his capacities for observation, comparison, analysis, reasoning, and deduction. After he has acquired sound methods, he must then develop good habits of using them in studying patients. The student should acquire from a well-designed curriculum and good teaching methods a body of knowledge, habits of study, and a capacity for independent thinking which will enable him to continue his education after he leaves the medical school.

Development of scientific knowledge has probably created the greatest demand for the inclusion of new courses in the curriculum, but changing concepts of social needs, public interest in medicine, and many other factors and forces have influenced its development and expansion. Although there is no single pattern since each school designs its curriculum to meet its local needs, there is a general basic structure common to the curricula of all schools. This general pattern stems from the early days of modern medical education when the medical student was first given a progressive and systematized series of courses instead of a series of lectures. The general pattern of the curriculum is as follows.

THE FOUR YEARS

FIRST YEAR

Three major subjects, anatomy (including the subdivisions histology, neuroanatomy, and frequently embryology), biochemistry, and physiology, are presented to the student in the first year of medical school. Gross anatomy as such is usually taught in a block of time in the first half of the year, and in less than half the schools surveyed instruction in anatomy continues into the second half of the year. The department of anatomy has the greatest allotment of teaching time in the first year. This department must bear the major responsibility of the student's readjustment of study habits and the change from college standards to those of a professional school, at a time when he is also busy acquiring a new vocabulary. In approximately half the schools biochemistry is taught concurrently with anatomy, and in some schools physiology parallels the course in anatomy. In seven schools bacteriology is included in the first-year curriculum.

In addition to these three or four major subjects most schools give short introductory courses during the first year, usually utilizing didactic methods of instruction in such subjects as psychology or psychiatry, statistics, public health, medical history, and medical physics.

The large majority of schools are also making use of correlation clinics, in which clinical departments cooperate with the medical basic science departments in the presentation of patients who present problems in the understanding of which anatomy, physiology, or chemistry play important roles. Such clinics are commonly held once a week through the entire year.

Thus the student is exposed to three or more major subjects and to four to six minor subjects in the first year, covering 32 to 36 weeks of instruction and totaling 1,000 to 1,200 hours of assigned work.

SECOND YEAR

In the second year, pathology, pharmacology, bacteriology, physical diagnosis, and clinical laboratory instruction receive the greatest emphasis. Pathology generally receives the largest amount of teaching time and in this respect holds a position similar to that of anatomy in the first year. Physical diagnosis is commonly the responsibility of the department of medicine, although several other clinical departments may participate in giving the course. Clinical laboratory instruction is usually the responsibility of either the department of medicine or the department of pathology—more frequently the former—although in a few schools a subdepartment has been established especially for this course. Occasionally some of the instruction in physiology and biochemistry is carried over into the second year.

The second year, especially the latter part, is almost always considered a transition period between the medical basic sciences and clinical medicine. Clinical departments and their specialty subdepartments usually give series of lectures or demonstrations to introduce the student to their fields of interest. There may be short courses in medicine, psychiatry, obstetrics, surgery, pediatrics, public health, ophthalmology, orthopedics, etc. In the typical second year, therefore, a student faces 8 to 15 separately taught courses. It is the exception rather than the rule for there to be any appreciable amount of free time in the planned curriculum. Usually there is one half-day per week in addition to Saturday afternoon when a student can plan his own time. In two schools studied, however, two afternoons per week in addition to Saturday afternoon were left free throughout the year. In most schools, however, the student must do most of his individual study and reading in the evenings.

THIRD YEAR

More variability exists in the third-year curriculum. The majority of medical schools choose the third year for the inpatient clinical clerkships, in which the student is assigned to the study of patients on teaching wards. A few schools devote the major portion of the year to ambulatory patient or outpatient department work. The commonest pattern is to break the academic year roughly into quarters, and to allot one quarter to medicine, one quarter to surgery, one quarter to pediatrics and obstetrics, and the fourth quarter to psychiatry and public health. Pediatrics, psychiatry, obstetrics, and public health and preventive medicine together are allotted as much time as the departments of medicine and surgery. Departments are usually jealous of their blocks of teaching time and resent another department's attempting to offer any concurrent instruction.

The class of medical students is divided into quarters or thirds according to the blocks of time allotted to the departments, and each section of the class rotates through the various departments. Each clinical department is responsible for instructing groups of students throughout the entire academic year. In addition to the daily work with patients on the wards, the student has daily conferences, clinics, and lectures. In some schools these constitute half or more of the instruction.

Pathology may play a minor role in the teaching of all departments, but it is only rarely that any other medical basic science department has teaching responsibility in the third year. The subspecialties of the clinical departments participate in instruction if patients on their services are assigned to students as part of the clerkship.

Usually, there is very little free or elective time in the third year. In only two or three schools studied, the curriculum was so organized that approximately one-fourth of the year was free for the student to participate in research or to carry on clinical work in some particular department or clinic of his choice.

FOURTH YEAR

The fourth year is commonly devoted to outpatient teaching and to clinical instruction in the specialties. A few departments may give the student some work with patients on the wards during the fourth year, but usually inpatient and outpatient work are sharply differentiated and are taught in the third and fourth years, respectively. In the fourth year a student may rotate through 10 to 15 general and special clinics, spending the equivalent of a few weeks in each. The longest periods are usually spent in medicine and surgery, and rarely extend more than 8 to 12 weeks. In this year the curriculum commonly allows a student some free or elective time.

FORCES AFFECTING CURRICULUM

Within the established four-year curriculum, many changes are taking place which appear to be the result of an interplay of contrasting and often contradictory forces (see also Chapter 9, "Medical School Departments"). One of these is the participation of clinical departments in first- and second-year teaching through demonstration of clinical applications of medical basic sciences.

The stated objectives in undergraduate medical education fall into two broad groups in the schools surveyed. One group tries to educate and train the student for the general practice of medicine, with the assumption that graduation from medical school and the completion of one to two years of internship adequately prepare him for general practice. The second group tries to educate the student so that upon graduation he can continue his study and training in any field of medicine he may elect.

A definite trend is toward emphasis on the study of man as an individual and the effects on him of his environment, and at the same time another trend is toward continued emphasis on science and its application in understanding the function and specific diseases of the human body. Many medical educators make the charge that laboratory science is being overemphasized. Various types of teaching and forms of orientation such as emphasis on growth and development, psychosomatic medicine, family and home-care programs, comprehensive and preventive medicine are the medical school's attempts to focus student attention on man as an individual related to his environment.

There is a movement toward prolonging the academic year, and at the same time the long and costly period of medical education is decried. Nine medical schools studied have extended one or more of their academic years of 34 to 36 weeks to periods of 38 to 48 weeks.

Although the allocation to departments of specific blocks of time for instruction has been firmly established, there are now many attempts to cut across departmental lines. Strenuous efforts are being made to integrate and correlate the teaching of a multiplicity of departments and subdepartments while at the same time new bodies of knowledge or techniques are struggling to obtain departmental status (biophysics, geriatrics, general practice, etc.). There is a definite conflict between the desire to add new subject matter and a reluctance to discard much of the old.

The medical basic sciences face a change in their orientation. A few schools are attempting to ally them more closely with the science departments of the university, but the general trend is to direct their teaching and research toward clinical medicine.

Although didactic methods of teaching have been steadily losing ground, many faculties still strongly support them. Medical schools should be graduate professional schools, but some are obliged to use collegiate methods of instruction because of the size of the classes and because college education has been inadequate to equip the student to function as a competent graduate student.

Many of these forces and opinions influencing the curriculum have laid more emphasis on the facts to be taught and the methodology to be used than on guidance of the student in his learning process.

THE BLOCK SYSTEM

The distribution of time in the teaching program is of basic importance in any curriculum. The block system of allocating instructional time to departments has certain definite advantages. As originally conceived, its purpose was to allow a student to focus his attention on only one or two subjects in any one portion of the academic year. It also allowed faculties of the various departments large blocks of time relatively free from teaching which they could devote to the instruction of graduate students or other students, to research, or to their own personal interests. Disadvantages have developed from the trend to specialization and from the consequent growth in the number of departments and subdepartments. The blocks of time have become shorter and shorter, and their content has become more intensive and more concentrated. In order to cover the teaching of all departments, therefore, the student, in any one period of the academic year, may be faced with four or more blocks of teaching. This system also makes it difficult to plan continuity of instruction between departments. Faculty members frequently feel that responsibility for the student ends with the completion of their period of instruction, and they are relatively uninterested in the student's activities in other departments unless these encroach on their own activities. To obviate some of these disadvantages, and to give the student continuity of study as he progresses from department to department, a few departments plan their courses jointly.

INTEGRATION AND CORRELATION

Practically every medical school studied was making a conscious effort to integrate and correlate the teaching of the various departments. Three approaches were being tried.

A correlation clinic was the method most frequently used. Under this plan, clinical and medical basic science departments join forces, usually once a week, for a session in which the clinician emphasizes and illustrates to the student the importance in clinical medicine of the subject under study. Some medical basic science professors feel that such correlation conferences are not essential. One made the statement that the student cannot correlate facts which he has not yet acquired, and that integration takes place within a student's mind and not within a course. The students themselves were often critical of such teaching because the clinician was frequently unable to appreciate the stage of their development and their actual knowledge and was inclined to talk over their heads. The greatest value of the correlation conference appeared to be in stimulating student interest in the work at hand.

In a second approach, two departments designed their courses jointly so that the student might study similar material and problems in the two departments at the same time. This method was used most frequently in neuroanatomy and neurophysiology and in bacteriology and pathology. Occasionally the department of biochemistry was attempting to integrate its work with that of the department of physiology.

In physical-diagnosis courses, in which the student is taught methods of examining a patient, it was common to find several of the clinical departments participating in the instruction of the medical student. As a result, in certain instances no one department had responsibility for coordination of the teaching. Each teacher, being a specialist, stressed the examination of one system or one segment of the body from the viewpoint of his own special area of medicine. Students may pass through such courses without ever taking a complete history or completing a physical examination on one patient.

A third method of integration is attempted by giving a faculty member appointments in two departments. As observed during the Survey, usually this integration is between a clinical department and a medical basic science department, but it may also occur between two clinical departments or between two medical basic science departments. The method has definite advantages in that at least one member of a department is intimately acquainted with the teaching that goes on in two departments. However, the faculty member invariably feels he owes major allegiance to one department and is on loan to the other. In order to obviate this difficulty, two departments may pay the faculty member's salary jointly. The effectiveness of this system as of most systems of medical education depends not upon the mechanics of its organization but upon the individual involved.

EXAMINATIONS AND OTHER METHODS OF EVALUATING STUDENT ACCOMPLISHMENT

Examinations are by far the most important method in use for evaluation of student accomplishment. Students are ranked in their classes, selected for honors, given warnings, or failed on the basis of their grades.

In the medical basic science departments, 80 per cent or more of the student's final grade in the department is based on a written examination. In some instances, 10 to 20 per cent of the final grade may depend upon the student's laboratory work, notebooks, or oral examinations. In the clinical departments more often than in the medical basic science departments, evaluation of the student as an individual is given weight in his final grade.

Grading systems have become extremely complex. Because of the number of courses and departments reporting grades, many schools carry out their mathematics to the third decimal point, which then determines a student's grade point average for the year and his class standing. Students are generally aware of such methods and are extremely grade conscious. They are frequently told that class standing will determine their ability to obtain a good internship.

There is a wide variety of opinion in medical faculties as to the purposes of examinations. Some of the faculty members interviewed felt that frequent examinations were necessary in order to make the student work, while others felt that the chief purpose was to enable him to evaluate his own accomplishments. In some schools examinations were devised to test the student's ability to use facts in making decisions and judgments. In a few instances examinations were used as true teaching tools, and each student's paper was returned to him with written suggestions and criticisms so that he could discuss the results with an instructor. In general, this practice was unusual, as few faculties had sufficient time to devote to such a program.

Although every professor stated that his department made an evaluation of the student and his personal characteristics, attempts to record such information in an organized manner were found only three or four times during the course of the Survey. Where there are 75 to 160 students in a class, it seems highly improbable that any professor or instructor can carry in his mind careful evaluation of individual students.

Examination schedules emphasized the sharp boundaries between departments as only rarely was one department aware of the number and timing of examinations given by another department. Thus when students are receiving instruction from several departments, they are frequently required to take one to three written examinations a week and at the same time carry on their work in other departments.

One department head said that the examination schedule for his course included 12 written examinations, two of which were two hours in length. He was greatly disturbed when informed by the Survey team that two other departments gave 8 to 12 examinations in the same period of time. When asked what effect these multiple examinations had on the student, he admitted that he was entirely unaware of the number of examinations given by other departments, but that he had been extremely careful to change the time of a test when students informed him that they had other examinations on the same morning.

In another school with an excellent reputation, one department head stated that he did not believe in frequent examinations but was forced to use them in order to compete with another department for the students' attention. The other department offered such frequent examinations that the students were slighting his course, and he used examinations in order to direct some of the student's energy to his department.

These are not unusual examples of the emphasis on multiple examinations. They should call attention to the fact that the time and energies of students may easily be dissipated in preparing for and taking numerous examinations. Examinations, properly designed, have educational value especially if grades are not the chief objective. Several schools of excellent standing report no grades to students to the great satisfaction of both students and faculties.

In a few shools the faculty members have debated seriously whether they should be responsible for examining their students. They feel that examination of students by them detracts from the spirit of common purpose and aims that should exist between instructor and student, and so have made attempts to have extramural faculty members give the examinations. Certain schools rely upon the National Board of Medical Examiners for the grading and rating of their students. The idealism of such faculties may be high, but it would seem that they are evading a responsibility a faculty member should assume. Having worked with a student day by day and week by week, a faculty member is in a much better position than an outside examiner to evaluate intelligently and accurately the over-all ability of the student, his strengths, and his weaknesses.

The Honor System

The honor system is not widely used by medical schools, and proctoring of examinations is fairly widespread. Students from some of the best colleges, to whom it is a new experience, resent the fact that in a graduate school it is deemed necessary that they be watched while taking examinations. It is a tragic commentary that young men being educated for a profession in which integrity is as important as a high level of intelligence should have to work under a system which clearly implies that they are not to be trusted.

It would appear that cheating, although common in college, usually disappears within the student's first year or two in medical school. Many students stated that, having once entered medical school, they found the studies so interesting and important that it seemed foolish to attempt to cheat, and they realized that if they did so they would only be cheating themselves or their patients. In the vast majority of medical schools, the tension and grade consciousness usually disappear in the second or third year athough in a few schools, because of the examination system, it lasts throughout the four years and becomes intensified again at the end of the third year or in the middle of the fourth.

FREE OR ELECTIVE TIME

Most faculty members interviewed felt that the student should have some free or elective time within the curriculum. In only three or four schools, however, was the curriculum so designed that the student had a useful amount of time for pursuits that interested him. In one school one-fifth and in another one-third of the total curricular hours are elective. In another there are two free afternoons throughout the four years. In some other schools, although the calendars showed time free for elective work, the students stated that the electives were really "compulsory electives." They said the courses were usually in subdepartments and minor specialties. It was understood that if the student did not elect to take them he would have difficulty in answering questions in the final examination.

In a surprising number of instances, faculty members were opposed to the inclusion of any free time in the curriculum because they thought the student would waste this time and because there was already insufficient time for them to cover their subjects. In departments where this attitude prevailed, it was unusual to find many students taking the few elective courses offered by the department.

Good lectures can have great educational value. If they make the student think and if they give him the benefit of the experience and competence of an alert teacher outstanding in a particular field, they will stimulate the student's interest in further knowledge. However, the theme of insufficient time to cover a field or a subject was constantly repeated by faculty members throughout the Survey, and it was cited as one of the chief reasons for continuing to use didactic teaching methods with a large number of lectures. One lecture could cover a vast amount of subject matter for an entire class. Many specialties are assigned 10 to 20 hours for instruction of the student. Here the common practice is to cover the field by means of lectures.

An associate professor in one of the best financed schools with high educational standards covered in a one-hour lecture all the diseases of the genitourinary system of man. It was a recitation of the headings of chapters in the textbooks, and it barely touched on new knowledge developing in the field. Such men are covering subjects. They are not teaching students, and they have little or no appreciation of the true educational value of a lecture.

LENGTHENING ACADEMIC YEAR

It is extremely rare for a faculty to look at the curriculum as a whole and judge its cumulative effect on the student. This failure to evaluate the curriculum and time requirements in terms of student capacity and student freedom comes into sharp focus in the growing tendency to lengthen academic years in an attempt to cover more fields and more material than the traditional period of nine months allows. Usually it is the third and fourth years that are lengthened.

The student's traditional summer vacation is being taken for curriculum expansion. Some schools state definitely that the vacation period is "allowed" the student for elective work. This tendency is leading to progressive encroachment on the student's freedom, so that he has little time to spend outside the confines of the medical school environment. He no longer has the opportunity to build up his health and to make broader contacts with individuals in other fields. He is handicapped by the loss of his earning capacity during the summer months. Many students need the additional income obtained in summer vacations. Faculties of many medical schools apparently think a student's mind can rapidly recuperate during vacation periods at Christmas and Easter with a short recess during the summer months.

Frequently, when the faculty cannot decide on the amount of material to be covered in a limited time, the easiest solution is to add more material and then lengthen the school year. Students at one school where the academic year had been extended said they could see no difference in the curriculum except that they went to school longer. One student said that the faculty could have done as good a job by teaching more effectively without lengthening the year.

ACCELERATION TO THREE YEARS

A few schools have organized the curriculum to cover the entire year. One such school was surveyed. Each year's program is organized on a quarter system, and the student can finish in three years by attending all four quarters during each year. He covers in three years the same material as the student who goes to school for three quarters of each year for four years.

This system allows the school to produce more graduates over a four-year period. At the time of the Survey it was the consensus of both students and faculty that the system was not desirable. From the faculty's point of view the teaching load was unduly heavy and gave the faculty members little chance to take stock, carry on research, refresh themselves, and redesign their courses each year to include new material and methods. Some faculty members recalled the deterioration in the quality of teaching and medical education which resulted from such accelerated programs during the period of the Second World War. The students felt that three years of four quarters each were hectic, tiresome, and exhausting. If they had sufficient funds, they would much prefer to spend four years in medical school. They stated that they needed the additional time to think about and digest the material presented to them. Many students, being veterans, had chosen to go through the medical school in three years, but none of those interviewed thought it wise.

At the time of the Survey, this school was considering abandoning the four-quarter system and returning to a plan which included a yearly vacation period and allowed the student to obtain his M.D. degree in four years.

INPATIENT CLERKSHIPS

In the majority of medical schools, the inpatient clerkships are given in the third year. In this year the student usually serves as a clerk on the medical, surgical, pediatric, obstetrical, and gynecologic services. The assignment to any one of these services may vary from 6 to 12 weeks in length, although most of the time is spent in medicine and surgery. During any one of the services, the student may rotate through two or three wards. Thus he will have opportunity to work both with male and with female patients as well as with patients in wards for special diseases.

The common pattern is for students to be assigned to patients as they are admitted to the wards. The student is usually the first person to take the complete history and carry out the complete physical examination of the patient. This he does under the supervision of the intern or the resident. He then proceeds to carry out simple laboratory tests. In many schools the student's history, physical examination, and laboratory work become an official part of the patient's record; in other schools, only the history or the laboratory work is recorded. Two to four new patients per week for each student are generally thought to afford him with ample problems for study.

The actual instruction of the student may be given by several methods. Much of the direct supervision and instruction is given by the interns and residents, who are directly responsible for the patients being studied. There may be teaching conferences, at which a student presents a patient before a professor, or there may be ward rounds, in which an instructor walks the wards with the students and discusses the problems of their patients. There is a trend to hold small group conferences so that each student can participate in the discussion and be asked questions by the instructor. In addition to the teaching which takes the patient as its text, the student may be required to attend several lectures or conferences each week.

In well-designed clerkships, the student is made to feel that he is a member of the team, striving to study patients and to deliver excellent medical care. The amount of work assigned to him is limited by his background of experience and knowledge, and sufficient time is allowed for him to peruse the medical literature pertinent to the problems presented by his patients.

Weaknesses exist in inpatient clerkship teaching. One weakness is the practice of rotating the student through several wards during his clerkship on one service. The student, being a neophyte doctor, requires time to become acquainted with the patients as well as with the personnel and routine of a ward. If this assignment to any one ward is only for a two- to four-week period, he rarely has time to learn its routine before being transferred to a relatively new environment on another ward. He also has some difficulty in following the course of the patients he left behind him. It would seem wise to assign students to fewer wards for longer periods so that the study of individual patients will be more complete and thorough.

A continuing difficulty is that of resisting the pressure from specialties to include in the clerkship a multiplicity of didactic lectures and conferences. This difficulty is especially common in large medical centers in which there are numerous strong specialty groups. In some institutions, two or three such conferences and clinics are held daily, and although the student is not required to attend them, it is nevertheless made clear to him that he will miss teaching of great importance if he is not present. Such conferences and clinics may greatly reduce the time available for his work on the wards.

Some schools find difficulty in designing the proper type of ward rounds for students. In several instances, the rounds made by the instructor include residents and interns as well as the third-year students. This plan is a logical outgrowth of the point of view that this group works as a team. However, if the instructor carries on his discussion at the level of the resident and the intern, the student does not have the knowledge or experience to understand it. On the other hand, if the instruction is designed for the student, the intern and resident may be bored by the repetition of material they already know. Taking cognizance of the differences in background, some institutions have sharply differentiated between student rounds and rounds designed to help the house staff.

One of the greatest weaknesses of clerkships exists when medical schools must utilize affiliated hospitals, in which they exert little or no control. In many instances, such hospitals utilize the students as interns. Under these circumstances, the student is forced to assume responsibilities beyond his ability and, while he may have many interesting experiences, his instruction becomes secondary to his service functions. In many such institutions, students are assigned 6 to 12 new patients per week and are barely able to do more than record histories and carry out a certain amount of laboratory work. Hospitals utilizing the student in this fashion do not afford him high-quality education.

TEACHING IN THE OUTPATIENT DEPARTMENT

Instruction of medical students in the outpatient departments of teaching hospitals is carried out by most medical schools in the fourth year of the curriculum. The student's educational experience with ambulatory patients, who pay brief, intermittent visits to the outpatient clinics, is very different from his experience with the hospital's inpatients.

The theory behind outpatient instruction is that it enables the student to see ambulatory patients with minor and major complaints—patients who represent the bulk of an office practice. Outpatient instruction is intended to give the student opportunity to follow the patient from his first complaint through diagnosis and treatment of minor illness. In addition he will see patients with early complaints, where serious illness can be prevented, and he will see patients during convalescence after their discharge from the hospital.

Practical difficulties exist, however, which detract from the effectiveness of outpatient-department instruction. These difficulties are probably responsible for the dissatisfaction with this type of teaching that was encountered, both in faculty and in students, at the majority of medical schools visited during the Survey.

ORGANIZATION AND FUNCTIONS OF
OUTPATIENT DEPARTMENTS

In order to understand the difficulties, it is necessary to know how the clinics are organized.

Almost universally, in both university-owned hospitals and hospitals related to the medical schools, outpatient departments function primarily for service and instruction, providing service to large numbers of charity or low-income patients in the local communities. Outpatient visits may number 50,000 to 500,000 a year in a single institution. One of the privately supported integrated teaching hospitals visited cared for more than half of the ambulatory charity patients in the state. In contrast, a few schools, because of their location, have small outpatient departments and give little ambulatory-patient instruction.

Usually, the only factors limiting the number of outpatients are the financial resources of the hospital, the available space, and the number of physicians who can be persuaded to devote time to giving free professional care or who can be employed as interns and residents. In an attempt to exert some control over the number of outpatient visits, many institutions make use of the appointment system, in which only those patients are seen who have been given an appointment. Acutely ill patients are seen without appointments.

Outpatients are cared for by one or several of numerous clinics dealing with groups of diseases, organ systems, methods of therapy, or specific disease entities. Large outpatient departments may have within them 25 to 50 individually organized clinics. A department of medicine, in addition to maintaining a daily general clinic for various illnesses and complaints, may have special clinics, meeting once to several times a week, in such fields as neurology, epilepsy, chest diseases, cardiac diseases, hematology, endocrinology, dermatology, allergy, liver diseases, gastrointestinal diseases, and peripheral vascular diseases. Each major department of the medical school may have 5 to 10 such special clinics.

The patient usually receives excellent specialized care in these clinics, but to have his various complaints and illnesses properly diagnosed and treated, it is frequently necessary for him to be referred from clinic to clinic and to attend two or three individual clinics. All the clinics operate on different time schedules, so each referral to another clinic means a delay of a day or two for the patient and at least one more clinic visit. Appointments are also needed for special tests, which are performed in various hospital laboratories. Thus responsibility for the care of the patient is divided and fragmentized, and there are delays and waiting periods before all the examinations are completed.

The position occupied by the outpatient department in the hospital–medical school organization also is important, since it affects the potentialities of that department for the best quality of patient care and student instruction. The outpatient department is considered by the medical school and by the hospital as an activity secondary to the inpatient service. The outpatient department is not a self-sufficient unit: for x-ray, pathology, and clinical laboratory examinations, it depends upon the hospital's service laboratories, which were designed primarily for the inpatient services. Medical school administrators and heads of departments often feel that one of the primary functions of an outpatient department is to act as a feeder to the inpatient services for ward teaching; hence, the larger the outpatient department, the greater the variety of patients from which to select ward teaching material.

Generally, none of the patients attending outpatient clinics pay physicians' fees; and the clinic charges, which vary according to the patient's means, rarely cover the costs to the hospitals of maintaining their facilities and the salaries of all the ancillary personnel such as secretaries, nurses, social-service workers, and technicians.

DIFFICULTIES IN DESIGNING OUTPATIENT DEPARTMENT INSTRUCTION

In outpatient departments there are several major difficulties in designing instruction for the medical student.

How can the faculty provide adequate professional care for all the clinic patients and at the same time select and properly utilize a limited number for instruction of the student? The student cannot study thoroughly a large number of patients in a limited time; in most schools the students study only a small fraction of the total number of outpatients. The faculty members, many of them serving on a volunteer basis, are responsible for serving at once the separate and important needs both of large numbers of patients and of a few medical students.

Another defect is the multiplicity of clinics mentioned earlier. Routing the patient from one special clinic to another results in discontinuity and fragmentation of patient care, which is a great disadvantage in the instruction of the student. The disadvantage is further aggravated because volunteer faculty members responsible for teaching and patient care in the outpatient department are usually unable to contribute more than one or two half-days a week to these duties. For this reason, not only does the student seldom see the same instructor more than once a week, but he rarely sees the same patient more than once with the same instructor—and, indeed, the student is fortunate if he sees the same patient more than twice under any circumstances. This lack of continuity leads to inefficient care of the patient and lack of interest on the part of both student and instructor.

The block system of assigning teaching time adds another difficulty because the student is rarely assigned for instruction in any one department for more than eight weeks.

Many of the large teaching hospitals still maintain the old organization of medical records of separate units for inpatients and outpatients. The system arose in some instances from the fact that inpatient medical records were kept in a location not conveniently accessible to the outpatient department. When a patient who has been an inpatient comes to the outpatient department, an abstract of his inpatient record is incorporated in his outpatient record. Similarly, an abstract of the outpatient record is requested when a patient is admitted to the hospital. Overworked medical-records librarians, however, find it difficult to give prompt attention to such requests without neglecting other important duties, and delays are inevitable. In any event, the abstracts cannot be sufficiently detailed to allow thorough study without going back to the original.

The schools that maintain this system of medical-records organization encourage a practice detrimental to the best patient care. They are also immensely handicapped in their clinical teaching. When two separate records of a patient must be studied, it is extremely difficult for an instructor to present to a student the whole picture of a patient's problem, including the story of his illness, the therapy he has received, and the effect of that therapy on his progress.

Special Clinics for Teaching Purposes

Aware of deficiencies in their outpatient department instruction, several medical schools have organized separate clinics for teaching purposes, insulated as well as possible from the hurly-burly of their surroundings. In these clinics, if located in large outpatient clinics, patients are carefully selected and limited in number. These teaching clinics cannot be entirely divorced from the outpatient department, however, since the services of the special clinics are usually indispensable. From the standpoint of good instruction there is a major defect in these special clinics. When the teaching clinic refers a patient to a special clinic, the student rarely has opportunity to observe the special examination or to take part in the consultation.

In an effort to correct this defect a few schools assign to the student an examining room of his own, to which his instructor and the consultant come in order to examine the patient with him. This system, in two or three instances, has worked fairly successfully because of good organization and a high degree of cooperation, and is well liked by the students. There remain several flaws which have not yet been corrected. The consultant may not be able to bring with him the instruments and equipment that he needs for his examination. Consultants must be in daily attendance or resort must be had to an appointment system, which breaks continuity by causing several days of delay between visits. If consultants are required to be in daily attendance, there must be a large flow of patients; otherwise consultants feel that their time is being wasted and they soon fail to attend clinics.

An example of a special type of clinic within an outpatient department was seen at one of the large, well-financed medical schools with an excellent reputation where the general outpatient department cared for approximately 160,000 patient visits per year. Space in the outpatient department was inadequate for the constantly increasing number of patients, and temporary partitions had been erected to provide examination areas with a modicum of privacy and space for physician and patient. Almost all the patient care was given by members of the volunteer faculty and by interns and residents, all of whom were under constant pressure to see large numbers of patients in limited periods of time. Some of the patients had to wait hours before being seen.

Since the optimum in care of the patient was practically impossible under these circumstances, a special clinic had been established to provide a careful and thorough study of selected patients. The clinic functioned strictly on an appointment basis and allowed an hour and a half for each new patient. Staffed by a team of salaried physicians and other professional people, the clinic studied the patient, his home, and his working environment. Usually, three to five persons applied their several skills to the study of each patient. The work of this clinic revealed many mistakes made in the general outpatient department, including superficial study of patients and other errors difficult to avoid under crowded conditions. The patients of the small clinic were well pleased with the attention they received. Unfortunately, only a few students worked in this clinic and only for short periods. Most of the students received the greater part of their instruction in the general medical clinic.

The cost of a patient visit to the small clinic had not been determined, nor had any study been made to see whether the same methods could be applied and the same type of care could be provided for the majority of patients in the outpatient department.

Family-care, Home-care, and Preceptorship Programs

"Family-care," "home-care," and preceptorship programs have been instituted by schools in an effort to provide continuity in the study of patients by the student and afford opportunity for a broader point of view of effects of illness on the home and effects of the environment on illness.

Family Care. In the family-care program, the second- or third-year student is assigned for one or two years as medical adviser to the family of a patient. Usually, the family selected is dependent upon charity or welfare agencies, and the student is enabled to see for himself how one stratum of society lives. Meeting members of the family and getting to know them in the home environment, the student obtains an experience far different from his later, fragmented experience in the outpatient clinic. He can observe emotional aspects of illness, its economic aspects, and its impact on each member of the family and the family as a whole.

The possible advantages of this program for a second- or third-year medical student are very much open to question, as he does not possess knowledge necessary to a medical adviser, nor does he have knowledge or techniques for accurate and intelligent study of patients. Experience of this sort does not correct the present defects in the organization of patient care and student instruction in outpatient departments. If it has a place in the education and training of the young physician, might it not better be instituted at the intern level, when he will have acquired a broader medical background? Fourth-year students commonly stated that family-care programs were overrated and did not yield returns commensurate with the time required. One of them summed up his experience in a family-care program by stating: "I learned much more about families by being a member of one and by being married and having a child and a home of my own."

Home Care. In the home-care programs initiated by a few schools, the third- or fourth-year student, supervised by residents or instructors, acts as a family doctor for a number of families in the vicinity of the hospital. When the patient calls the hospital and asks for a physician, the student goes to the home, takes the patient's history, performs a physical examination, and decides whether to send the patient to the outpatient department or to send him to the hospital for admission. The student then reports back to his instructor or his resident, who may or may not accompany him on a second visit to the home to confirm his decision.

All the students interviewed liked this type of experience because they were given responsibility for the care of the patient. The plan has the advantage of the family-care programs, since it takes students into the homes of patients. Here again assignment of teaching time interferes with continuity since only two to eight weeks are allotted for this program.

Variations in home- and family-care programs include a plan in effect at one school in which two instructors held paid part-time appointments in the city's welfare department in addition to their medical school appointments. Accompanied by two students, they visited welfare patients in their homes. The department head stressed the value of this experience in introducing the student to some of the social aspects of medicine, and stated that the plan had reduced the number of patients hospitalized and had lowered the cost to the welfare department tremendously.

Experience in home- and family-care programs has a certain value in the early training and orientation of the medical student, but whether it has sufficient educational value to warrant the time required is open to question. In view of the limited time available in the curriculum, it is essential that students be provided with conditions which offer opportunity for thorough study of patients. Physicians today require tools and facilities for thorough patient study, and the trend is to visits of patients to doctors' offices and clinics and away from visits of the physician to the homes of patients.

Preceptorships. The preceptorship was the earliest form of medical education. When medical schools changed from vocational to university orientation, there was no place for preceptorships in the educational program and they were gradually abandoned. Interest in this system of teaching is being revived. In 1950 a preceptorship had been added to the program in 19 schools, and in 9 schools it was a required part of the undergraduate course.[1]

Medical schools are reestablishing preceptorships for various reasons. In some schools the outpatient departments are small and the number of patients is inadequate for ambulatory-patient instruction. The most common purpose of the plan is to interest the student in general practice. In other instances, preceptorships are being established in an attempt to provide the student with a type of experience not offered by the outpatient clinic. The promotion of good public relations for the school is sometimes the motive.

Seven of the medical schools studied had preceptorships in operation. In four schools the preceptorship was compulsory for the students; in two it was elective. In the seventh school, it was on an informal basis and the students were given an opportunity to take preceptorships for part of their summer vacation.

Methods of selecting preceptors varied. One school selected them from a panel of names prepared by an academy of general practice. Another selected them from a panel proposed by the state medical society. The society made up its panel from physicians practicing in small communities, and the medical school, after obtaining as much information as possible about these physicians, selected 35, who were then instructed as to their duties. In a third school a member of the faculty selected the preceptors from among his friends and acquaintances.

Time spent by a student with his preceptor varied from three weeks to three months. Usually the student served his preceptorship when he had finished his third year, but in one school half of the class were sent to work with their preceptors before they had served a ward clerkship in the university hospital. In another school, in which the program was initiated to interest students in general practice, a number of students were questioned about their experiences. They had all been assigned to physicians practicing in small towns. None of the preceptors had had more than two years of hospital experience, and the majority had had only a one-year internship, but had had experience in the armed services. Their practices included office, home, and hospital care. They saw 20 to 50 patients per day, caring for general illnesses, minor surgery, and obstetrics, and on some occasions carrying out major surgery with the help of another physician. One of the preceptors kept rather careful records of his patients; according to the students, the others made only perfunctory notes. The students felt that they had been well treated and had not been exploited by their preceptors. They felt they had an "interesting" and "enjoyable" experience; often the doctor had "taken time" to discuss the patient's complaints and illness. With one exception, the students stated that they did not wish to practice the same way as their preceptors and did not want to live in small communities. One of them, because of financial difficulties, thought that upon graduation he might take over the practice of his preceptor, who expected to go away for special training.

In a second program several preceptors and students were interviewed. The preceptors in general were well-qualified physicians by training, but only one showed any insight or interest in teaching. They looked upon students as bystanders who would learn the practice of medicine by watching. Two students were assigned to one surgeon. Their routine day was to work in the preceptor's office in the afternoon where they saw him examine patients and occasionally had opportunity to examine a patient. They were never allowed to take a history or to do a complete examination themselves. They then had an early supper and went to the hospital in which the surgeon and his assistant practiced. In the evening they did complete histories and physical examinations on three to six patients who had been admitted during the day, and they usually finished work between 10:00 and 12:00 P.M. The next morning they helped the surgeon and his assistant at the operations, often acting as third assistant. They gave infusions, transfusions, and postoperative care, and occasionally made brief rounds with the surgeon or his assistant to see the patients who had been operated upon that day. Both students were extremely unhappy with their experience and were anxious to return to the medical school.

A student with another preceptor spent half his time in the doctor's office watching him examine patients and the other half in a hospital.

He had considerable freedom in the hospital and could work on the various wards and with various patients, but no one carefully supervised his work. There was a small library in the hospital as well as in the doctor's office. This student felt that his experience was fairly worth-while, but that he was wasting a considerable amount of time because of lack of instruction, supervision, and encouragement.

Another preceptor, a very busy practitioner, had given his student considerable responsibility. This student was treating a patient at home who had a high fever and was extremely ill, but whom his preceptor had never seen. The student was not sure of the diagnosis but thought the patient probably had pneumonia. He was a little fearful, but he liked the experience of being treated as a full-fledged physician, and said this was in marked contrast to his experience in medical school, where he was given very little responsibility and was never allowed to make decisions regarding a patient's treatment.

In a third school in which the students were questioned, they all stated that the preceptorship was an interesting experience and that they liked the contact with patients and the responsibility they were given. This again was in contrast to their experience in medical school.

A preceptorship for the undergraduate medical student may have a valid place in the curriculum if the medical school has an inadequate number of ambulatory patients for such instruction. It may also be justified if the medical school is unable to organize outpatient-department work so as to offer the best type of ambulatory-patient instruction.

The weaknesses of the preceptorship system are numerous. It confuses experience with true education; the time factor for study of patients is obviously disregarded, and the student may either be a passive onlooker or be given responsibility for which he is not qualified. The methods of selecting preceptors are extremely weak since they do not select physicians primarily for teaching ability. It must be remembered that preceptors are busy practitioners to whom patients—not students—are the primary responsibility. If they are busy, they cannot devote sufficient time to the student, or even allow him time for thorough study and understanding of the patients he sees. Requiring a student to take this type of experience either in the curriculum or in his vacation period adds rigidity to the program of education. The curriculum and the student should not be exploited in the public relations of a medical school. Such practice is an expediency only; it is not sound from the educational standpoint. The preceptorships studied are unsound at the level of instruction of the undergraduate medical student. It is doubtful whether they can be designed to meet requirements of true university educational standards.

Combined Inpatient and Outpatient Teaching

A few instances were encountered in which a department of a medical school attempted to arrange for the student to follow the same patient both as an outpatient and as an inpatient. Departments of surgery were making the greatest efforts in this direction. These departments so organized their teaching that the student followed a patient from the outpatient department through the surgical ward of the hospital and back to the outpatient department. He had opportunity for complete study of the patient and the course of his illness, beginning by taking the patient's history and continuing through diagnosis, preoperative, surgical, and postoperative treatment, recovery, and convalescence. Time assignments are not compatible with this system because the student rarely has opportunity to complete the study of a patient.

All the plans described have been adopted, with varying degrees of success, in an effort to supplement the student's learning experience in the outpatient department, or to provide him with a continuity in the study and care of the patient not provided elsewhere in the curriculum. The plan in which the student follows the patient from the earliest recital of his complaint in the outpatient department, through his stay in the hospital, and on subsequent visits to the clinic during his recovery and convalescence comes closest to the educational ideal for the student.

ANALYSIS OF THIRD- AND FOURTH-YEAR SEQUENCE

The curriculum is generally so organized that the student studies inpatients during the third year and outpatients during the fourth year. To the student, outpatient-department work, with its organization into specialty clinics, its voluntary teachers, and the limited time in which the patient is avaliable for study, is a disappointing experience. The student finds his fourth year less challenging than the third and that the pace of his learning process slackens (see Appendix I, "Student Opinion").

In many medical schools visited, half or more of the members of the fourth-year class held positions in small hospitals in the evening, where they were paid to work as interns and often given a room. In most instances, the students stated, they sought such positions because of the experience and the responsibility for patients they offered them rather than for the financial rewards. They had more than enough time and energy left for such activities in their fourth year. Many described the last year in medical school as "a waste of time."

The full-time faculty member commonly spends little time in outpatient departments, unless it is in a clinic for the study of some disease of particular interest to him. The volunteer faculty members carry on most of the instruction and devote one to three half days per week to this work. They find they can work in their own private offices more effectively and with more satisfaction to themselves and to their patients than is possible in the outpatient department. In their offices, laboratory facilities may be readily available and are under the physician's control. The man whose office is adequately equipped not only can take the history and complete the physical examination, but in a very short time he can obtain x-rays, electrocardiograms, and the results of blood, urine, and other specific tests. In the outpatient department as now organized, at least two visits are required of the patient before all the necessary tests can be completed. The volunteer instructor, often spending only two half days a week in the clinic, frequently must wait several days to more than a week before he can accumulate all the facts and arrive at an adequate understanding of the patient. Many such faculty members interviewed during the Survey described their outpatient work as "a chore."

Why is outpatient work given in the fourth year? Faculty members gave various reasons, the commonest of which was that experience in ambulatory medicine is a natural transition from medical school to the practice of medicine. Other faculty members felt that—because of the limitation of time for the study of individual patients and the need to work more rapidly with the ambulatory patient in the outpatient department—the student required skill and experience that could best be obtained in the inpatient service given in the third year.

In reasoning that by assigning the student to the outpatient department in the fourth year he will be better prepared for practice, the fact is ignored that practically all students will spend at least one or more years as interns or residents before entering practice. The reasoning was probably valid in the days before internships were so generally accepted.

In the time available, the hospital wards offer better opportunities than the outpatient department for the careful, searching study of the patient that must be taught to the medical student. The inpatient is avail-

'able for study 24 hours a day; all laboratory tests can be carefully observed and controlled; the effects of therapy can be watched and measured; consultation is readily available; and family members visiting the patient can be interviewed by students. In contrast, the ambulatory patient is available for study for only a few hours a day; laboratory tests cannot be instituted immediately or their results obtained without delay; only occasional observations of the effects of therapy can be obtained; and usually there is no opportunity to talk to other members of the patient's family.

The sequence of third- and fourth-year teaching is a subject on which there has long been arduous discussion, and no final dictum can be pronounced that will be applicable to all situations. It can be argued that the sequence violates a basic principle in education that the student should be led gradually in his study of medicine from the simpler to the more difficult aspects of illness. At present, however, in his third year he is introduced to the difficult diagnostic problems and the serious illnesses found on hospital wards before being introduced to the simpler problems of the ambulatory patient that represent the bulk of practice. This violates that principle, though other principles and practical considerations argue for the present arrangement. Further experiment and debate are essential.

Why is there such a sharp differentiation between inpatient and outpatient teaching? The practicing physician cannot so sharply divide his patients. To him the patient is a person—not an ambulatory patient or a hospitalized patient. To the student the division of patients into inpatients and outpatients is conducive to the point of view that the patient is a disease entity, an organ system, or a case either in the hospital or on two feet. It does not give the concept of the patient as a whole.

In a redesign of the curriculum for the last two years, the care of the patient and the instruction of the student with especial reference to time sequence should be given first consideration.

CONCLUSIONS

1. The primary purpose of the curriculum is to help the student develop habits of study and acquire basic knowledge as a foundation for continuing education and training throughout his professional life.
2. Failure to distinguish between the relative value to the student of

new knowledge as compared with the old contributes to the lengthening of the medical school year and continuation of excessive amounts of didactic teaching.

3. Some faculties, in planning the curriculum, fail to appreciate time now spent by medical school graduates in training and do not differentiate what can best be given in the period of formal medical undergraduate instruction and what should be left for periods of hospital training.

4. Multiplicity of clinical departments, subdepartments, and clinics makes it almost impossible to plan continuity in teaching and decreases effectiveness of instruction. Medical schools have had to adapt teaching programs to hospital organization.

5. Inpatient services offer much better opportunity for study of the patient and instruction of the student than do outpatient services.

6. Outpatient departments, as presently conducted, in general provide inefficient and ineffective care of the patient, and both faculty and students find the work uninteresting and unsatisfactory.

7. Sharp division of the patient, according to degree of illness, into an inpatient or an outpatient breaks the continuity of patient study, is not the way medicine is practiced, and fails to give the student the concept of the patient as an individual.

8. Clinical departments are giving more instruction in the medical basic sciences than formerly and are orienting their teaching toward the practical applications of these sciences to the practice of medicine.

9. The curriculum is becoming more rigid from attempts to include too much material, and as a result elective time is decreasing and the student is losing freedom.

10. Examination systems in general increase rigidity of the curriculum, interfere with the student's learning, rob him of time for study, and fail to promote his sense of integrity.

RECOMMENDATIONS

1. The curriculum should be adapted to student needs and not the student to curriculum needs.

2. It is urgent that faculties carefully weigh the value to the student of old and new knowledge and study and employ the best methods for its presentation and timing in the curriculum.

3. Mastering of techniques and specialty training should be left for internship and residency periods.
4. The curriculum should be designed to allow the student to follow the same patient both as an outpatient and as an inpatient.
5. The outpatient departments of teaching hospitals should be designed and organized for teaching and for efficient and effective care of patients, and not primarily for service. Service loads should be limited to teaching needs. When this is accomplished, both faculty and students should find greater satisfaction in working with outpatients.
6. The curriculum should provide more freedom and elective time for the student than it now does.
7. Examinations should be used as teaching tools and not simply as a means of evaluating and grading students.
8. Proctoring of examinations and formal honor systems should not be necessary if the student has intimate contact with teachers of integrity and if methods of judging his accomplishment are based on observation of his daily work.

Part VI

ADVANCED EDUCATION AND TRAINING

14 INTERNSHIP AND RESIDENCY TRAINING

The internship is a period of hospital service, training, and education, usually of one year's duration, which follows graduation from medical school. The residency is a period of special service, training, and education, in hospitals, of one to five or more years following the internship. The house staff of a hospital is composed of both interns and residents. In 1950, more than 24,000 young physicians served in hospitals as interns and residents.

THE INTERNSHIP

Historically, the internship was developed before the residency. The term "intern" came into use in the United States approximately 100 years ago, to identify those young physicians who served in a hospital or almshouse for the purpose of gaining practical training under the guidance of a senior physician on the staff of the hospital. Frequently the young doctor paid a fee for this privilege. There was a real need for such practical experience because medical school instruction was chiefly didactic and students had little opportunity to examine patients and study them carefully.

In the late nineteenth and early twentieth centuries as hospitals became more closely associated with medical schools, internship training gradually became accepted as a routine part of a young physician's training. Physicians serving internships in well-established hospitals, with able staff members, were soon recognized by the public as having special competence. After the turn of the century many hospitals found young physicians useful in the care of their charity or ward patients and developed internship programs. The intern lived in the hospital and could be called upon to render patient care both day and night.

The need for establishing standards for hospitals offering internships was first discussed by the Council on Medical Education of the American Medical Association early in the century. In 1914 the Council published its first list of hospitals approved for internships.

Three general patterns of internship training emerged. The first became known as the "rotating internship," in which the young physician spent periods of time on 5 to 10 or more services (medicine, surgery, obstetrics, urology, etc.). The number of services varied according to the hospital's organization of them, and the rotation periods varied from a few weeks to two or more months. Such internships offered the trainee experience in several fields of medicine and were said to be designed to train him for general practice. The second pattern became known as the "mixed internship." In this type of training, the trainee spent longer periods of time on fewer hospital services and was often allowed to select one service in which to devote a major portion of his time. In the mixed internship, it was recognized that more time was needed than the rotating internship could provide if the physician was to gain any mastery of one particular discipline. The third pattern was the "straight internship," which developed primarily in the older teaching hospitals in the East. In this type, the trainee devoted his entire period to one field such as surgery, medicine, or pediatrics. It was designed for specialty training, although many of the young men, after completing it, continued with one or more years of training in a residency.

The internship in the teaching hospitals that are owned or affiliated with the medical school was primarily designed for work with charity patients on the wards, where the undergraduate medical student received his instruction. The intern commonly did little or no work with private patients. On the teaching ward he carried considerable responsibility for his patients. He recorded their histories, he performed physical examinations, he carried out certain laboratory work, and he wrote orders for the care of his patients. He also carried out many therapeutic procedures. He was an integral part of a team composed of the senior faculty member, a resident, and a medical student, whose purpose was to study thoroughly a group of patients for whom the team provided professional medical care.

Some teaching hospitals clearly differentiated between the interns assigned to teaching wards and those assigned to private wards. Interns working exclusively with private patients received larger stipends; it was understood that one of the major purposes of the interns on the private wards was to give service to private patients under the direction of the patient's private physician and that the educational opportunities on the private wards were not equivalent to those on the ward teaching services.

In some of the university-affiliated hospitals, in which the majority of patients were private, the intern spent a large portion of his year of training with private patients and had opportunity for the more varied experience with charity patients for perhaps only two to six months. Frequently the medical students clearly recognized the disadvantage of these internships, and those graduates who wished to continue their training under close supervision chose university-owned or -integrated hospitals for this purpose.

Education or Service

Since the establishment by the Council on Medical Education of standards for hospitals offering internships, there has been a constant and continuing effort on the part of educational bodies to make the internship a truly educational experience. At the same time, the demand by the hospitals for the services of interns has continually increased. The Council,[1] in defining the essentials of an approved internship, has described the internship as "one of the most important phases of medical education," and has stated:

The purpose of the internship is to supplement the undergraduate medical course by a well-rounded experience of closely supervised clinical practice in diagnosis and therapy. There should be a progressive increase in the intern's responsibilities.

Internships designed without a well supervised educational program, or arranged merely to provide hospitals with resident personnel to assist in the clinical work of the hospital, cannot be approved.

In 1920, 593 of the 6,440 hospitals in the United States sought annually 3,420 interns, or about 400 more than the number of students

[1] "Essentials of an Approved Internship," prepared by the Council on Medical Education and Hospitals of the American Medical Association, Chicago, American Medical Association, 1951, p. 3. [Revised to December 1948; originally published by the *Journal of the American Medical Association*, Vol. 25, p. 1757 (June 14), 1919.]

graduated in that year by the medical schools. Commenting upon that fact, an editorial in the *Journal of the American Medical Association*[2] stated:

Nevertheless, these hospitals represent a very small proportion of all hospitals in the country, and the number seeking interns is increasing. It can be seen, therefore, that the number of students graduating annually is not sufficient to supply interns for all the hospitals seeking them, far less to meet the demand if all general hospitals should desire to use them. This, meanwhile, is one of the bases for the claim that there is a dearth of physicians. It can readily be seen, however, that sufficient interns could not be provided for all hospitals even if the annual number of graduates exceeded by several times the normal output for this country. The intern problem must be solved in some other way. Many hospitals, even now, are employing physicians as residents or house officers at increasing salaries or with gradually increasing privileges in the way of practice. Interns, also, should be relieved of much of the work required of them which should be done by orderlies employed for that purpose. History-writing and records, which have depended largely on intern service, can be kept up by staff physicians through the use of stenographers. It is certain that the increased demand for interns does not justify either the lowering of educational standards or a multiplication of medical schools.

It is apparent from this editorial that as far back as 1920 there was a definite conflict between the desire of the hospitals on the one hand to obtain interns because of the value of their services and the ideal of educational organizations on the other hand to make the internship predominately an educational experience.

The Commission on Graduate Medical Education[3] published a report in 1940 in which it stated its views concerning the internship.

The internship . . . should be an educational opportunity which rounds out the training received during the medical course and which continues the clinical clerkship with enlarged responsibilities. It should, therefore, be considered as a part of the basic preparation of the student for general practice; in addition, it should provide him with the foundation on which he can, by graduate training, develop proficiency in a specialty.

The Commission went on to describe what should be included in the internship. It advised that general medicine, pediatrics, surgical diagnosis, minor surgery, first aid, and normal obstetrics should be included

[2] Editorial in *Journal of the American Medical Association,* Vol. 75, p. 418 (Aug. 7), 1920.

[3] "Graduate Medical Education, Report of the Commission on Graduate Medical Education," Chicago, University of Chicago Press, 1940, p. 5.

in the internship experience. Patients were to be treated as an entity from both the mental and the physical points of view. Public health and preventive medicine were to be stressed. The intern was to have considerable outpatient-department experience; he was also to deal with chronic diseases; and he was to carry out laboratory work. He was to spend considerable time in diagnosis and in preoperative and postoperative surgical care. Periods were to be set aside for educational pursuits with one or more hours per day for formal educational opportunities. The Commission also recommended that each hospital keep a record of each intern's work and report to the dean of the medical school from which he graduated.

In spite of the efforts of such organizations, the hospital-intern problem continued to grow. Interns became so valuable that many more hospitals sought approval by the Council on Medical Education and Hospitals. In their competition for the medical school graduates, the hospitals began to offer appointments to the students before they had completed their third year of medical school, with the understanding that the student would intern in the hospital upon graduation. Those hospitals encountering difficulty in obtaining interns frequently offered $100 to $200 per month plus board and room. In large teaching hospitals the intern rarely received more than $25 to $50 per month. In many instances he received no stipend whatever.

The problem became increasingly acute as more and more hospitals were approved for intern training. By 1950 the 799 hospitals approved by the Council on Medical Education and Hospitals offered nearly twice as many intern places (9,398) as there were medical school graduates (5,600).[4] The competition among hospitals for interns led the medical schools and certain national hospital organizations to meet for the purpose of devising some plan for standardizing internship appointments. A so-called "matching plan" evolved which gave the medical students a maximum of freedom in their choice of hospitals in which to intern. The Council on Medical Education and Hospitals, also realizing that many hospitals were increasing the number of their internships, attempted to set some standard for the number of interns each hospital could appoint. This issue has never been settled, however.

[4] LEVEROOS, E. H., W. R. ALBUS, W. W. CORBETT, and W. W. SOUTHARD, Approved Internships and Residencies in the United States, *Journal of the American Medical Association*, Vol. 142, p. 1145 (Apr. 15), 1950.

Except for a matching plan which deals only with the mechanics of appointing the interns, little progress has been made in the solution of this problem in the last 25 years.

The Real Issue

The real issue is whether or not the internship can be made truly educational or what portion of it is truly educational. In order to grasp this problem it is essential to realize that there are at least five parties who determine to some extent the character of an internship. They are the medical student, the hospitals, the Council on Medical Education and Hospitals, certain state boards of licensure, and the medical schools themselves.

At present the medical student is essentially a free agent in deciding at which hospital or hospitals he will attempt to obtain an internship. In a few instances the medical schools have definitely directed their graduates to intern in certain hospitals affiliated with the school, but these are unusual examples, and it is the general tradition of the medical schools to allow their graduates to apply for any internship they may choose.

The hospital has sole responsibility for its internships. It appoints its staff, and it maintains the services that it can afford and that are necessary for good patient care. A hospital is not primarily an educational institution; its main purpose is service. It does not receive its charter as an educational institution and, although it can issue certificates, it has no legal right to grant educational degrees. In some states, when a hospital appoints unlicensed physicians as interns, it assumes legal responsibility for their professional services.

The Council on Medical Education and Hospitals of the American Medical Association, because of its interest in improving medical education and hospitals—and with the support of the medical profession—has established itself as an agency for the approval of hospital internships and residencies. Its position as such has been accepted both by the hospitals and by the medical schools.

State boards of licensure have a decided influence on many internships. The boards in 24 states require the graduate of a medical school to serve one year in an internship in a hospital which they approve, before the young physician is allowed to take an examination for licensure. Most state boards accept the list of hospitals approved by the Council on Medical Education and Hospitals. Thirteen state boards specify the type of internship (rotating or mixed) a man must serve.

The medical schools are involved in internship training in two ways. If the faculty of the school has the authority to appoint the interns in its teaching hospital or hospitals, the school is directly involved and takes the responsibility for the interns' training in these institutions. A school may also have an indirect influence on internships. The faculty and the administration can advise and direct students to certain hospitals that are considered to offer excellent internships or that are connected with the medical school. Six medical schools have gone farther than this and have required their graduates to serve internships before they can be granted M.D. degrees. This practice is being abandoned. It is generally considered unsound from an educational point of view unless the medical school controls the hospitals and the staff appointments, and thereby the content, quality, and method of intern instruction.

The internship in its present form and use does not lend itself to the continuation of medical education in a formalized way. From the standpoint of medical education there are drawbacks in any training program conducted in a service institution. Hospitals are not primarily educational institutions, and the staff is not selected primarily on the basis of teaching ability. Few if any hospitals make a careful evaluation of the intern's educational accomplishment. In fact, there are as yet no standards of accomplishment for interns to achieve by the end of their internship training.

There is considerable confusion in the thinking about the educational aspects of an internship. Several medical schools and medical educators have advocated that the interns should be charged tuition in the teaching hospitals, basing their belief on the theory that the internship is primarily educational. In this way, it is said, the intern could partially repay some of the "high cost" of the more formalized medical education that he received in medical school.

Of considerable significance is the change which is taking place in the internships because of three factors. The first of these factors is the adoption and the widespread use, by the medical schools, of the clinical clerkship. It should be recalled that the intern period of training developed as a result of the need for practical experience with patients—experience which was not offered by most medical schools before the turn of the century. When the schools adopt clinical clerkships, however, the medical student has the opportunity of carefully studying and following the patients from day to day and from hour to hour. He takes their histories, he carries out physical examinations and certain laboratory tests, and he may participate in certain technical therapeutic procedures. At present he is given less responsibility for patients than the intern. Patients must be available to the medical student, and the student must be enabled to spend time with the patients to whom he is assigned. The time factor is of great consequence. As clerkships have grown in importance, there has frequently been competition between the intern and the medical student for the patient's time and attention.

The second factor is the marked growth in residency training. The major teaching hospitals more than doubled their number of residencies in the years following the Second World War. In many instances the number of ward patients available for study did not increase correspondingly; therefore the intern found himself frequently competing with the resident for work with patients. The resident, being the intern's superior, almost invariably won out in this competition.

Obviously, in these major teaching hospitals, the intern was caught between the clinical clerkship for the undergraduate medical student and the marked increase in the number of residents who were also seeking work with patients. Other medical schools expanded their hospital facilities by affiliating with smaller hospitals, rotating the interns and residents from the teaching hospital through those affiliated hospitals. In a typical program operated by a privately endowed medical school, the reports of the interns showed that in general they felt that their experiences in these small hospitals had been interesting and of some value. They severely criticized, however, the lack of supervision and planning, the inadequate libraries, and the laboratory facilities. They felt that such an experience should be limited to short periods, and none of those interviewed wished to continue in service at these hospitals.

In another program, also typical of its kind, conducted by a state-supported medical school, the faculty of the medical school appoints interns to work in several smaller hospitals. Half of the intern's time is spent at the university hospital and the other half at the affiliated hospitals. There were not enough interns available to cover all the services in these hospitals, and the hospital administrators desired to have the number doubled. One intern had contracted tuberculosis, and the program did not have its full complement of men. Although the interns in the affiliated hospitals were supposed to do complete histories and physical examinations on all new patients who were admitted, this became impossible in hospitals in which the average daily number of new admissions ranged from 25 to 50. The interns were also responsible for covering the emergency room and the delivery room. On all services except pediatrics, the intern was overworked. The intern was usually given alternate nights and week ends off duty. On days when he was on duty, he commonly worked until midnight. In contrast, on returning to the university hospital these interns found that there was insufficient work for them because of the large number of residents who were caring for the patients.

The third factor effecting a change in the internships is the increase in the number of private and semiprivate patients, and the decrease in the proportion of ward patients. Half of the total number of major departments (medicine, surgery, obstetrics and gynecology, psychiatry, and pediatrics) in the four-year medical schools included in the Survey reported that their interns spent 25 to 75 per cent of their time with private patients. With the growth of hospitalization insurance, more patients have sought admission to hospitals as semiprivate or private patients with their own physicians. The hospitals are finding it increasingly difficult to finance the ward services, where interns receive most of their training. In large city and county tax-supported institutions this problem was found to be less acute. It has already been stated that many major teaching hospitals realized that a definite difference existed between work with charity or ward patients and work with private patients, whose professional care was the responsibility of their private physicians. The teaching hospitals, finding difficulty in obtaining interns and residents for their private wards, assigned interns to private patients as well as to ward patients. Thus they immediately detracted from the quality of the educational experience of the internship.

These three factors combined have made the internships in many teaching hospitals less attractive to the graduates of the medical schools. In 1950–51 those major teaching hospitals affiliated with the medical schools surveyed were unable to fill 23 per cent of their internship places.

Remuneration

Such figures do not tell the complete story, however. Many of these hospitals, which in the past had several applicants for every intern position, have been faced with the opposite situation: they have barely enough applicants to fill their internships, and they do not have the opportunity of selecting only the most promising candidates. At present this situation may partly be due to the low remuneration for the intern in these hospitals. Federal hospitals, which in general pay more than teaching hospitals, filled all but 15 per cent of their internship places in 1951. However, according to the interviews held with the students during the Survey, the most common complaint about their own medical school teaching hospital was that the intern was not given sufficient responsibility. They stated frankly that they did not wish to serve a further period of time in these hospitals.

What is the status of the internship today in medical education? Is it any longer necessary as an educational instrument? It is time to face the hospital-internship problem realistically, and in a broad sense.

THE RESIDENCY

The residency period of training was designed for the purpose of developing physicians as experts in special fields of medicine. In recent years it has been utilized for training in general practice also. In its early beginnings the residency was a rather informal period of training with neither definite time requirement nor precise goal of accomplishment.

The Johns Hopkins Hospital is said to have established the present form of residency training. Dr. Osler[5] in reporting the plan in 1890 wrote, about the resident physician:

It would be well to use for this officer the term First Assistant at the Medical, Surgical and Gynaecological Clinics, respectively. Ultimately we should look forward to having Second Assistants, as at the German Clinics. These men should, as now, be salaried. They should be selected with the greatest care by the Staff, with the approval of the Medical Board and of the Trustees. Though appointed annually, it is expected that these men remain for an indefinite period, so long in fact as they do their work satisfactorily.

Perhaps the one special advantage which the large German hospitals have over corresponding American Institutions, is the presence of these highly trained men who remain in some cases three, five, or even eight years and who, under the Professor, have control of the clinical material.

[5] CHESNEY, ALAN M., "The Johns Hopkins Hospital and the Johns Hopkins University School of Medicine," Vol. I, Baltimore, Johns Hopkins Press, 1943, p. 161.

It is apparent from this statement that the residency was designed for the development and training of a few young physicians with special interests and abilities who might become professors or men especially competent in one field of medicine.

The teaching hospitals and a few of the nonteaching hospitals at first established their own patterns and standards. The length of time the resident might spend in a hospital was frequently determined by his own wishes. In a teaching hospital the resident was responsible for the professional care of patients under the supervision of the chief of his service. He usually participated in the instruction of the medical students, helped to supervise the work of the interns, and frequently he carried out some research.

At the beginning of the century, with the growth of scientific and technical medical knowledge, the need for and the value of specialists became increasingly apparent. There were various methods by which a young physician could obtain such specialty training. He could go to one of the large European clinics for a period of time; he could attend one of the numerous postgraduate medical schools which existed at that time in the United States; he could work as an assistant with a specialist of proved ability; or he could obtain one of the few good residencies that then existed. The quality of the training was extremely variable and often unsatisfactory. No standards or examinations existed for men wishing to claim that they had special qualifications. A physician could become a specialist simply by declaring that he was one.

In 1917 a group of ophthalmologists, dissatisfied with the training of physicians in their specialty, established the American Board of Ophthalmology for the purpose of examining candidates and certifying as to their competency. Between the First and Second World Wars, as medical science became more complex and the public demand for the services of specialists increased, the number of specialty boards grew rapidly. During this same period residency training was inaugurated by a steadily growing number of hospitals. The Council on Medical Education again expanded its approval functions. In 1920 the words "and Hospitals" were added to its title, and in 1927 its first list of hospitals approved for the training of residents appeared. In 1933, the American Medical Association recognized the special certifying boards and began to cooperate with the Advisory Board for Medical Specialties, which had representation from each of the approved specialty boards, and was organized "to act in an advisory capacity to such organizations as might seek its advice concerning the coordination of the education and certification of medical specialists." Upon the advice of this advisory board of medical specialists, the Council on Medical Education and Hospitals of the American Medical Association might, or might not, approve the establishment of a new board for specialty certification.

The growing emphasis on specialization was given tremendous impetus by the policies of the Federal government services during the Second World War. The armed forces, faced with grave problems in the identification of specialists, recognized certified specialists by giving them higher officer's rank and resulting increases in pay. The Veterans Administration introduced the pay differential at the end of the war. The younger physicians serving in the forces were made acutely aware of this fact and, often fearing greater government control over civilian medicine, sought residency training in the specialties upon returning to civilian life. The number of certified specialists tripled between 1940 and 1951. The number of specialty boards had increased to 19, with subspecialties and special certification in 24 minor fields. By 1950 there were 1,079 hospitals with approved residency and fellowship training programs offering 18,669 positions of which only 6 per cent were vacant. At the same time there were 9,370 approved internships of which 25 per cent were vacant.[6]

Growth in Demand for Specialized Training

This growth in the demand for specialized training, and in the number of the boards with their specific requirements, had a decided influence on the residency training in all hospitals. Before the First World War, a majority of the teaching hospitals had established a pyramidal system of residency training. Under such a system a hospital might have, for example, 40 interns, 20 first-year assistant residents, and 10 second-year residents, and only five men would reach a senior resident's posi-

---

[6] By 1951 there were 1,120 hospitals offering 20,257 resident and fellowship places, and 25 per cent of the 19,364 resident places were unfilled; and 828 hospitals offering 10,044 intern places, of which 32 per cent were unfilled. This was an abnormal period of war emergency when physicians were being called to military service. Figures are from the 1950 and 1951 reports on Internships and Residencies of the Council on Medical Education and Hospitals of the American Medical Association, published in the Apr. 15, 1950, and the Sept. 29, 1951, issues of the *Journal of the American Medical Association.*

tion in the fourth year after graduation from medical school. This system was competitive, and the hospital and the medical school staff attempted to select the most promising young men for their top residency positions. However, since the Second World War, with so many men wishing to specialize, many of the teaching hospitals have changed to a parallel system of training by which twice as many or more men become senior residents each year. Fifty-eight per cent of the departments in the teaching hospitals of the medical schools surveyed had parallel systems of residency training. The parallel system was found to be necessary if large numbers of men were to meet their board requirements, which in most instances are a minimum of two and sometimes of four years of hospital training following an internship.

In the major teaching hospitals of the schools surveyed, the number of residencies more than doubled in the period between 1940 and 1950, increasing from approximately 1,000 to more than 2,500. In the same period the number of internships increased less than 5 per cent. Some of the teaching hospitals, in order to obtain enough patients for their expanded residency programs, affiliated with other hospitals in their vicinities. The hospitals were extremely anxious for this affiliation because it increased their opportunity of obtaining the services of residents. In such newly affiliated hospitals, the medical schools attempted to establish training programs that would meet the requirements of the Council on Medical Education and Hospitals; they tried to give advice to the hospital staff and sent faculty members to help to direct and to participate in the training of residents. In many instances the residents in the outlying hospitals were brought back to the major teaching hospital for a term of service or a formal course in one or more of the medical basic sciences. There were obvious defects in this system which soon became apparent when it was found that the medical school might have little or no control over the appointment of the staff in the affiliated hospital and therefore found it almost impossible to maintain the medical school standards of medical care and close supervision of each resident.

To meet this defect some medical schools have established standards to be met by those hospitals desiring affiliation for residency training. In other instances, in which the teaching hospitals were either unable to or did not increase the number of patients, in order to keep the residents busy the men were assigned to services that were not designed for residency training, such as outpatient clinics, accident rooms, and private services. This practice frequently lowered the quality of training when it diminished the individual responsibility of the residents.

These defects may be illustrated by the complaints of the residents in a hospital that was affiliated with a medical school and in which the majority of patients were private. The residents' views were obtained in interviews during the Survey, and the comments in this example are typical of the comments of residents at other, similar hospitals. In the hospital mentioned, the residents stated that the surgical training was of little value; they were permitted to do little more than watch and hold retractors. Both the resident and the intern were responsible for the work-up of the private patients of the hospital staff. Since these patients were admitted to the hospital in the evening, each member of the house staff usually had three to six patients whose histories and examinations had to be worked up and who had to be prepared for operation the following morning. All morning, these young physicians helped with the operations; in the afternoon they tried to sleep. The residents stated that the resident in surgery was given little or no responsibility for the surgical patients. The resident in urology also was critical of the hospital; he stated that he had been sold the job on the basis of education but found it was chiefly service, and also that he was not receiving adequate compensation for the service he was rendering.

There was considerable dissatisfaction on the part of the residents interviewed with the lack of responsibility given to them for private patients. In general they were anxious to spend more time on the teaching ward service, where they could be responsible for patients' care, but such assignments had been shortened by the hospital so that each resident would have some of this type of experience.

A surprisingly large number of young physicians accepted the fact that it was necessary for them to spend three to four years in a type of hospital training with which they felt dissatisfied in order to meet their time requirements for the boards. Some of them were acutely aware that they were in a lock-step system and must serve their time and move up the ladder year by year as was prescribed.

Rigidity of Requirements

As is common in the development of new educational programs, the time requirement and the content of the training are stressed by the boards; less emphasis is given to the quality of the training and the ability of certain young men to advance more rapidly than others. The time requirement has been given such weight that many young physicians have been refused the opportunity to take board examinations because they lacked two or three weeks of the time requirement in hospital training prescribed by their boards. Rigidity is a definite handicap to the clinical departments of a medical school which wish to try new designs and new approaches in residency training.

Rigid requirements may also restrict the freedom of the young physician to explore new fields which might interest him. A young man is anxious to complete his long years of training in order to fulfill the requirements; he is loath to step out of the prescribed path for fear it will prolong the time until he can receive his certificate and be qualified to practice as a specialist in his field.

Specialty boards were established to meet a definite need, and they are performing a definite service. As any field of education develops, firm, clear, and regular standards need to be established. It is in this field that the specialty boards, whose membership usually includes a high percentage of medical school professors, have made their real contribution. As the boards develop, however, they need to analyze and evaluate their programs constantly in order to avoid excessive and continued rigidity in the time and content requirements.

Professors in certain departments were rather rebellious at the board requirements. For instance, in one medical school the department of gynecology was a part of the surgical service and, partly because of this administrative organization, the American Board of Obstetrics and Gynecology had refused to approve a residency in the specialty in the teaching hospital. The professor of obstetrics felt that the Board was exceeding its authority, and that it might better have given its "provisional approval" until more effective rotation between obstetrics and gynecology and surgery had been arranged. The professor stated that he was encountering increasing difficulty in maintaining a resident staff because young physicians would not apply for resident positions on his service unless the training would qualify them for their board examinations. A point of view encountered in several instances was that of the dean of another medical school, who stated:

In their approving activities the boards have taken on responsibilities which they do not have the staff, the mechanism, or the authority to properly discharge. The medical school should largely ignore the American Boards and should protect and develop their own residency programs and emphasize that the medical schools are certifying that their own residents are competent.

However, the public recognition of specialists and the resultant prestige have led many hospitals to require that a man hold a board certificate before he can be appointed to a senior staff position. Young physicians are acutely aware of this fact and realize that if they are to have full hospital privileges for their patients when they enter practice they will be wise to conform with the hospital and board requirements. The boards are opposed to this attitude on the part of the hospitals. The medical school teaching hospitals are, therefore, caught in a cycle of influences which to a large extent determine their residency training programs. First of all, the medical schools themselves must be approved by the Council on Medical Education and Hospitals and by the Association of American Medical Colleges. Their internships and residencies must be approved by the Council on Medical Education and Hospitals. The establishment of specialty boards must be approved by the Council on Medical Education and Hospitals. The boards then require fixed time periods of training before certification and often specify the experiences the trainees should have in hospitals approved by the Council on Medical Education and Hospitals. In turn, those hospitals which have been approved for internship and residency training attempt to obtain diplomates of the boards for their staffs; and hospitals wishing to establish residency programs feel it increases their opportunity of gaining approval if they have board-certified men on their staffs. The charge has been brought that this policy prevents general practitioners from gaining hospital staff appointments. Thus the cumulative effect of the present requirements of the Boards and the Council has reached beyond the goals that were intended.

Private Patients

Another factor having a decided influence on residency training is the increase in the number of hospital-insured and private patients, as has already been mentioned under the section on the Internship. In 1950, 76,961,000 people in the United States held hospital insurance, which was an increase of 17 per cent over the number in 1949. There were 54,477,000 people carrying some kind of surgical-expense insurance, which was an increase of 32 per cent over the 1949 figure. There were also 21,589,000 individuals carrying medical-expense insurance, which was an increase of 28 per cent over the 1949 figure.[7] It is obvious that the number of people carrying insurance which allows them to become private or semiprivate patients in hospitals is rapidly growing. It must be remembered that residencies, in their full development, were based on the principle that young men grew and developed with responsibility. When a second-year or third-year resident was placed on a teaching ward under a consultant appointed by the professor of a department, the resident was held strictly responsible for the over-all professional care of the patients and for the quality of the work of the resident and interns who worked under him. He could admit and discharge patients, and he was given considerable authority. Upon finishing his residency he was considered by his professor to have demonstrated his ability to handle those problems which he would meet in the practice of his field of medicine.

In dealing with the private patients of individual physicians it has been almost impossible to give a resident the degree of authority and responsibility that could be assigned to him on teaching wards. The amount of authority and responsibility that can be delegated to the resident depends upon the patient's private physician and upon legal aspects of the practice of medicine. To allow a resident to decide when to operate and what type of operation to perform, and then to have him perform the operation on a patient who had selected the senior staff physician as his doctor, is practically impossible. The increase in prepayment insurance plans will continue to accent this problem as more and more people are able to afford private professional medical care. Only a few surgical departments were encountered which had found a satisfactory answer to this question.

Remuneration

The remuneration of residents has always been small in the major teaching hospitals. Forty-two teaching hospitals which were visited in the course of the Survey gave an average monthly stipend in 1941 of $35 for the first-year residents in the departments of medicine and

[7] "Survey of Accident and Health Insurance Coverage in the United States," prepared by the Survey Committee of the Health Insurance Council, September, 1951.

surgery. By 1951 these had been increased to an average of $60 per month. They ranged from $25 to $175 per month in the various hospitals, but in many instances those residents receiving the larger amounts also paid for their board. In the second year of a man's residency he might receive as much as $50 to $200 per month, and in the third year it would be common for him to receive $100 to $300 per month in addition to his board and room. Thus, a few young physicians four or five years after graduation from medical school at the age of twenty-eight to thirty receive their board and room and an average of $1,200 to $2,500 per year. The hospital and its staff are assured of his services, usually on the basis of a seven-day week, and he may be on call 24 hours a day when he is on duty. He may be assigned to work anywhere in the hospital at the discretion of the chief of his service.

The arrangements between the hospital and medical school for the payment of residents vary considerably. In many instances the hospital pays the whole of the resident's stipend; in a few instances the medical school pays all of it; and in other cases the medical school and hospital jointly pay the residents, who are considered by the medical school as instructors.

The scales of pay for residents in teaching hospitals were designed before so many men were demanding long periods of residency training. Because of the higher monetary reward that is offered, many young physicians are obtaining residencies in hospitals of the Veterans Administration. They can frequently receive a similar professional experience to that in the teaching hospitals, because in many hospitals of the Veterans Administration the faculties of the medical schools supervise and participate in the residency training.

In general, young men serving residencies are looking for some added source of income. This question was discussed with residents in all the teaching hospitals surveyed. There were three general suggestions as to how their compensation could be increased. The majority of the men thought that pressure should be brought to bear on the hospitals to increase their stipends, although they realized that hospitals were having difficulty in meeting their expenses. A second group, commonly including those residents who were spending considerable time on private pavilions or wards for private patients, suggested that the staff physicians responsible for these patients should pay the resident for helping with the care of their patients. These residents made the point that the private physician was able to care for a large number of patients only because of the number of interns and residents who helped him. A third group suggested that the Federal government should pay them a salary while they were in hospital training. It was rather surprising that this suggestion came from residents who had served five or more years in a private hospital offering excellent residency training. These men had also graduated from private medical schools. However, they had come through a period when they had been indoctrinated with the point of view of looking to the government for financial help, and it seemed to them perfectly logical that the government pay for a part of the expense of their education in medical school, and that it should continue to pay a part, if not all, of their stipends while they were in hospital training. This same point of view was shared by other young physicians as well as by some of the medical students who, during the Second World War, had come to rely upon the Federal government for part of their education and also for a salary while they were attending medical school.

The training of those residents serving a considerable portion of their training period with the private patients of the senior hospital staff physicians should be carefully considered. The quality of their training and the degree of supervision they receive from individual physicians is extremely variable, and their responsibilities are limited.

The teaching hospital may take the point of view that, by providing interns and residents to aid with the care of private patients, it is partially remunerating the volunteer staff members of its faculty for their teaching services. Nevertheless, by providing the services of young physicians the hospitals are offering their senior staff members professional assistance, and not merely hospital facilities for the care of private patients.

It would be impossible for many senior staff members to care for more than a fraction of the number of their private patients were it not for the work of the interns and residents. This is especially true of the surgeon, who requires a team of residents and interns in order to provide him assistance at the time of operation and in the preoperative and postoperative care of his private patients. This situation exists in both university-owned and affiliated teaching hospitals. Occasionally, in fact, staff members take advantage of their hospital connections to increase their private incomes.

In one instance the head of a department in a state-owned medical school was reported to have an income of well over $100,000 per year. He had a large resident and intern staff and also made use of medical students to help in the care of his private patients. This individual was collecting private patients' fees from 50 or more hospitalized patients daily. In another teaching hospital the Survey teams were told that the heads of several departments had incomes from private patients ranging from $25,000 to $50,000 per year, and that most of the routine daily care given to these patients was furnished by interns and residents of the teaching hospital. These are exceptional instances, however, and by no means represent the contribution made by hundreds of physicians throughout the country who teach in medical schools, many of whom either donate their services or earn less than they could from private practice.

The Young Physician

The system of residency training, which was developed in medical school teaching hospitals whose staff members were selected because of their teaching ability, has spread to involve more than 1,000 hospitals in the United States, in most of which staff members are selected for their professional rather than pedagogical qualifications. In spite of this fact there can be no doubt that those young men who have spent two to five years in residency training are generally well equipped by experience and practice for work in their chosen fields. However, the rigidity of the system, its time requirements, and the low remuneration for residents and interns may well contribute to the development of at least three different attitudes in young men who have completed such training. One attitude is that of resignation to a lock-step system of training, and its acceptance, which in some individuals tends to stifle initiative and imagination. Second is the point of view that, if they must submit to this system of training with its low pay, it would be logical to look to some sort of government aid or government pay to help in their remuneration. Already many of these young men are seeking positions in hospitals of the Veterans Administration, which are competing with private hospitals for their services.

The third attitude is one which should be decried in the practice of medicine: that is, that the charging of high fees is justified. One is reluctantly forced to the conclusion that some aspects of the system of medical education and hospital training are conducive to this point of view. The young man who has paid a fairly high tuition for four years of medical schooling and has then spent another three to five years in residency training with a low salary is generally twenty-eight to thirty years of age when he has obtained his board certification. During this period his maximum earnings have not averaged more than $1,200 or $2,500 per year, and in many instances he has either delayed marriage or has required financial assistance. When he enters the practice of medicine, he can usually anticipate a maximum of 30 to 35 years of real earning capacity. In the first few years he may have difficulty in establishing his practice and a reputation. Thus, when patients do seek his services, he feels justified, on a logical basis, in charging high fees in order to make up for his earlier lack of earning capacity.

It would seem entirely reasonable for staff physicians to pay for the valuable services they receive from these young physicians in the care of private patients. The questions should be asked: Are the costs of maintaining internships and residencies properly a charge against the costs of hospital care or against the cost of professional medical service? To what extent should these costs be considered the hospital's contribution to medical education?

CONCLUSIONS

1. Internships, as presently organized, are primarily periods of training and service with marked variations in educational opportunities.
2. Internships and residencies are the responsibility of hospitals which receive approval for that purpose from the Council on Medical Education and Hospitals of the American Medical Association, and in some instances from state boards of medical examiners.
3. Interns and residents are frequently exploited. They perform valuable service functions for the hospitals and their staffs but receive far from adequate compensation in the form either of educational opportunity or of financial remuneration.
4. The internship as an educational instrument is no longer so essential as it was 25 years ago.
5. The internship is generally deteriorating in educational value as it is encroached upon to an increasing degree both by the clinical clerkships and by the expansion of residency training.
6. Residency training is designed primarily for the development of

specialists, and residents also contribute greatly to the teaching program.

7. Teaching hospitals have more than doubled the number of their residencies within the last 10 years.

8. The duration and type of residency training are largely determined by agencies other than the teaching hospital and the medical school. These institutions pattern their residency programs to fit the requirements of the American Boards for certification in the specialties.

9. The method of residency training developed by teaching hospitals utilizing wards designed for teaching is jeopardized by the increase in the number of private and insured patients. This problem has not been adequately solved by teaching hospitals, and it is becoming increasingly acute.

10. The period of residency training has tended to become longer and the program more rigid.

11. More than 24,000 young physicians were serving as interns and residents in 1950.

12. In many hospitals, interns and residents assisting in the professional care of private patients make it possible for practicing physicians to care for large numbers of hospitalized patients.

13. Insufficient thought has been given to the effect on the young physician as a person of long training periods with low income and rather rigid regimentation.

14. The question arises whether the cost of maintaining internships and residencies should be charged to hospital care, professional service, or medical education.

RECOMMENDATIONS

1. Medical school faculties should give their students more helpful advice and counsel concerning internships.

2. Medical schools and their major teaching hospitals should reexamine their internship and residency programs from the standpoint of their total impact on the young physician.

3. Medical schools should exert greater leadership in the field of residency training, and attempts should be made to establish more flexibility in residency training and more freedom for both the trainee and the teaching hospitals.

4. Medical schools should assume responsibility for intern and resident training only in hospitals in which the schools control staff appointments and the educational program.

5. The concept of the private patient's position in a teaching hospital and the status of the resident physician must both be redefined if responsibility for patient care is to be maintained as a basic principle in residency training.

6. Exploitation of interns and residents should be stopped. Interns and residents provide valuable services. In return they should receive a true educational experience and adequate financial support. They should not be exploited and expected to serve solely as salaried staff officers.

15 GRADUATE EDUCATION IN THE MEDICAL BASIC SCIENCES[1]

Anatomy, biochemistry, physiology, pharmacology, bacteriology, and pathology are important sciences in their own right, apart from their basic relevance to medicine. As such they attract the interest of certain students who are inclined toward careers of investigation or teaching in one or another of them. For these students, the American universities have adopted the pattern of graduate education which was first developed in the German universities. The medical schools, having developed strong scientific departments in these subjects, conduct graduate programs in which they train the young scientists, some of whom will be the teachers and investigators of the future. By devoting all their talents to one of these fields, men with this type of training have made enormous contributions to knowledge and to medical education.

Any department conducting such graduate education immensely enhances its contribution, provided it adheres to the objective of graduate education by giving the student an opportunity to delve into the study of the subject of his major interest amply provided with time, stimulation, facilities, and supervision. The department is strengthened by the stimulus the graduate students give to the interest of the teachers, the assistance they give in the teaching of medical students, and the investigations they pursue. On the other hand, the graduate program may have only limited value if the department is overrun with graduate students seeking degrees. Mass production of this sort may destroy

[1] For the purpose of this report, use of the term "graduate student" is restricted to students who take courses in the medical school as candidates for a Master's or a Doctor of Philosophy degree. The term does not include interns and residents, because few physicians are candidates for Master's or Ph.D. degrees while serving in those categories.

rather than enhance the quality of the teaching of both the medical student and the graduate student.

Large numbers make impossible the closeness of contact between student and teacher that is essential in higher education. Furthermore, the fact that the members of the department are so deeply interested in the subject may incline them to direct their teaching toward graduate rather than medical students, thereby weakening rather than strengthening the department's value to the primary purpose of the medical school.

The general pattern of these programs is fairly uniform. After the student has demonstrated his ability and interest in the field in certain collegiate courses, has received a Bachelor's degree, and has been accepted as a candidate for a graduate degree, he spends one or two school years taking advanced courses in the field of his main interest (his "major") and in certain related subjects (his "minor"). After passing an examination, he may then receive a Master's degree. Subsequently, he may spend a year or more in original investigation of a problem in his field of interest, working under the immediate supervision of a senior member of the department. During this period he receives highly individualized instruction. He must prepare a scholarly report of his investigation and present it for review and criticism to designated members of the faculty, before whom he must also appear in order to defend it. A comprehensive written and oral examination in the subject then follows which, if the student has successfully completed the program, leads to the granting of a Doctor's degree.

When these graduate programs were first developed, the careers open to the men who completed them were largely restricted to teaching and research in similar departments in medical schools, and there was no other means of obtaining thorough training in the scientific aspects of medicine. At this mid-point of the twentieth century both of these factors have changed markedly. The growth of research institutes, the development of research in industrial organizations and Federal services, and the requirement of advanced degrees in some of these fields for teaching in secondary schools and colleges have created a demand for men with this graduate education in many careers outside the medical schools.

Only a few universities maintain strong departments in five of the subjects in other schools on the campus. It has become customary, therefore, for graduate students from other parts of the university to take as

"minors" parts of the graduate courses in the medical school departments, even though their "majors" are in nonmedical subjects.

An effort was made by the Survey to obtain data on the growth and
magnitude of the graduate programs in the medical schools, on the
number of course hours devoted to graduate students, and on the amount
and distribution of tuition fees from these students. This effort was only
partially successful because of the medical schools' lack of information
on the number of students for whom they were responsible and their
tuition fees.

Such data as it was possible to collect indicate that the number of
graduate students taking work in medical departments increased sharply
between the academic years 1939–40 and 1948–49 (Table 49). Only

Table 49. TOTAL GRADUATE STUDENTS AND MEDICAL STUDENTS ENROLLED
IN 19 MEDICAL SCHOOLS, 1939–40 AND 1948–49

Year	Graduate students	Medical students
1939–40	1,335	5,912
1948–49	2,060	6,382

19 schools gave usable data for both years. In these schools the total
number of graduate students rose from 1,335 in 1939–40 to 2,060 in
1948–49—an increase of 54 per cent. During the same period the enrollment of medical students in the same schools rose from 5,912 in
1939–40 to 6,382 in 1948–49—an increase of about 8 per cent.

The Council on Medical Education and Hospitals[2] reported only
2,898 graduate students in all the medical schools in 1948–49, 1,133
of whom were physicians working for advanced degrees, and the remaining 1,765 of whom were graduate students. This apparent dis-
crepancy is another illustration of the fact that the medical schools'
records of their activities in this area are inadequate.

Only seven medical schools supplied usable answers to the question
regarding the total tuition fees paid by graduate students and the portion
of those fees which went to the medical school. In these schools the
fees paid by graduate students in 1948–49 totaled $238,726, of which
the medical schools received $168,538 (71 per cent). On the basis of

[2] ANDERSON, D. G., and ANNE TIPNER, Medical Education in the United States
and Canada, *Journal of the American Medical Association,* Vol. 141, p. 27 (Sept. 3),
1949.

the total graduate enrollment of 507 in the seven schools, it is estimated that in this very limited sample the students paid an average of $470 each.

The question of tuition fees from graduate students is complicated by the wide variation in programs for graduate students. In some schools the graduate student is expected to give active assistance in the courses for medical and other students. Such aid usually consists of preparing material and supervising work in the laboratory. Occasionally, however, graduate students are responsible for a substantial part of the lecture work in the courses for medical students. In many of these schools the graduate students' contribution to teaching is recognized to the extent that most of them hold appointments as teaching assistants. They may receive some salary; commonly they receive remission of all tuition fees. In other schools, however, the graduate student is neither asked nor permitted to take any part in the teaching of other courses, and he is expected to pay fees comparable to those in other parts of the university.

In the 41 schools visited, graduate students were enrolled in a total of 148 medical basic science departments. Of these, 112 (76 per cent) reported that graduate students were utilized to some extent in teaching.

In most schools the candidates for graduate degrees are registered in the university's graduate school, which recommends them to the university for the granting of degrees. The department of the medical school in which the student is to do his major work is largely responsible for the selection of the graduate students, although of course complying with the general rules of the graduate school. In most instances the medical school departments make every effort to select only well-qualified and promising students, but there have been many instances of poor understanding by the graduate school as to what constitute "proper" qualifications. In the selection of highly competent graduate students, and in the quality of the programs conducted for them, the medical school departments compare favorably with the strongest departments in the other schools of the university.

In 20 of the schools visited some difficulty was being encountered because of the medical school's distance from the main university campus. In these schools it has been difficult for the faculty of the graduate school of the university to keep well informed on the aims and practices of the medical school departments. It has also sometimes been difficult for certain medical school departments to keep in touch with the graduate school, and to avoid the unsound practice of accepting graduate students whose qualifications are poor in order to use the incentive of a graduate degree as a means of getting additional help with the department's research program.

Master's or Doctor's degrees in clinical departments were offered in 19 of the 41 schools visited. The programs followed by candidates for these degrees vary, but they have little in common with such programs in the medical basic sciences.

In a few schools the regular work of the medical school may be counted toward a Master's degree. A little extra work is required of the student, usually with little or no original investigation. This practice amounts to giving the student double credit for his work; it enhances his education little if any, and has the net effect of cheapening the degree.

In most other instances advanced degrees are obtained by going through the usual intern and residency program for about three years, and supplementing it by writing a scientific paper, with or without taking a special examination for the degree. This, too, approaches the practice of giving the candidate double credit for the work he has done, and violates the purpose of graduate education described earlier.

More graduate students were enrolled in departments of bacteriology than in any other basic medical science department (Table 50). This

Table 50. FULL-TIME GRADUATE STUDENTS* IN BASIC SCIENCE DEPARTMENTS OF 41 MEDICAL SCHOOLS, 1949–50

Department	Departments reporting	Departments taking graduate students	Departments not taking graduate students	Total graduate students
Pathology............	39	13	26	78
Pharmacology........	33†	24	9	196
Anatomy............	39	31	8	240
Physiology...........	40	31	9	328
Biochemistry.........	40	35	5	344
Bacteriology.........	40	34	6	516
Total..............	231	168	63	1,702

* Does not include residents.
  † Seven departments are combined with physiology.

finding is probably influenced by the fact that in a number of instances the department of bacteriology in the medical school serves also as a general university department of bacteriology and thus has large numbers of graduate students who plan careers in nonmedical fields such as the teaching of science in secondary school.

The smallest number of candidates for advanced degrees was found in departments of pathology. This circumstance is due to the fact that much of the graduate training in pathology follows graduation from medical school and is conducted by means of internship and residency programs in clinical departments, rather than by means of graduate programs in the other medical basic science departments. Only the students of pathology who are candidates for a graduate degree are included in this section.

About one-fourth of the basic medical science departments in the schools that were visited had no graduate students enrolled at the time of the Survey. In most of the other departments about eight or ten graduate students were doing their major work. In about six of the schools, however, the average number of graduate students per department was several times as great, and in a few departments as many as 50 graduate students were doing their major work.

This extreme variation in numbers represents a similar variation in the concept of graduate education. In many schools which enjoy the oldest and best reputations for graduate work of high quality, the faculty holds the view that a senior member of a department should supervise the work of only one or two graduate students at a time. With this arrangement the graduate student receives a large amount of personal instruction.

In contrast, in a few of the schools—particularly in large tax-supported schools in the Middle West—great emphasis is placed on the courses the graduate students take and the degrees they receive, and many departments have so many graduate students that faculty members hardly know them by name. Since the work arranged for such large numbers of students must be tightly scheduled and formalized, great reliance must be placed upon written tests and grades, and little individual instruction of the student is possible.

Examples of this mass-production approach to graduate education are revealing. In one department of a medical school there were 25 candidates for the Doctor of Philosophy degree in the field. The department was staffed by a professor, an associate professor, and two assistant professors. In another school a department had 52 candidates for the Ph.D. degree. This department was staffed by a professor, five associate professors, and five assistant professors, and the department also gave courses to 180 other graduate students who were taking their major work in some related discipline, as well as courses for medical students.

Obviously the educational experience of graduate students in these very large programs has little to compare with that of graduate students in other institutions who spend three or more years working closely with a master of the subject.

Some of the disciplines, notably biochemistry, apparently attract a large number of able students, who seek graduate degrees in those fields. In most schools, according to the heads of these departments, those students are highly competent and show great promise. Other disciplines, however, are not in such a fortunate position. In many schools, according to the department heads, the caliber of the graduate students they attract is not high and many of them have been refused admission to medical school.

In some schools it is a regular phenomenon for students who have been refused admission directly to gain it by enrolling as a candidate for a graduate degree in one of the medical school departments and transferring to the medical school after obtaining the degree. This represents an unfortunate inversion of an originally sound educational program. At some times in the past—and in occasional instances still— highly competent graduate students, whom the medical school would have been glad to accept on direct application, have been encouraged to complete the medical school program before entering careers in the disciplines of their major interests. The basis for that encouragement was that better orientation could thus be obtained for a career in medical education and research. With this background, a man not only was highly talented but was so dedicated to the discipline of his graduate degree that his effectiveness in that discipline was enhanced. However, when a department is unable to attract such highly competent students and accepts men whom the medical school has refused, an entirely different result ensues. Such a student, having used the graduate program as a means of gaining entrance to medical school through the back door, usually does not return to the department of his graduate degree. Instead, he continues in medicine, a field for which he was not only deemed unpromising but to enter which he was willing to spend two or more years in subterfuge.

Before the Second World War it was common for a promising medical student to drop out of medical school after the first or second year to spend a year or two in the department which attracted his interest, going deeply into the study of that subject in a manner comparable to that of graduate students. This program was followed only by students with special interests whom the faculty considered especially promising. For those students, however, it proved a highly effective educational pattern. Many of the men later returned to fruitful careers in those disciplines, and thus the method proved a means of recruiting able men in the several fields. For those who did not return but continued in clinical medicine, it was also highly effective in enhancing their interest and improving the quality of their clinical work. Indeed many of the most productive men in medicine today followed some variation of this educational pattern.

The department heads reported to the Survey that it is now far less common for promising medical students to follow this practice. Some of them show interest in the subject and a considerable interest in research, but they now tend to complete medical school without interruption and then seek residency or fellowship training in some clinical specialty. Some of the department heads of long experience deplore this tendency, but they reported that they now advise promising young men who have developed a keen interest in research to complete medical school and go into some clinical department. They point out that it is no longer necessary for a young man to forego an opportunity to obtain training in research if he is a physician, and that a man with an M.D. degree has an opportunity for a career either in research and teaching or in practice, whereas a man with a graduate degree alone is limited to a career in teaching and research.

This trend toward the clinical departments is also apparent in the recruitment of younger men to the faculty. According to the information supplied to the Survey, and as described in Chapter 9, "Medical School Departments," clinical departments are now finding it far easier than the medical basic science departments to attract not only financial support, equipment, and facilities for their research, but also the more talented young men.

The proper organization of the course work for graduate students has become a matter of concern to the heads of some medical basic science departments. This problem is obviously much greater in the departments with large numbers of graduate students, but it is also felt in those schools whose graduate programs have long been small in size and high in quality. In many schools it has been customary for the graduate student to take the course for medical students in the field of his major interest. In addition he usually takes several other courses given to medical students in the first two years, supplemented by one or two advanced, highly individualized courses in the field of his own interest. This pattern is sometimes defended on the ground that the courses for medical students should be both elementary and thorough; that the graduate student is headed for a career in the medical basic sciences; and that, therefore, he should be as familiar as possible with the material of importance to a medical student. Two disadvantages of this pattern are apparent.

If the graduate student already has some leaning toward medicine as a career and then completes satisfactorily most of the courses taken by medical students in their first two years, the likelihood of his wanting to change his program and go on through medical school is increased. If he has been successful, the school has little ground on which to forbid his transfer. This is a symptomatic defect and one that is related to the fact that medicine exerts more attraction for some of these students than the field of their stated interest.

The other disadvantage has to do with the selection of the subject matter. The medical student is headed for a career in medicine; his program is crowded, and each of the disciplines deals with a large body of knowledge. For the medical student, therefore, the subject matter must be carefully selected; those principles and facts of most importance to medicine must be included at the expense of other material which, although highly important, is less relevant. But the graduate student is headed for a career in that discipline; his need for those portions of the subject most relevant to medicine is less great and his need for other highly important material is much greater. Thus, a course designed to be as good as possible for the medical student cannot at the same time be as good as possible for the graduate student. If the two groups of students must take the same course, the needs of one must suffer for the sake of the best interests of the other. The subject matter is so great, and the needs of the two groups of students are so different, that a course designed to compromise between the needs of the two is unsatisfactory for either.

The extent to which members of the faculty are concerned about the problems created by the great appeal of the clinical departments and the necessity to improve and redesign the education and training of graduate students in the medical basic science departments varies considerably.

One school has attacked the problem from the point of view of better organization of graduate work for students seeking the Ph.D. degree in one or another of the medical basic sciences. This is one of the strongest and best supported medical schools in the United States with an excellent reputation. The caliber of its students and of its faculty compares favorably with the best in the country, as do its physical facilities. Concern over the problem was real. The chairman of the division of medical sciences stated that the departments in his division had "felt for a long time that course offerings to graduate students could be improved in content, variety, and number," and that for medical students, too, "a careful reassessment of teaching in medical science [was] long overdue, to determine where the burden of facts [could] be reduced and replaced by more emphasis on fundamental principles."

In attacking the problem, one basic assumption adopted was that the design of courses for graduate students should be different from that of courses for medical students. Funds have been made available, therefore, to provide an additional member of the faculty in each of the medical basic science departments, at the academic level of assistant professor. This person has, as his prime responsibility, the organization of an integrated program of work for graduate students, in collaboration with his opposite number in each of the other preclinical departments. A small "pilot" group of students, 20 in number, has been selected to undertake graduate study in this experimental program. The general qualifications of these students is as nearly comparable as possible to those of other graduate students entering at the same time and pursuing the regular curriculum. The present pattern for the other graduate students will continue without change. The faculty members from the various departments responsible for the program are also collaborating in working out courses for the pilot group that are as well designed for the needs of graduate students as they can make them. They are working very closely with the students, with each other, and with the heads of the respective departments. At the completion of their program, the graduate students in the pilot group will be compared with the students in the control group. It is anticipated that it will require three or four years for students in the pilot groups to complete their graduate work and thus permit the experimental program to be evaluated.

It is expected that this experimental program not only will lead to improvement in the teaching of graduate students, but will also prove effective as a means for showing the faculty members of the several departments how to work together more closely and effectively. It is expected also that it will improve the quality of graduate education to such a degree that the medical basic science departments can compete more successfully with the clinical departments for the most talented students. Lastly, and perhaps of most significance, it is expected to lead rapidly to more successful teaching of medical students in the fields of the medical basic sciences.

In the other school the point chosen for attack is the relation between the sciences of anatomy, biochemistry, physiology, pharmacology, and bacteriology to the basic sciences of chemistry, biology, and physics. This is a small, compact institution of high quality. The caliber of its students, faculty, and physical facilities is also excellent. Concern over these problems has led to a program aimed at their solution.

The basic assumption in this instance is that, through being in the medical school, the departments have become too remote from basic research and graduate teaching in the broader fields of biology, chemistry, and physics. Although the university is small and the medical school is on the university campus, contact between the medical school departments and the other scientific departments of the university is not great. The departments in the medical school are burdened with teaching of medical students and a few graduate students. In the same physical plant the faculty members of the clinical departments constitute the staff of the university hospital. They have access to patients for study, and they have financial support, facilities, and equipment for research on problems closely related to the patient that are at least as good as those of the medical basic science departments. The latter departments have some time, support, and facilities for research, but in the institution as a whole the university hospital and its patients operate as a strong magnet pulling the interest of students and faculty toward the problems of the patient.

The plan under way is to construct a wing to the building that will immediately adjoin the medical basic science departments of the medical school. This wing is to house the graduate departments of physics, biology, and chemistry. The new wing is to be equipped with elaborate instruments necessary in basic research, which will be available to the faculty in the graduate departments of physics, biology, and chemistry and the medical basic science departments of the medical school, as well as to the graduate students in all those departments.

It is hoped that this arrangement will counterbalance the strong attraction of the patient and the clinical departments by creating a research environment in which there is opportunity to pursue knowledge for its own sake as well as for the faculty to remain in close contact with graduate students in the basic sciences. A young man developing an interest in one of the preclinical fields might then be attracted toward clinical investigation, but might also be strongly attracted toward more basic research. And the faculty in the preclinical departments will have the advantage of intimate contact with men in the fields of physics, biology, and chemistry, as well as with the clinical investigators of the clinical departments, thus bringing their intellectual position into better balance. In this way, it is expected, the opportunities for basic research will be improved without impairing the opportunities which now exist for research in the clinical departments.

It is beyond the scope of a Survey to measure the full accomplishment of either of these imaginative and courageous attacks on the problems. In any event both programs, which deal with some of the most important long-range problems in medical education, are now in their initial stages. For this reason the pilot programs described will be observed with care and interest by other schools which must give thought to the problems and search for their solution.

CONCLUSIONS

1. Graduate education in the medical basic sciences is a primary means of educating future faculty members. Working with the graduate students vitalizes the department and its research.
2. In many medical school departments these programs are of very high quality. In others, however, so many students are enrolled for their major and minor work that the quality of all the work of the department suffers.

3. Some departments are not successful in attracting talented young men and enroll students of inferior quality.

4. Many departments enroll too few graduate students to supply the needs for faculty members.

5. Students unable to gain admission directly enroll in graduate programs with the hope that they may later transfer or gain admission to medical school.

6. Departments of biochemistry and bacteriology apparently attract an adequate number of highly competent students. The other medical basic science departments are having difficulty competing with clinical departments and other fields for talented young men.

7. A certain number of medical students drop out of medical school at the end of the first or second year to obtain graduate education in some department of the school. This program greatly enhances the training of the talented young men suited to it, whether their later careers lie in that department or in some clinical field. Unfortunately this practice is becoming less common.

8. It is a frequent practice for graduate students to take some of the same courses as medical students.

9. The medical schools do not keep complete data on their graduate educational activities. Nevertheless, it is apparent that graduate programs are growing in size, complexity, and cost.

10. The opportunities for careers in industry and research institutes have apparently contributed to the increase in the number of graduate students in the last decade.

11. Graduate degrees in clinical subjects are awarded by a few medical schools, but they usually have little in common with graduate degrees in medical basic science departments and amount to a means of formalizing the internship and residency training.

RECOMMENDATIONS

1. Medical schools should keep more completely informed of the load of graduate education carried by their faculties.

2. Medical schools should continue to conduct graduate education in the medical basic science departments as a primary means of enhancing the work of these departments in the present and preparing men to conduct this work in the future. They should, however, take

every precaution to prevent these aims from being thwarted by over-crowding with large numbers of graduate students and the resultant low quality of programs.

4. Medical schools should not accept as transfers from graduate programs students whom they would not accept on direct application.

5. Medical schools should study carefully the fact that some of their departments are not now successful in the competition for talented young men, and should take thoughtfully considered steps to correct the situation. One means of correcting it is to improve the graduate programs in the departments concerned.

6. The size and character of the graduate program in any department should be such as to enhance the quality of the program for medical students.

7. The awarding of graduate degrees merely for training in clinical departments should be discontinued.

8. The universities and the general public should be aware of the large size and the high quality of the graduate programs in the medical schools when they consider the cost of operating the medical school.

16 POSTGRADUATE PROGRAMS

In medicine, courses that are designed for physicians who have completed their formal training are known as postgraduate programs. The programs are organized by medical schools as part of their traditional obligation for the continuing education of physicians. Courses may be part-time or full-time, and may last a day or two or as long as nine months. They usually do not lead to a degree. Training of interns and residents is not included in this discussion of postgraduate education.

Local, county, and state medical societies, and other special organizations also conduct extension courses for physicians, sometimes sponsoring programs jointly with medical schools or borrowing faculty members.

History shows that the need for extension courses dates from the days when America had no medical schools. Students were trained by the only qualified physicians among the early settlers, who had been educated in Europe. Many young physicians felt the need to supplement the knowledge obtained from their preceptors, and those who were able to do so journeyed to the medical centers of Europe. On their return with valuable medical knowledge, some of them formed into groups in centers of population to offer instruction to less fortunate physicians in such subjects as anatomy, materia medica, and midwifery. This group teaching and sharing of knowledge was the forerunner of today's postgraduate programs.

Some of the oldest medical schools and postgraduate medical schools in America today are direct descendants from the early private teaching groups. In 1910, according to Flexner, 13 well-established postgraduate schools functioned as self-sustaining, independent organizations. New York City and Chicago each had four, Washington had two, and Philadelphia, Kansas City, and New Orleans each had one. In addition a number of medical schools offered lectures and short courses for physicians, on an informal basis.

In the twentieth century the development of internship and residency training largely replaced postgraduate medical education. However, with the establishment of the specialty boards with their individual requirements, many physicians preparing for board examinations seek postgraduate courses either of their own volition or because certain medical basic science courses are required by a particular specialty. After the Second World War there was a great increase in the demand by physicians for postgraduate work. Returning veterans felt the need for refresher courses on returning to civilian medical practice. The practicing physician also feels the need for this type of education because of the rapid scientific advances in medicine.

Deans and heads of departments, directors of postgraduate programs, presidents of universities, secretaries of state medical societies, and physicians taking the courses all agreed that postgraduate education was necessary.

ORGANIZATION

Postgraduate education can be either informal or formal in its organization. The informal type includes the day-by-day education of physicians, who attend conferences, seminars, clinics, and ward rounds with no formally planned program of instruction.

The organization of formal postgraduate education falls into three patterns. The first and most highly organized is conducted in the postgraduate medical school. The two such schools studied have their own deans, budgets, and faculties although medical school faculty members may be used by them. The next pattern is that in which the medical school appoints an "assistant dean in charge of" or a "director of" postgraduate medical education. This individual is responsible for organization of courses, acceptance of students, and selection of medical school faculty members to give instruction. In the third type the dean and faculty of the medical school design and carry out programs of postgraduate education. In the last two types costs are borne as a rule by the medical school.

All three of these forms of organized postgraduate teaching may cooperate with city, county, or state medical societies and health departments in designing and giving medical educational programs. The larger part of the cost of these programs may be borne by the outside agencies or by the medical school.

TYPES OF POSTGRADUATE COURSES

Postgraduate courses, designed to meet the needs of practicing physicians, vary greatly in duration, in subject matter, in frequency, and in location. Some courses are designed for physicians who can leave their practices long enough for an "in-residence" course at the medical school; others are designed for those who find it difficult to leave their practices.

In-Residence Courses

In-residence courses may be of the short refresher type lasting a few days, or the larger type lasting as many as nine months.

Refresher Courses. Refresher courses are usually conducted by clinical departments, although occasionally members of the medical basic science faculties participate. Some type of refresher course was offered during the academic year 1949–50 by 31 of the 41 schools visited during the Survey. One tax-supported medical school conducted 22 courses during the year, each lasting three days to two weeks. The faculty of this school considered a three-day course with a tuition fee of $20 the most effective.

Longer Courses. Another type of in-residence course requires the full time of postgraduate students for periods of two to nine months. Most of these courses, which schools recommend as preparation for specialty board examinations, include a basic science review, clinical lectures, demonstrations, and conferences.

Many medical schools offered programs of this type to meet the need for refresher courses of physicians returning from service in the Second World War, but the demand for courses of this length appears to have subsided.

Extension Courses

Courses are also designed for physicians at some distance from the medical school who cannot leave their practices. For this group some medical schools have organized courses which are given in places more easily accessible to the practicing physician.

The programs may be organized at the request of county medical societies or other medical groups. The courses, which members of the faculty may conduct individually, in teams, or in cooperation with leading physicians in practice, include lectures, demonstration clinics, or consultation services.

The programs may be sponsored by the medical school alone, or in cooperation with medical societies, state departments of health, or voluntary agencies. The Academy of General Practice deserves mention, since it has increased the demand for postgraduate courses by its requirement that all its members spend a certain amount of time annually in organized postgraduate programs.

EXAMPLES OF PROGRAMS

The following examples of courses encountered during the Survey illustrate some of the variations in sponsorship and fees, and some of the adaptations to meet various needs.

One school, over a period of eight years, had instituted five different types of courses of varying duration in an attempt to meet the needs of local physicians. All but one had been abandoned. A course of $1\frac{1}{2}$ days duration had met with the greatest success. At the time of the Survey the school was conducting a series of short courses in cooperation with the state medical society and the Academy of General Practice. In 1949–50, 700 of the state's 2,600 physicians attended these courses. This registration surpassed that of any courses the school had previously offered. The school received no compensation for the time and services of its faculty members.

In another school the program organized by the state medical society and conducted by the medical school consisted of a series of six courses, four days in length, held at hotels in cities throughout the state. Teams composed of a faculty member and a practicing physician gave the courses, receiving honoraria of $50 a day and expenses. Twenty-five per cent of the physicians in the state attended these courses in 1949–50. At the time of the Survey plans were under way for changing to a less didactic form of instruction, in which clinics were to be held in hospitals with the hope of increasing the value of the courses and the attendance of physicians.

Another program, organized by a committee whose members represented the state department of health, the state medical society, and faculties of the medical schools in the state, consisted of four courses each year conducted at 12 to 15 centers in the state. Instruction was designed to meet regional needs as shown by requests of physicians or by study of the vital statistics of the state. Each group contributed to the support of the program, and there were no fees for instruction. The medical schools supplied 90 per cent of the instructors, who were paid $40 a day with no travel allowance. Over 1,000 physicians attended these courses in 1948–49.

This same committee on postgraduate education supervised the program of the annual meeting of the state medical society and gave a $3\frac{1}{2}$-day postgraduate institute conducted by eight faculty members and four nonfaculty physicians. One thousand nine hundred physicians registered for the institute in 1948–49 and received credit toward requirements of the Academy of General Practice. The medical schools received no compensation for the time and services of faculty members, who had to be absent from the schools a week or more.

MAGNITUDE OF POSTGRADUATE EDUCATION

It was impossible to determine accurately the magnitude of postgraduate activities as the schools seldom keep complete records of enrollments.[1] The deans of 26 medical schools gave data for the year

Table 51. TOTAL POSTGRADUATE STUDENT ENROLLMENT AT 26 MEDICAL SCHOOLS, 1948–49, AS REPORTED BY THE DEPARTMENTS, THE DEANS, AND THE COUNCIL ON MEDICAL EDUCATION AND HOSPITALS OF THE AMERICAN MEDICAL ASSOCIATION

	Departments' *figures*	*Deans'* *figures*	*Council's* *figures*
Basic science departments.....	3,638	Not obtained	990
Clinical departments..........	11,093	Not obtained	10,513
Total all departments.......	14,731	15,014	11,503

1948–49. This information did not agree with that given by the department heads or with the figures published by the Council on Medical Education and Hospitals (Table 51). Discrepancies are probably due

[1] It is of interest to note, however, that, according to the figures reported to the Council on Medical Education and Hospitals of the American Medical Association, a total of 65,935 of the nation's physicians attended postgraduate courses during the 1951–52 academic year. [ANDERSON, D. G., F. R. MANLOVE, and ANNE TIPNER, Medical Education in the United States and Canada, *Journal of the American Medical Association*, Vol. 150, p. 130 (Sept. 13), 1952.]

to multiple registrations in different courses by the same student. However, most deans stated that careful registration and attendance records were not kept for extension courses. Enrollment information was available from 15 of the 41 schools visited, which indicated the growth of postgraduate education from the year 1939–40 through 1948–49. In these schools the number of postgraduate students rose from 2,431 to 5,169 in the nine-year period—an increase of 113 per cent (Table 52). Five of these schools had no postgraduate programs in 1939–40.

Table 52. INCREASE IN SIZE OF POSTGRADUATE ACTIVITY AS INDICATED BY POSTGRADUATE ENROLLMENTS AT 15 MEDICAL SCHOOLS, 1939–40 AND 1948–49

	Postgraduate enrollment	
	1939–40	1948–49
	0	474
	0	75
	0	136
	0	344
	0	80
Total 5 schools......................	0	1,109
	55	168
	70	70
	292	352
	1,392	2,097
	200	823
	44	247
	4	24
	185	100
	178	112
	11	67
Total 10 schools......................	2,431	4,060
Total 15 schools......................	2,431	5,169
Increase, 1948–49 over 1939–40..........	....	113%

According to the figures given by department heads in medical basic sciences, physiology had the largest enrollment with pathology second and anatomy third. In clinical departments, medicine had the largest enrollment, followed by pediatrics, psychiatry, and surgery.[2]

[2] See Appendix 5, Table 59, for departmental enrollment figures for 26 schools in 1948–49.

FINANCES

Fifty-seven medical schools supplied financial data on postgraduate programs for the fiscal years 1940–41, 1947–48, and 1950–51. Many schools which conducted such programs on an informal basis during those years were not able to report the expenditures for them. The number of schools reporting such expenditures and the total amount they spent rose from $385,694 spent by eight schools in 1941 to $1,436,000 spent by 23 schools in 1948. During the next three years the number of schools with postgraduate programs increased from 23 to 29, but the amount spent on them declined from $1,436,000 to $1,074,000. A large part of the total for each of the three fiscal years was spent by one school with an unusually large program, which cost $340,243 in 1941, $600,849 in 1948, and $523,849 in 1951. The decline in expenditures by all schools from 1948 to 1951 undoubtedly shows that the demand for postgraduate programs created by physicians returning from military service passed its peak.

Income for postgraduate courses is derived from tuition fees paid by students, appropriations made by state legislatures, subsidies paid by medical societies and public health departments, or grants from foundations. A number of medical schools charge no fees for postgraduate courses while others make nominal charges. A typical tuition-fee schedule is $5 for a course of one day, $20 for a three-day course, $35 for a week, and $50 to $100 for a month of instruction.

Very little effort has been made by medical schools to determine the actual cost of postgraduate programs. Only one school was found in which a real effort had been made to estimate the cost of giving these courses and where adequate tuition was charged to meet such cost. The faculty assumed that physicians who wanted good courses would be willing to pay for them. The assumption was correct as there was no falling off of attendance.

Under the present system of financing postgraduate education, the medical school absorbs many indirect costs. Out of its general funds it provides administrative supervision, office and teaching space, clinical material, and the services of its faculty. Although individual faculty members frequently receive honoraria, the only benefit to the medical school is improvement of faculty incomes. Without accurate knowledge of total costs, it is impossible to determine how nearly the funds from tuition, medical societies, and foundations meet such costs, and what portion is taken from the medical school budget.

THE FACULTY

The deans of 26 medical schools reported that during the year 1948–49 their faculties gave instruction, in one form or another, to more than 15,000 postgraduate students. This figure is nearly twice the number (8,390) of undergraduate medical students taught in the same schools in the same year. Not all faculty members participated in postgraduate teaching, but in every medical school included in the Survey some full-time or part-time faculty members participated.

The great number of extension courses places a heavy strain on the faculty members. In some instances they travel as much as 300 miles and neglect undergraduate medical students for periods of a week at a time in order to give lectures and clinics in postgraduate programs. Added to the fatigue incidental to this obligation is the time that must be spent in preparation. In only a few schools studied were replacements provided for faculty members absent on postgraduate teaching assignments.

Medical school faculties in general are understaffed. If, in addition, a faculty loses 226 undergraduate teaching days and travels 25,000 miles in a year—as reported by one school—both faculty and students suffer. The quality of undergraduate medical education cannot be properly maintained where postgraduate education makes such demands on present-day faculties.

The Commission on Graduate Medical Education,[3] in 1940, warned against the dilution of undergraduate teaching, and recommended additional faculty for postgraduate teaching in order to avoid weakening the program for medical students. Undergraduate and postgraduate teaching compete for funds, for the time of faculty members, for clinical material, and for space and equipment in the medical school, and often the medical student comes off second best.

Faculty members are often anxious to participate in postgraduate programs because of the additional remuneration they receive as a supplement to their relatively small salaries.

[3] "Graduate Medical Education, Report of the Commission on Graduate Medical Education," Chicago, University of Chicago Press, 1940.

POSTGRADUATE MEDICAL SCHOOLS

Two separately organized postgraduate medical schools were visited, and the deans, faculties, and students were interviewed.

The dean of one school stated that its program was directed primarily toward the medical basic sciences in preparation for board certification. In addition a short refresher course was given in the fall of each year. As the demand for courses in preparation for board certification had decreased, the school had been accepting increasing numbers of foreign students, who wished to supplement their education and training to meet requirements of medicine in this country or to improve their practice of medicine in their native countries. The second school had a program of internship and residency training in the specialties, carried on in its own postgraduate hospital and in a number of associated hospitals. It also gave short and long clinical demonstration courses for practicing physicians.

The purposes and needs for such courses were brought out by interviews with faculties and students. Faculty members felt that separate postgraduate medical schools served a need in preparing physicians for the specialties and for training practicing physicians in new diagnostic and therapeutic techniques as well as correcting and supplementing educational and training defects.

Students said that they enrolled in these postgraduate schools in an effort to improve their medical background. Some felt that their courses in medical basic sciences in medical school had been inadequate in preparing them for specialties. The overwhelming majority of these men stated that the postgraduate courses gave them stimulation and time to study that had been lacking in their internships and residencies. During this period they had had a great deal of practical work on a large number of patients with little supervision and no time for study. Whatever the motivation for taking these courses, none of the physicians felt he could continue his own education through daily reading and study.

EVALUATION OF EFFECTIVENESS

The vast majority of medical schools offering postgraduate courses evaluate their effectiveness on the basis of attendance and requests for more courses. Little or no attempt is made to evaluate the student's accomplishments or his understanding of the material presented.

CONCLUSIONS

1. Postgraduate medical education is of growing importance in the continuing education of the physician.
2. The demand for postgraduate education is due to
    a. Demands of practicing physicians for instruction in new techniques and application of new scientific knowledge in medicine.
    b. Weaknesses in internship and residency training programs.
    c. Need for courses in medical basic sciences in preparation for specialty board examinations.
    d. Poor instruction in some medical schools.
    e. The trend for foreign physicians to seek training in this country.
3. Programs are sponsored and organized by the medical schools or in cooperation with city, county, or state medical societies and health departments. Foundations have helped promote and support such programs in medical schools.
4. A variety of courses have been offered, many of which lack sound educational design.
5. Demands on the medical school and its faculty for postgraduate instruction have become so great as to jeopardize undergraduate education in some schools.
6. Costs of postgraduate programs have not been accurately determined. They are borne in part or entirely by the medical school budget.
7. Faculties have not been increased in proportion to teaching loads imposed by postgraduate programs.
8. Little or no attempt has been made to evaluate the effectiveness of teaching or the student's accomplishments.

RECOMMENDATIONS

1. Four major types of courses should be emphasized.
    a. Informal weekly conferences and clinics at teaching hospitals or large local hospitals, in which physicians participate and their continuing education thus becomes routine.
    b. Short courses given once or twice a year at the medical school or

a hospital center for the physician practicing at a distance from the teaching centers. Courses should be designed to cover the application and techniques of new knowledge in the study and treatment of disease.

c. Courses in the medical basic sciences designed to meet requirements of specialties.

d. Courses for foreign physicians, which to a limited extent may be given by the medical school, but the postgraduate medical school should be much better adapted to give them.

2. Courses should be designed so that students actively participate and so that their accomplishments and understanding of the courses may be evaluated.

3. Medical school faculties should be increased to meet the present demands of postgraduate education.

4. Costs of postgraduate education should be determined. At present it is impossible to know to what extent tuition charges, contributions of medical societies and foundations, or other sources of income meet these costs.

5. Undergraduate medical school instruction and internship and residency training should be improved. This would reduce the demands for postgraduate education.

Part VII

A SUMMING UP

17 A SUMMING UP

The future of medical education will be decided, not by a survey, but by the public and the future leaders of medical schools and universities. Spread across the country in the medical schools are men who have given thought to most of the questions described in this volume. Because for them the principles at the heart of true medical education exist for all time, they have not needed a survey to help them to set their course.

When a number of such men are found on one faculty, a spirit of common purposes permeates all the medical school and the hospital— the students, the interns, the residents, and all the other members of the health team. Such institutions stand out above all the others for the quality of the educational opportunity that they offer. They are doing their job in medical education often in spite of inadequate facilities and in spite of pressures from all sides that threaten to dilute their effectiveness. In many other schools, a single department is outstanding for its vitality because of the qualities engendered by one faculty member. These men are developing in their students the leadership for the future of medicine. Their spirit, their vision, and their intellectual vigor must be nurtured. They must be allowed to grow, and their students with them.

Clear and well-directed thinking was never more important in medical education than it is today. Certain broad questions are in urgent need of an answer before the plans and policies for the future of the medical schools can be determined.

The first question is one of definition: *What is medical education?* The facts found by the Survey shed a new light on medical education as it is generally understood. The term is used freely by educators and the public alike to refer to the instruction leading to a degree of Doctor

317

of Medicine, with little regard to the various other educational and training programs carried on by the medical schools. In practice, medical education is becoming virtually all-inclusive, embracing or participating in the education and training of practically all types of ancillary health personnel essential to the present-day health team. Many universities include in the teaching program of their medical schools the instruction of students in no way directly related to the field of health. There is no consensus as to what groups of students belong in medical education. Are all the members of the large health team to be included?

At the same time the term "education" is used to include what is more accurately defined as training. Although education may include some training and training may offer some true educational opportunities, the two terms are not synonymous. Education should be concerned with teaching and study for the purpose of understanding; training has to do with habits and technics. How much responsibility for training should a professional school assume?

The proper role of the medical school in the education and training of health personnel must be considered in relation to the responsibility of the colleges, hospitals, and other schools and institutions for such students. In the present trend, the medical school is assuming part of the roles of all those institutions, and losing its effectiveness as a school for instruction in a learned profession. If the trend continues, radical reconstruction will be needed of the medical school, its faculties, and its departments.

In addition to assuming responsibilities in these various areas of education and training, the schools have been under increasing pressure to enlarge their enrollments of medical students. In order to meet the demands of the country for more physicians, enrollments of undergraduate medical students have been increased from 21,379 in 1940–41 to 26,186 in 1950–51, and further expansion is planned.[1]

Study of schools revealed that in most instances finances, facilities, and faculties are overtaxed by all the activities that they have assumed or that have been thrust upon them. The quality of instruction has deteriorated in some schools because of enlarged classes of both medical and nonmedical students.

---

[1] Enrollment in 1951–52 totaled 27,076. [ANDERSON, D. G., F. R. MANLOVE, and ANNE TIPNER, Medical Education in the United States and Canada, *Journal of the American Medical Association*, Vol. 150, p. 109 (Sept. 13), 1952.]

Ideally, students enrolled in any one class in a medical school should not exceed the number who can have contact with the faculty members of professorial rank. Time and the number of students are the limiting factors that determine the intimacy and frequency of contact between the professor and the students. The principle of close student-teacher contact is fundamental to all high-quality education. The administrators and faculties of many schools, believing firmly in this principle, have strongly resisted pressures to enlarge their classes. More than two-thirds of the medical schools admit classes under 100, and many educators feel that a class of more than this number exceeds the ability of the departmental faculties to become acquainted with the student and to help him with his individual needs.

If more physicians are demanded, new medical schools should be established. To expand the classes of existing medical schools would result in mass production of physicians and make impossible the application of the most fundamental of all educational principles.

The development of medical schools into centers for medical research and service in which the education of the medical student is often of secondary importance poses a question that concerns both focus and boundaries. *What is a medical school and what are its responsibilities?*

Although research is vital to a medical school, should it be the major goal and receive the greatest financial support? What type of research is the medical school best qualified to pursue? The present methods of financing research tend to lead to its isolation in special institutes, and to a certain degree of separation from the educational activities of the schools. Concern over the dangers of project research is growing. Acceptance of grants for specific research projects, the needs for which are decided by the granting agencies, leads to loss of freedom—freedom of the school to choose projects to strengthen its educational program, and of the individual to seek new knowledge unhampered by periodic deadlines for evaluation by the outside grantor.

What of the role of the medical school in providing medical care and professional medical service? The role of the medical school in a medical center serving large population areas has been delineated and promoted, but the effects on the medical school per se have rarely been analyzed. Too commonly a medical school is judged by its size—by the magnitude and multiplicity of its activities rather than by the quality of its instruction to the medical student. The trend has been encouraged by those philanthropic agencies which actively exert pressure on the schools to expand their social and welfare functions.

Many leaders of medical education today are busily engaged in building up large empires which serve as welfare and semicharitable institutions, steadily spreading their influence and control over many segments of health care. Should this be the role of an educational institution? And should these institutions assume responsibility for professional medical care on a national scale?

Such questions cannot be answered with authority by a survey. Nevertheless, these expansionist policies would seem unwise when they are judged in relation to the present facilities and resources of the medical schools. If the assumption of these roles is to be part of the responsibilities of the medical schools, those policies should be clearly stated and presented to the public for its support. Six or seven medical schools were encountered in which thoughtful leaders had resisted the pressure for expansion in the field of medical service.

The financial affairs of the medical schools cannot be put in order until these primary issues are faced realistically. Medical education must first be defined, and the responsibilities of the schools must be clearly stated.

It is time to examine carefully the activities of the medical schools and to weigh their relative values in order to put them in proper balance for the future. The public recognition and approval given to the medical schools and medical education because of their great contributions to human welfare have tended to make medical educators less critical of themselves and their work. In addition the schools have been expanded so rapidly that their greatest worry in the last decade has been with finances. It is true that many schools are vigorously attacking problems dealing with the mechanics of admitting students, with expanding enrollments, with the correlation and integration of complex departmental organization, with defects of instruction in ambulatory-patient care, and with the desirability of a broader approach to the patient. But far more important are the problems arising from the adoption of broad and poorly defined policies and the assumption of increasing responsibilities without regard to their effect on the primary purpose of the school. Philosophers have pointed out that when size transcends quality that is the beginning of decadence.

As the medical schools expand into medical centers, they assume the shape of big business, and in their administration a knowledge of business, finance, and administration becomes of greater importance than knowledge of education. Far too frequently, major policies are decided and programs are undertaken on the basis of financial expediency, public relations, or to make a direct contribution to social welfare, without due regard to the effect on the educational opportunity of the students.

The type of man attracted by faculty positions and selected by the schools reflects the objectives and relative values placed upon the various activities. In the selection of faculty members, interest and ability in research have been the dominant qualification; teaching experience and ability have been secondary, and often clinical ability and interest in patients have come last. With the growth of individual departments into half-million dollar enterprises, administrative ability is of increasing importance as a qualification of department heads.

A complaint common to all medical schools is the inability to attract young men into the medical basic science fields because salaries are inadequate to meet the competition of industry, government, and research institutes. These reasons are only part of the cause. What has not been realized is that those departments are in direct competition with the rapidly growing clinical departments, which not only are applying the medical basic sciences at the bedside but are also carrying on fundamental research in those fields.

In the establishment and organization of the departments and subdepartments of the medical schools, no definite principles or policies appear to be followed. Departments have been established on the basis of techniques, special fields of interest, and methods of therapy, and not infrequently they owe their existence to one person's personality and energy. Although this method appears haphazard, it does give the schools great flexibility. But it has led to such a multiplicity of departments and subdepartments that the effective utilization of all of them in the educational program of the medical student has become practically impossible. It is imperative to decide what the primary purpose of a department is to be and which of the units are to carry on the major functions in undergraduate medical education. Departments for these latter functions should be established on the basis of broad recognized fields of knowledge. Specialized divisions should function primarily in specialty training of residents and postgraduate students and in the field of specialty service.

Perhaps of the greatest importance is the question of the future of medical basic science instruction. In the college preparation of prospective medical students there is a growing tendency to deemphasize the amount of basic science instruction and to emphasize the humanities for the purpose of making the student a more broadly educated man.

In the medical schools social and economic studies are being introduced in the first and second years of the curriculum. The clinical departments are extending their teaching into the first two years of medical school—the so called "preclinical" or "medical basic science" years—and the medical basic science faculties are being urged to teach their subjects from a more practical, clinical point of view.

If the basic science teaching in college is reduced and the medical basic science departments in medical school are to orient their instruction toward the immediate application of their fields of knowledge to medicine today, what of tomorrow? No one can tell today what facts from these sciences will be applicable tomorrow. The graduates of the medical schools may be poorly prepared to understand and apply those advances of science which will be applicable to medicine in the future.

This question demands thought in universities and medical schools. It will be necessary to decide whether medical basic science instruction should be more closely allied to university basic science departments, or whether more responsibility should be given to the clinical departments for instruction in these fields.

Scientific knowledge is rapidly expanding. With the relatively long periods of hospital training now served by most medical school graduates, an increase in the medical school curriculum for the purpose of including more basic science instruction would be neither feasible nor desirable unless the internship year were included and replaced a large part of the present clinical clerkship. Before any such plan is considered, the faculties of the schools should give thought to strengthening the four-year period by means of more emphasis on the fundamental sciences and to their careful application in the study of a limited number of patients, leaving more of the experience and the technics in their application to be obtained in the periods of hospital training.

Such an approach might be in conflict with the policies of those schools which state the objective of undergraduate education and internship training to be the preparation for general practice. It would decrease the amount of training and experience in the undergraduate period and allow only the internship for practical training. This is inadequate preparation for general practice.

General practice, however, is but vaguely defined. It generally includes surgery, medicine, pediatrics, obstetrics, and psychiatry; but what phases of these subjects are to be included and how much training is to be given have not been clearly stated.

If the general practitioner is to hold the respect of his colleagues and of the public, he must be competent in certain fields. The public demand for care by specialists has been steadily growing and, unless the general practitioner is to become only a clearing station—as is the case in England—he must have skill in diagnosis and ability and competence in the care of certain of the commoner human illnesses. Training for the type of general practice that may be envisioned for the future should be such as is now given to the internist, including pediatrics and psychiatry, and perhaps also some obstetrics and minor surgery. The training must be thoughtfully designed to develop competence in diagnosis and real skill in treatment. The student being trained for general practice should be given responsibility during his training period; he should not work as a subordinate in a system of residency training designed for the training of specialists.

To the majority of medical schools, the curriculum is a matter of vital concern. Shifts and changes are constantly being made in the content and duration of the whole and of its separate parts. New programs are frequently tried, and it is claimed that they are experiments. Where, however, is there evidence of a planned, scientific approach, in which the results are measured by their effect upon the student and in comparison with carefully established controls? Little or no evidence is to be found throughout the country of real experiments in medical education, even though experimentation and research are part of the armamentarium of medicine. Even when circumstances bring about a situation that would permit of a real experiment, with ready-made controls, the experiment is not carried out. In one school, for instance, in which a greatly increased enrollment had necessitated division of the class for teaching in two sections, the faculty and the dean rejected a proposal made by the professor of pathology that a different teaching method be utilized in one of the two sections of the class and that the results be measured and compared. The faculty should ask itself how effective a new program or a change in the curriculum really is. There is a real need for such experiments in medical education and in the study and testing of teaching methods. Too much reliance is placed on tradition and authority.

The concepts of education and teaching in the medical schools vary in the extreme. Some of the large schools are still giving most of their instruction by didactic methods; a few have only recently introduced true clerkship teaching, and it is still not well understood by some of the faculty members. Many schools rely upon voluntary clinical faculty members for almost all the clinical instruction, and are just beginning to employ a few men on a salaried or a part-time basis. In medical education, acceptance and adoption of new developments and concepts take time. In fact, the educational methods in use by today's medical schools run the full gamut of the educational ideas of the past 25 years, and the educational opportunities offered to the students by some of the schools are of a lesser quality than those offered by others a quarter of a century ago. Some of the excellent recommendations contained in the Flexner report of 1910 have not yet been carried out.

The responsibility of the medical schools in the training of physicians after graduation from medical school is vaguely defined and performed, and in this area, again, education and training are confused. At present, internship and residency training is primarily the responsibility of hospitals, although medical schools, through their clinical faculties, are assuming roles of increasing importance by expanding such programs. *Should the medical schools assume responsibility for all internship and all residency and specialty training?*

Some medical educators advocate that internships be under the control of the medical school. An internship as well as an M.D. degree has become a requirement, either by law or by custom, for obtaining a license to practice medicine. Responsibility for the design of the internship program is now divided among the state licensing boards, the Council on Medical Education and Hospitals of the American Medical Association, the medical schools, and the hospitals. In reality, internships are primarily service and training periods and, all too frequently, even in the university teaching hospitals, their educational opportunities are extremely variable and sometimes can hardly be found. There is a trend to increase the amount of training in the formal medical school curriculum. If it continues, there will be little need for the internship, except for the interns' services to hospitals and to practicing physicians.

Although a large proportion of the residency training is carried on by the teaching hospitals of medical schools, the demand of young physicians for specialized training and the demand of the hospitals for their services have increased the number of programs in nonteaching hospitals since the Second World War. In duration and content, the programs are to a large extent determined by agencies outside the medical school; the schools themselves have not been sufficiently closely knit, or demonstrated sufficient strength, to assume the authority and the responsibility for setting their own standards in this area. Today, even in some of the university hospitals, residency programs are designed to provide routine professional services for the hospital rather than for the primary purpose of training the young physician; and in hospitals only loosely affiliated with a medical school, they are often designed primarily for the improvement of the professional care of patients.

The medical schools and their teaching hospitals took the leadership in establishing the residency system of training; they should reestablish this leadership. And they should make sure that the training in their hospitals is clearly defined as to purpose and educational opportunity, and that it is conducted accordingly. The young men in such programs should be permitted to advance as rapidly as their individual abilities will allow. Clear distinction should be made between salaried staff officers employed to provide services, and interns and residents serving in programs in which education is the primary objective.

The patient is an inseparable part of the teaching of medicine, and in medical education his cooperation is essential. Through tradition, only one segment of the population—the charity or welfare patients—has cooperated with the medical schools in their teaching and in the study of human disease. Patients with private means have in the past sought the benefits of the teaching hospitals without being included to any extent in the teaching activities. The fact that they are private or semi-private patients has denied them the advantages of the teamwork on the teaching wards. Social and economic trends will no longer allow of such distinction, and it has become imperative that the teaching hospitals and the medical schools enlist the cooperation of private, semi-private, or insured patients in their teaching and research programs.

Certain phases of patient care in teaching hospitals require analysis and improvement. In the search for knowledge concerning disease, the medical schools have focused their attention on smaller and smaller segments of the human body, and medical knowledge has become divided into more and more specialized fields. As has been stated previously, teachers are often selected because of their knowledge and research ability in special fields. The professional responsibility for patients is often divided among a team of specialists and a house staff. Thus there develops such fragmentation of the patient that often he is described in the teaching hospital as a "case," or is referred to by the name of a disease. The trend is antagonistic to the impression the student should be given that patients—not diseases—are the subject matter of medicine. The impression is reinforced by the numbers of clinics for the study of special diseases that are found in outpatient departments of medical schools and hospitals.

The trend has been recognized, and in attempts to counteract it, and to focus the attention of the student on the patients and their environment, the schools have developed family and home-care programs, psychosomatic clinics, preceptorships, and other plans intended to correct the concept of the patient in the student's mind. Thus side by side exist factors which give rise to fragmentation and factors which attempt to correct it. The dilemma can be partially resolved by maintaining special clinics for the sole purpose of clinical research, and increasing the use of general clinics for the care of patients with all types of diseases and for the teaching of students.

*   *   *

The medical student should be the focus in all the activities and policies of the medical school. *What are the effects of present educational and training programs on this student?* To the Survey, this was the most important question in its study.

The young physician of today, before entering the practice of medicine, has spent three or four years in college, four years in a medical school, two to five years in hospital training, and 21 or more months in the armed forces. His income may have totaled $8,000 to $10,000 in the four- to eight-year period after graduation from medical school, with most of these funds accruing to him during military service. Marriage has been possible if he has had private funds or has received veterans' benefits, or if his wife has been willing and able to add to the family income by holding a job. He has been told that he owes a financial debt to society for his educational and training opportunities. With the payment, out of Federal tax monies, of the tuition of the majority of students because they are veterans, the young physician has been led into a philosophy of dependence upon others for the financing of his career without acceptance of this responsibility as his own.

The physician, regimented to a degree, and conditioned to living in a protective, institutional environment, at the age of thirty to thirty-two must now enter practice. He hesitates to practice medicine in a small community with limited hospital and clinical facilities but prefers to stay in a larger city or within the shadow of a medical center where the facilities and consultations to which he has become accustomed are readily available.

If he is successful in practice, his income soon increases and he can afford the home, family, and car to which he has been looking forward. For the first time in his life he has achieved a degree of financial security. Occasionally he may become avaricious and be accused by the public for this tendency. As a member of organized medicine he is criticized for defending his independence and financial security. At times his ethics are questioned as well as his interest in patients as people. There is a constant demand by the public for his leadership in improving their health services.

The system of education and training is conducive to the development of certain characteristics and attitudes which bring forth such criticism. It does not develop independence and leadership.

The medical schools are the gateway through which all physicians must pass. If the schools fail to comprehend and to appreciate the intrinsic value of the young men whose development is the very purpose of their existence—if they fail in their emphasis and do not stimulate the curiosity, initiative, and freedom that are the essence of the profession of medicine—if they do not allow the student responsibility to the limit of his capacity—if they do not allow him to associate with men of the highest ideals of practice and ethics—then they will fail in their most important mission. Such a failure will leave medicine without leadership in the future, and there will be constant criticism of medical education, as well as increasing supervision by outside and government agencies.

The vision of greatness must be preserved. It must not be lost in the medical school in a welter of service, research, training, and welfare functions. The greatest need of the medical schools today is clear, critical thought, by men who are sincerely interested in the education of students and who have an understanding of educational principles, a knowledge of science, and a familiarity with social and economic trends. Such men must have courage and faith in the idea that the quality of medical education in the last analysis will determine the future of medicine in the United States.

Appendixes

APPENDIX 1   STUDENT OPINION

An interview with approximately 12 students was held at every medical school surveyed, with the purpose of obtaining a cross section of student opinion concerning the strengths and weaknesses of premedical and medical education. The students were selected by the deans from the third- and fourth-year classes and represented all levels of academic attainment. In two or three schools the dean, although he had been requested not to select all the students because of their brilliant performance, had obviously picked the cream of the crop. On the whole, however, the Survey teams felt the students were a well-chosen and representative group.

The interviews were informal affairs, and the students, once the purpose of the Survey had been explained, were obviously glad of the opportunity to state their views. Many inquired whether their criticisms and suggestions would do any good, or whether the results of the interviews would be put to any use.

THE MEDICAL STUDENT IN 1950

In evaluating student opinion, it must be remembered that on the whole the medical student in 1950 was more mature than the student 10 years earlier. Many students were married and had families; most of them had served in the armed forces; some had served in active combat. Marriage provided maturity and fixity of purpose, as well as the incentive to get out into practice as early as possible. Family responsibilities made it necessary to consider the size of the stipend for internships, and the length of residencies, when the students planned for the future.

At the same time, marriage provided a degree of economic stability. In most cases the student was financing his medical education with the help of the GI Bill of Rights, which, in addition to providing tuition and part of the cost of books and instruments, paid $90 to $120 a month for personal expenses. When the wives held relatively well-paid positions as secretaries or teachers, and the family income was supplemented by benefits from the GI Bill of Rights, the couple was economically fairly comfortable.

The Survey teams were impressed with the students' earnest interest in medicine. They were struck by the fact that students who differed so widely in family, community, and college educational backgrounds were all imbued with definite purposes, high ideals, and a sense of responsibility. These young men and women had evidently thought critically of their education and its impact on them.

It is obviously impossible in the space available to publish all the views of nearly 500 students. Only the most commonly expressed and most representative views are therefore included.

COLLEGE PREPARATION

Most commonly expressed was the statement that the medical schools and the colleges "ought to get together" on what was required of a prospective medical student. Many students, finding their college advisers ill-informed, had therefore depended upon medical school catalogues for clues to the college courses that would best improve their chances of admission to medical school. There constantly recurred the statement that if an adviser was a science professor he urged the students to take science courses, and that if he was in liberal arts, he urged a broader background. Some students explicitly stated their belief that their advisers were "plugging their own courses."

Often, the students said, their advisers had said that the best expedient was to take as many science courses as they could and to get A grades in all of them. However, they had found that the science courses, particularly chemistry and physics, most often were designed for students preparing for careers in engineering and industry, and not for premedical students.

In general, the students felt that the best advice concerning premedical courses came from men with medical backgrounds, especially from friends who were physicians.

Many students said that if they could do it over again they would take more courses in the humanities because they felt the need for a broader background. Much of the science background they had tried to acquire was wasted, they said, because in medical school they had had to learn the subjects again from the point of view of medicine. While they lacked especially the ability to express themselves in writing, almost universally they agreed that this difficulty stemmed from high school or earlier. No matter what premedical program they had pursued, however, the students complained of a degree of rigidity and the lack of freedom to choose—or time to take—elective subjects.

The large sizes of some classes in college had handicapped many students. Among students making statements to this effect were those who said they had been in a physics class of 1,200 in which there was only one laboratory session a week. In another typical comment, however, a physics class of 40 students was said to have been badly taught; the subject matter had allegedly been both too advanced and unnecessarily broad to be useful in their medical school studies.

It was interesting to note that, throughout the 41 schools, the matter of college preparation had been a big enough problem to cause earnest discussion among the medical students. In several schools students were conducting polls of their classes on the subject.

Other subjects discussed with regard to college years related to cheating, competition, and grades.

While its incidence apparently varied greatly, cheating was common in more than half the colleges the students attended. Students from some colleges said it had been virtually nonexistent; students from a few others said it was not apparent, often adding that the examinations were carefully proctored. Where cheating did exist, the students were inclined to blame it on the emphasis their professors placed on factual knowledge, and on examination methods, as well as on the competition for admission to medical schools.

MEDICAL SCHOOL

Methods of selecting students from among the applicants were apparently thought to be 75 to 80 per cent effective. While they felt that some of their fellow students were probably weak and should not have been admitted and that others, who were not admitted, were better qualified than themselves, the students felt that on the whole the results of the selection methods were fairly good.

Transition from college to medical school is apparently sharp and difficult for most students. Not the least of the hurdles is the necessity for learning to "think like a physician" which some faculty members urge during the students' first week. Students apparently do the best they can with this advice and, when their work becomes absorbing or they have close contact with faculty members early in their medical school career, they soon appear to be at home in their environment of medical study. In any event, the impact of the first few weeks in medical school is borne surprisingly well in view of the new perspective he is shown of the human body and its functions, and the new experiences he is exposed to.

According to the majority of students interviewed, while adjusting to the longer 30- or 40-hour week from the 15-hour week in college is another of the first hurdles, it is one they have anticipated. The fewer extracurricular activities in medical school partly compensated for the extra hours, the students said.

Competition for grades continues in medical school. In some schools it lasts throughout the four years and apparently is associated with an intense fear of failing and being dropped by the school. In other schools it subsides during the first year. In a few schools, among which is one of the largest and most highly regarded, it is intensified in the first year.

Students were preponderantly in favor of examinations as an incentive to study and as a means of estimating their progress. They thought essay-type questions more helpful than multiple-choice questions, which they found were usually too easy. Impressively frequent was the opinion that examinations were helpful if (1) the results were discussed with the students, and (2) no grades were given but the student was merely told his rating from time to time in terms of whether his work was satisfactory or unsatisfactory. Such a system, the students declared, would be of immense assistance to them and free them from the nervous tension that builds up when examinations follow closely upon one another. In a school in which no grades were announced to the students, tension and fear of being dropped from school were almost completely absent, and the students stated that their interest in their work left no room for fear of survival.

Cheating is not common in medical school. Students who described competition for grades at their schools as "cutthroat," "more intense than in college," or in similar terms, however, invariably reported a prevalence of cheating, especially in the first two years. They were unanimous in their condemnation of the practice, but seemed discouraged at any prospect of its complete elimination.

Transition is often sharp for the medical student entering his third year, when he begins his clinical work. After two years of study predominately in the medical basic sciences, he begins to take responsibility for patients, in the care of whom he must apply knowledge that so far has been largely theoretical or technical. Methods of study that have been learned must be put into practice, and at the same time clinical judgment must be acquired.

Students who made the transition slowly, from well-taught courses of physical diagnosis and pathology in the second year, felt that the transition was fairly smooth and logically planned. Students who found the transition the sharpest blamed the inadequacy of teaching in the first two years, but said that a good hospital service in the ward clerkship helped them to correct their deficiencies.

Opinion was sharply divided as to whether ward teaching should precede outpatient teaching or vice versa. But there was universal agreement that rotation through the various hospital services was immensely valuable, and also that experience with inpatients gave better opportunity for learning than experience with outpatients. In this respect, the statement that the fourth year was "a letdown" was echoed at almost all the schools. Students said that in the fourth year, far from feeling that they were advancing, as they did in the first three years, they felt suddenly jerked back to more elementary problems and the pace of their learning noticeably slackened. At one school, for example, the fourth year was described by one student as "a waste of time," and by another as "like a prolonged vacation." At that school, students were spending their evenings in externships at other hospitals, and stated that they were doing so in order to gain experience rather than for the monetary reward.

On the other hand, at one school the students said that in the outpatient department, although they were "required to work like mad" and were given a great deal of responsibility for patients, they badly needed more and closer contact with faculty members. Here, too, the students preferred their inpatient experience.

Criticisms of ward clerkship teaching also were found. At many schools, the students were disappointed at the amount of routine laboratory work required of them when they felt they should be spending more time with patients and developing clinical judgment. There recurred the statement that they were being used to provide services instead of being taught or given an opportunity to learn.

Criticisms of teaching were more frequent than praise, although this is to be expected under circumstances in which students are given opportunity to express opinions that they feel may be helpful. The criticisms were varied and too numerous to list in detail.

At one school, students felt they needed more guidance in their anatomy learning; at present they were given a book and told to learn its contents. At another, students expressed doubt regarding the logic in presenting to the beginning medical student the study of the detailed anatomy of cadavers, which was quite different from what they saw later in pathology or in clinical medicine.

At several schools, the students complained that faculty members lecturing to them in their first two years needed instruction in how to teach. The teachers "talked to the blackboard," or "mumbled into their beards," and many were obviously more interested in research than in teaching, the students said. In school after school, there recurred the statement that most of the preclinical subjects were "taught for their own sake," rather than from the standpoint of their application to medicine. At one of the largest schools, the students stated unanimously that most of their teachers, both in the preclinical and the clinical years, were not sufficiently interested in teaching. They explained also that the poor teaching in the preclinical subjects made teaching more difficult for the clinical faculty members. Many of them felt the need for better knowledge of biochemistry in their fourth year, and said that they wished, for instance, that they could have had more biochemistry taught by clinicians with special biochemical training.

Specific suggestions were made by students at a number of schools that they be given more case presentations during their first year so as to improve their understanding of the application of preclinical subjects. Such a plan, they said, would help them to correlate the knowledge of medical basic sciences with their clinical work and give them a sounder background for their third and fourth years.

The most bitter criticism concerned lack of student-faculty contacts. Statements such as "I wouldn't know the dean if I saw him," and "We would like more contact with the senior men on the faculty" were made at almost every school. The exceptions were in a small minority. Where they existed, the students were enthusiastic about their work and some were conducting research projects of their own in their free time or helping a faculty member with a research project. At one school only were the students unanimous in stating that their contact with all their faculty was frequent and highly satisfactory. Even here, however, they stated that they wished senior faculty members were more active in the outpatient department.

In general, the students at almost all the schools felt that, when it was time for them to think about applying for internships, they received inadequate advice. At some schools, the students stated that, thus far, neither the third- nor the fourth-year class had been given any form of advice regarding internships. At only a few schools, the students described the advice they received individually from faculty members as "adequate" or—at one school—as "excellent." It was noteworthy that in schools in which students had had little contact with the faculty, or where the emphasis was on research, students unanimously expressed the desire to seek an internship at some other teaching hospital. It was interesting to note also that they preferred not to seek internships at private hospitals because they wanted greater responsibility for patients than they would obtain in such hospitals.

APPENDIX 2   ADMINISTRATION

THE DEANS

According to the information listed in the American Medical Directory, the average age of the medical school deans in 1950 was 53.9 years; in 1920 it was 51.9 years. The deans both in 1950 and in 1920 had been in office for an average of about eight years. The faculty background of the dean was more frequently in the department of medicine than in any other department of the medical school, with preventive medicine and public health the next most common.

Data on the financial remuneration of the deans were obtained from 65 four-year and five two-year medical schools. They reveal that the earnings of the deans in the four-year schools were derived from one or more of three sources (Table 53). In 33 schools the dean's earnings were derived from the

Table 53. SOURCES OF DEAN'S PROFESSIONAL EARNINGS IN 65 FOUR-YEAR MEDICAL SCHOOLS, 1950–51

Source of professional earnings	Number of schools		
	Tax-supported	Privately supported	Total
Salary from deanship......................	13	20	33
Salary from deanship plus faculty position....	3	7	10
Salary from deanship plus consultant fees.....	10	6	16
Salary from deanship plus faculty position, and consultant fees..........................	3	1	4
Salary from faculty position, none from deanship.................................	0	2	2
Totals.................................	29	36	65

deanship alone; in 10 schools from the deanship and a teaching position on the faculty; in 16 schools from the deanship and consultations; and in 4 schools from the deanship, a teaching position on the faculty, and consultations. In two schools there was no remuneration from the deanship, and the only earnings of the incumbents were from the faculty appointments.

In the 65 four-year schools, professional earnings of the deans from all sources averaged about $14,700 (Figure 13), with a 95 per cent range of from about $7,100 to about $22,300. Eighty per cent of their earnings came from the deanship, 14 per cent from a teaching appointment on the faculty,

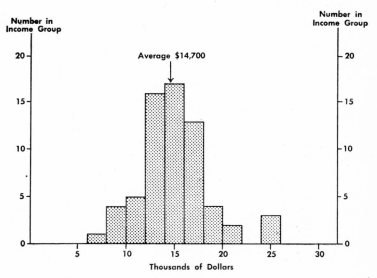

Figure 13. Frequency distribution of professional earnings of deans of 65 four-year medical schools in 1950–51.

and 6 per cent from consultation fees (Figure 14). The average in the privately supported schools, $15,083, was slightly higher than the average in the tax-supported schools, $14,262 (Table 54). The average earnings

Table 54. AVERAGE EARNINGS OF DEANS FROM ALL SOURCES, 1950–51

In 29 tax-supported schools.................. $14,262
In 36 privately supported schools............ 15,083
In 5 two-year schools...................... 10,706

almost coincided with the median figure of $14,750. In five two-year medical schools the average income of the dean was $10,706 with a range from $8,500 to $13,500.

It should be emphasized that these figures undoubtedly underestimate the actual earnings, since in certain cases the figures reported to the Survey bore a notation that consultation fees were received but gave no estimate of the income from them. In other instances, salaries were supplemented with benefits such as insurance, hospitalization for the dean and his family, a generous travel allowance, an entertainment allowance, and even an automobile for transportation to and from the medical school. This practice appears to be more common in tax-supported institutions.

The average earnings of the deans were approximately the same as the average maximum salary ($14,069) of the full-time professor on the clinical faculty. Here again, however, the figure is conservative because the salaries of clinical professors are frequently supplemented by consultation fees and private practice.

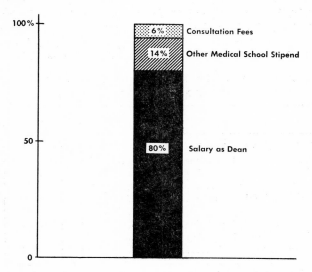

Figure 14. Sources of professional earnings of deans, and percentage of total from each source, 65 four-year medical schools in 1950–51.

Eleven schools gave the salaries of vice-presidents or directors of medical affairs where such positions were distinct from the deanship. The average salary of men holding such positions was approximately the same as the average income for the deans.

The position of the dean certainly carries with it modest financial rewards. The wisest and most able leadership is essential to meet the problems of the medical schools. The remuneration of the dean should be adequate to attract men of the highest caliber and sufficient so that it will not be necessary for him to supplement his income.

EXPENDITURES FOR ADMINISTRATION

The administrative expenses of medical schools, as reported to the Survey, varied widely, and it is almost impossible to compare one school with another. The medical schools and their parent universities differed in their policies concerning the allocation of administrative costs. In some schools certain costs were borne by the university, in others the same costs were carried by the medical school. In some instances only estimates could be made of costs of administration. Administrative expenditures by departments of a school appeared infrequently as part of over-all administrative costs. All these variations must be considered in interpreting the following figures.

Information was available on administrative expenses, share of university expenses contributed by the medical school, general operating expense, and funds restricted to research for 59 four-year medical schools for the fiscal years 1940–41, 1947–48, and 1950–51. Over the 10-year period 1940–41 to 1950–51, the percentage of general operating expense devoted to administration remained about the same (Table 55, *A*). However when funds re-

Table 55. ADMINISTRATIVE COSTS AT 59 FOUR-YEAR MEDICAL SCHOOLS FOR THREE FISCAL YEARS

	1940–41*	1947–48*	1950–51
A. *Medical-school Administration Alone*			
Expressed as % of general operating expense....	6.3	6.5	6.4
Expressed as % of general operating expense plus funds restricted to research.................	5.6	5.0	4.3
B. *Medical-school Administration Plus Share of University Expense*			
Expressed as % of general operating expense....	11.0	12.4	11.5
Expressed as % of general operating expense plus funds restricted to research.................	9.8	9.6	7.8

* Figures for 1940–41 and 1947–48 computed from data of the Surgeon General's Committee on Medical School Grants and Finances.

stricted to research were added to general operating expense, the percentage devoted to administration was found to have fallen from 5.6 per cent in 1940–41 to 5.0 per cent in 1947–48 and 4.3 per cent in 1950–51.

Table 55, *B* shows the cost of medical school administration plus its share of university expenses expressed as a percentage of general operating expense and as a percentage of operating expense plus funds restricted to research. The percentage rose slightly when only operating expense was considered, but fell from 9.8 per cent in 1940–41 to 7.8 per cent in 1950–51, when research funds were considered with general operating expense.

Over the 10-year period, research funds have shown the greatest growth of any of the expenditures of the medical schools. Only when research funds were considered with general operating expenses was a decrease observed in the percentage of funds devoted to administration. This can mean either that research funds are less costly to administer than funds for the support of other activities or that the expense of administering research funds is being met by reducing the funds for general administration. This question cannot be answered by the information available. It certainly deserves more careful study by the medical schools, especially by those expending large grants for research.

If all funds expended by the medical schools are considered, including funds restricted to research, the expenditures on administration are found to have decreased within the last 10 years while other expenses of medical schools have increased markedly. The period was one of tremendous and rapid changes, including the Second World War and its aftermath. Administration should have been strengthened—not weakened.

APPENDIX 3   DISTRIBUTION OF
GRADUATES OF
FOUR-YEAR MEDICAL
SCHOOLS

State	Univ. of Alabama	Univ. of Arkansas	Univ. of California	Univ. of So. California	Stanford Univ.	Col. Medical Evangelists	Univ. of Colorado	Yale Univ.	Univ. of Georgia	Emory Univ.	Univ. of Chicago	Northwestern Univ.	Univ. of Illinois	Chicago Med. School	Stritch (Loyola)	Indiana Univ.	State Univ. of Iowa	Univ. of Kansas	Univ. of Louisville	Tulane Univ.	Louisiana State Univ.	Univ. of Maryland	Johns Hopkins Univ.	Harvard	Boston Univ.	Tufts College	Univ. of Michigan	Wayne Univ.	Univ. of Minnesota	Washington (St. Louis)	St. Louis Univ.	Univ. of Nebraska	Creighton Univ.	Columbia Univ.	Albany	Univ. of Buffalo	Long Island
Alabama	258	17	1	1	1	1	3	1	23	158	3	17	13	1	4	5	3	4	31	362	33	8	29	31	1	2	8	1	5	49	7	2	1	21	2	1	
Arizona	2	7	6	12	2	22	12	4	.....	2	...	37	43	1	7	7	17	7	7	22	4	6	9	10	3	5	20	6	17	15	21	20	16	15	3	3	
Arkansas	2	602	1	...	1	3	1	3	3	7	2	9	12	1	4	10	4	5	23	77	4	3	17	2	.....	.....	.....	1	4	23	16	6	2	8		1	
California	6	51	1,541	690	1,092	1,240	192	79	12	29	55	521	544	6	153	129	216	151	122	108	32	67	204	306	43	103	306	106	344	261	293	300	369	176	23	64	
Colorado	1	7	4	3	5	24	594	6	1	3	10	79	34	...	10	28	34	30	14	16	2	6	25	48	5	6	35	4	18	47	35	65	39	17	2	9	
Connecticut	...	4	6	2	6	1	6	471	3	2	5	12	7	1	14	11	7	7	11	7	5	60	125	190	87	249	26	5	16	9	19	6	6	183	22	16	
Delaware								7		1		1	1		1	3	1	1	2	.....		29	16	2	.....		3	1	.....	3	3	1	...	2	4	3	
Florida	29	22	3	...	1	23	3	16	136	253	8	41	39	3	26	25	12	8	50	207	24	65	60	46	17	33	43	20	20	23	27	9	3	45	16	23	
Georgia	9	17	.....	...	1	5	1	5	740	748	6	7	9	...	2	9	5	5	27	72	4	40	64	31	.....	2	15	4	4	10	3	7	1	26	4	4	
Idaho	...		1	2	4	7	14	.....	...	6	61	11	1	1	3	5	20	7	13	1	2	5	6	10	.....	1	10	3	11	17	9	20	13	5	1	2	
Illinois	...	18	4	6	5	10	19	9	4	9	254	1,466	2,501	187	1,261	83	98	28	67	27	5	23	69	103	12	22	107	22	86	232	351	48	44	34	5	19	
Indiana	...	18	3	1	2	8	5	1	3	9	19	140	129	...	58	1,875	26	16	211	5	1	10	31	28	1	8	100	12	11	29	66	24	8	12	2	5	
Iowa	1	8	7	...	2	10	17	5	4	2	12	129	112	1	35	17	1,099	27	21	3	4	3	12	14	2	1	35	6	43	36	51	110	171	6	2	3	
Kansas	...	9	3	1	4	5	15	11	5	3	10	87	46	...	15	9	25	662	26	24	3	4	2	16	4	3	15	2	13	72	64	35	54	1	2	
Kentucky	1	12	1	1		4	5	5	8	10	3	16	21	...	12	24	8	3	1,068	25	2	10	24	19	4	3	22	3	5	9	9	4	4	11	2	2	
Louisiana	7	25	2	1	1	2	3	8	13	19	2	19	10	...	8	1	5	5	27	1,247	575	5	17	19	2	6	11	4	8	10	16	8	4	14	1	.....	
Maine	...					2		24	1		1	2		1			1		2	.....		8	17	95	82	126	6	1	1	3	1	1		18	3	1	
Maryland	...	4	10	1	8	30	5	16	9	13	16	10	11	1	6	11	4	3	11	12	6	1,152	517	32	6	9	13	3	8	16	6	7	7	31	5	6	
Massachusetts	...	2	22	3	10	14	10	112	10	9	7	31	12	3	9	15	10	10	9	14	3	54	122	1,710	657	1,916	59	10	16	30	16	17	8	133	35	16	5
Michigan	...	13	4	1	9	47	19	17	3	9	38	173	153	1	107	72	84	24	58	16	2	20	85	73	12	22	1,812	1,619	81	49	83	51	28	20	11	33	
Minnesota	...	5	7	3	14	14	15	10	3	1	23	192	94	...	35	36	60	27	23	20	3	11	52	85	9	8	64	12	2,005	21	43	61	41	32	1	7	
Mississippi	10	16	2	...		3	.....		2	42	3	18	10	...	2	.....	1		30	325	30	2	7	6	.....		1		2	7	3	2	2	8	1	2	
Missouri	1	66	5	1	2	4	16	16	3	6	6	80	56	...	14	16	27	282	80	30	1	8	43	70	3	5	27	5	22	989	922	40	53	23	2	3	
Montana	...	4	2	...	3	11	13	2	.....		5	45	26	1	7	2	16	7	6	3	1	2	9	6	2	1	24	3	78	19	27	13	36	5	.....	1	
Nebraska	1	2	.....	...	1	8	8	3	1	1	4	47	12	1	5	2	24	9	6	.....		5	6	16	.....	1	15	3	6	11	13	664	329	7	1	1	
Nevada	...	.....	6	4	5	3	3	.....		2	6	6	...	3	4	3	1	4	5	.....		6	1	5	2	.....	1		3	6	6	3	4	8		
New Hampshire	...				1	.....	4	15		1	1	3	.....		2	1	2	2	.....	2	1	4	10	83	57	118	7	.....	1	2	1	2	2	29	7	2	
New Jersey	1	24	9	1	1	2	4	49	5	8	5	24	13	...	51	22	29	10	35	42	10	192	59	71	52	55	73	9	24	19	89	11	21	411	45	27	26
New Mexico	1	7	.....	1	...	2	27	5	2	1	4	25	19	...	4	6	7	5	10	16	2	6	3	8	1	2	9	1	2	11	9	2	1	9	2	1	
New York	6	70	26	10	26	29	38	265	21	51	51	96	82	2	120	75	79	27	101	139	41	349	393	530	214	308	254	36	74	84	260	51	83	2,404	923	1,720	2,37
North Carolina	1	7	2	2	5	20	4	7	32	74	5	32	6	1	1	9	9	2	28	84	7	216	91	73	6	8	17	1	8	31	4	4	1	24	1	3	
North Dakota	...	3	.....	1	...	5	.....			5		48	34	...	5	5	14	3	4	1	1	1	3	3	.....	3	10	5	101	9	3	9	4	.....		
Ohio	2	24	5	3	2	19	21	35	10	17	33	119	76	...	123	93	66	39	172	20	9	59	114	128	16	17	306	51	31	62	340	39	37	38	5	57	2
Oklahoma	1	83	.....			10	10	6	6	12	5	53	21	...	3	7	25	39	44	47	2	7	9	8	.....	2	18	1	9	56	36	19	16	6	2	7	
Oregon	...	3	9	3	11	53	13	3	.....		9	48	30	1	8	10	40	17	16	5	3	3	19	47	2	3	22	5	48	25	33	42	46	13	3	1	
Pennsylvania	...	7	4	7	7	3	12	35	7	11	12	37	19	...	56	23	20	12	39	16	6	200	161	128	31	45	103	12	30	27	81	26	10	62	17	51	4
Rhode Island	...		3	.....		2	4	30	1	1		1	.....		3	1	.....		2	2	...	22	14	129	58	189	4	1	3	1	15	2	1	28	1	1	
South Carolina	...	1	.....			1	.....		58	54	2	4	2	...	1	.....	1	1	10	12	6	51	20	5	3	4	6	.....	1	1	2	2	.....	10	1		
South Dakota	...	3	.....			2	5	.....		3	57	36	...	5	3	34	2	9	.....	1	2	6	6	.....		7	.....	46	9	7	20	50	1		
Tennessee	4	18	2	...	43	6	3	11	15	46	...	20	22	...	5	8	9	4	55	73	7	14	40	29	1	3	16	3	6	19	7	9	.....	10	2	2	
Texas	9	125	3	4	3	26	33	8	11	26	15	81	60	2	30	50	50	40	140	533	66	25	62	59	3	12	35	13	43	76	63	52	20	35	2	13	1
Utah	...		8	1	8	2	11	6	.....	1	15	85	25	...	4	2	5	6	38	7	9	13	9	23	2	1	5	.....	11	42	12	11	12	19		1	
Vermont	...					1	2	7	.....		1	2	1	...			1		1	.....		5	3	24	7	17	3	1	1	1		2		13	6		
Virginia	1	7	1	...	6	5	11	17	25	1	7	8	...	3	3	6	3	29	23	3	106	86	23	4	6	10	2	7	10	2	7	3	21	1		
Washington	1	8	7	5	21	94	23	14	4	1	26	238	95	1	19	20	55	24	40	3	7	10	36	63	10	72	14	112	56	81	62	85	26	2	13	
West Virginia	...	10	1	...		4	2	4	7	21	...	29	5	1	12	8	6	2	129	12	2	153	20	15	4	6	14	3	5	18	13	1	1	7		3	
Wisconsin	...	5	5	1	1	9	7	6	5	2	16	260	186	...	58	17	42	8	30	6	3	7	40	58	5	7	65	9	93	51	48	27	19	33	4	5	
Wyoming	...	1	.....	1	1	2	15	2	.....	1	...	13	11	2	6	1	7	3	3	2	.....	1	1	8	.....		3	2	9	3	7	38	16	2		
District of Columbia	1	7	7	2	4	16	4	10	4	10	9	15	14	1	4	22	9	5	10	16	3	79	83	45	11	21	27	6	16	19	9	11	5	25	3	11	1
	356	1,332	1,733	775	1,276	1,852	1,226	1,360	1,195	1,699	716	4,543	4,677	220	2,324	2,786	2,323	1,584	2,894	3,689	945	3,137	2,851	4,539	1,444	3,369	3,864	2,030	3,509	2,625	3,236	1,971	1,677	4,094	1,179	2,149	3,17

Graduates of the University of Washington School of Medicine not included since the first class graduated in 1950.

Source: Compiled by the Bureau of Medical and Economic Research of the American Medical Association from 147,328 of its 202,000 punch cards for the 1950 American Medical Directory (effective date mid-year 1949, excluding June 1949 graduates).

New York Medical	Syracuse	New York Univ.	Cornell	Univ. of Rochester	Bowman Gray	Duke Univ.	Western Reserve	Ohio State	Univ. of Cincinnati	Univ. of Oklahoma	Univ. of Oregon	Univ. of Pennsylvania	Jefferson	Woman's Medical	Hahnemann	Univ. of Pittsburgh	Temple	South Carolina	Vanderbilt	Univ. of Tennessee	Meharry	Univ. of Texas	Baylor	Southwestern	Univ. of Utah	Univ. of Vermont	Univ. of Virginia	Med. Col. Virginia	Univ. of Wisconsin	Marquette	George Washington	Georgetown	Howard	Total	No. of 4-year schools
1	3	9	7	1	6	12	4	2	9	11	.....	46	29	3	13	3	4	19	134	145	49	5	8	...	...	1	46	6	.....	.....	14	1	15	1,729	1
6	1	10	7	2	1	3	15	8	7	6	5	14	20	4	6	5	9	4	12	13	.....	5	9	1	...	2	1	7	14	6	14	6	3	623	0
1	.....	2	3	...	...	2	3	...	1	9	1	4	12	1	1	.....	1	1	30	103	36	7	4	...	...	1	6	6	3	.....	2	1	3	1,101	1
76	28	109	100	72	4	33	100	85	118	88	230	225	191	68	101	68	66	21	70	58	68	66	55	5	15	32	35	28	78	110	146	48	40	12,664	4
4	4	10	10	10	2	4	13	7	4	22	6	23	23	7	5	7	6	2	19	10	1	15	11	2	...	3	6	2	10	8	10	4	1	1,541	1
71	26	96	92	35	1	20	10	5	6	3	3	58	109	23	54	6	25	2	10	9	5	6	6	...	1	126	13	18	6	13	34	87	13	2,687	1
1	1	2	2	1	...	2	.....	2	4	1	1	50	80	3	55	2	24	1	.....	1	1	.....	.....	...	...	1	11	5	1	.....	7	11	7	366	0
27	10	41	26	7	6	47	17	37	42	9	2	80	81	15	36	38	38	46	73	78	57	5	6	...	1	14	45	47	3	10	19	24	19	2,425	0
4	3	9	16	4	6	29	5	3	6	7	.....	21	25	4	5	5	4	35	46	42	92	9	9	1	...	4	39	21	2	1	12	6	18	2,383	2
2	2	1	2	2	...	2	5	.....	2	4	36	8	14	1	.....	...	4	1	3	5	.....	3	.....	...	9	3	1	1	3	4	11	2	.....	401	0
7	15	19	17	8	5	10	35	24	38	27	7	54	50	13	20	17	13	7	21	37	121	9	7	1	4	11	12	11	61	58	24	11	51	8,071	5
5	6	12	4	5	...	3	26	39	49	8	2	20	35	6	19	9	9	2	12	11	36	4	1	...	...	.....	3	6	8	22	11	5	12	3,270	1
2	2	9	7	6	3	2	13	5	10	4	6	18	22	6	8	5	8	1	6	9	4	5	3	1	1	2	4	2	12	12	3	2	3	2,218	1
4	1	9	5	4	1	2	8	14	6	20	1	16	17	2	3	1	5	1	10	15	14	14	9	1	...	1	2	.....	10	6	5	4	10	1,479	1
1	.....	3	6	3	7	9	6	13	94	1	.....	27	15	7	8	3	2	5	103	94	48	6	2	...	...	3	14	18	.....	3	6	1	11	1,887	1
3	2	7	6	4	2	6	2	4	7	5	5	18	7	4	4	5	6	6	43	85	43	30	28	6	1	...	16	13	7	1	5	3	20	2,510	2
2	2	7	13	7	...	2	4	3	2	.....	.....	17	28	3	13	1	7	...	.....	1	.....	1	...	1	44	2	3	.....	1	7	23	.....	600	0
7	10	22	19	13	3	26	6	5	8	10	4	44	57	8	37	9	29	9	12	7	35	4	3	2	6	42	43	6	1	94	88	79	2,772	2
33	21	64	63	40	1	19	22	15	17	6	4	102	84	38	41	8	27	2	17	15	4	5	8	3	5	168	33	9	8	11	25	113	7	6,203	3
10	24	18	15	8	7	22	55	61	58	23	9	65	51	15	23	18	18	4	30	17	88	21	9	3	1	15	15	16	22	87	18	25	51	5,783	1
5	9	3	7	7	2	7	15	15	15	15	10	60	28	4	11	16	20	7	2	9	.....	17	3	1	6	3	11	17	36	80	23	10	1	3,521	1
.....	.....	3	1	2	...	2	1	2	1	6	.....	18	26	4	2	3	2	2	71	256	44	7	6	1	1	23	6	.....	2	4	4	5	1,032	0
2	2	17	12	16	3	9	10	10	9	16	5	53	26	9	9	2	8	1	20	89	109	19	14	2	2	6	5	28	12	9	3	56	3,536	2
.....	.....	2	5	2	1	1	2	4	2	2	6	8	12	.....	1	3	.....	.....	2	1	.....	2	.....	1	1	1	3	3	6	3	4	.....	457	0
1	1	2	3	1	...	2	5	3	3	2	1	9	12	2	2	4	3	.....	4	7	1	2	...	1	.....	1	.....	1	.....	3	1	1,289	2
4	.....	4	1	...	...	2	3	3	1	.....	1	2	3	...	5	2	3	1	.....	.....	1	...	1	.....	3	4	4	.....	151	0
1	4	12	10	5	...	.....	1	.....	2	.....	12	11	13	10	2	2	.....	1	.....	70	1	5	.....	.....	2	16	.....	543	0
243	52	465	187	14	3	19	11	11	17	7	2	353	454	65	432	17	182	15	11	18	23	6	10	...	70	44	40	9	27	114	260	110	5,063	0
2	4	4	5	2	...	3	4	8	4	10	1	8	9	1	4	1	2	1	2	14	.....	16	30	1	3	2	2	4	2	4	2	...	369	0
1,450	1,038	2,669	1,318	382	11	62	76	60	75	20	23	315	269	124	206	43	117	27	77	56	72	46	55	4	6	213	136	148	25	105	229	493	198	21,561	9
5	12	26	17	7	117	221	8	8	22	7	3	279	268	19	7	3	63	101	56	46	78	3	8	1	...	5	81	320	3	3	24	13	45	2,716	2
.....	.....	1	.....	1	2	1	1	.....	1	1	2	8	2	2	.....	...	15	1	.....	.....	3	...	1	.....	1	2	9	2	3	.....	343	0
37	19	30	41	49	...	32	1,203	1,642	1,053	17	3	146	202	36	140	95	41	12	47	16	99	14	9	3	2	15	26	40	22	40	50	45	44	7,483	3
.....	3	4	1	1	...	9	3	2	690	.....	9	16	.....	4	3	1	1	43	74	39	24	29	6	...	1	12	2	3	2	7	3	6	1,575	1
4	2	4	3	8	...	4	5	4	4	13	708	20	19	4	6	.....	6	2	1	4	1	3	4	...	2	3	4	2	16	11	6	2	1	1,473	1
27	36	58	46	21	8	28	68	27	28	8	4	2,464	2,498	353	1,463	1,674	1,355	11	15	14	41	24	5	1	2	24	35	56	16	30	95	235	126	12,254	6
12	5	6	16	2	...	3	2	.....	1	2	.....	21	47	4	42	.....	2	1	3	1	.....	1	.....	...	18	1	3	.....	3	13	67	2	804	2
1	2	1	4	1	2	34	2	2	1	2	.....	19	24	6	.....	2	5	815	31	12	36	3	.....	...	1	25	28	.....	1	1	4	16	1,342	1
1	.....	.....	1	.....	...	.....	1	.....	6	1	2	3	7	.....	1	1	13	.....	1	6	.....	2	...	3	.....	1	1	4	3	1	.....	374	0
1	4	10	6	5	1	18	7	6	10	6	1	35	26	5	6	4	9	7	543	898	167	6	6	...	1	3	43	23	3	2	10	3	7	2,390	3
9	2	23	9	10	5	17	19	21	28	110	5	82	56	7	8	14	16	7	183	187	130	1,850	1,095	163	...	4	26	26	22	11	17	10	13	6,025	3
1	3	7	7	3	...	1	9	1	5	1	9	59	19	1	4	1	18	2	2	5	.....	1	1	72	.....	2	1	3	28	2	.....	662	1
3	.....	7	13	5	...	1	.....	.....	.....	.....	.....	5	4	4	4	.....	1	2	.....	.....	.....	.....	.....	340	1	.....	.....	2	2	.....	500	1
4	6	10	7	3	8	39	8	8	12	8	1	64	46	7	16	7	11	15	29	28	60	4	...	1	521	987	8	3	67	35	73	2,561	2
7	3	9	15	13	1	7	15	9	11	17	294	66	59	4	14	6	17	2	12	9	2	7	3	1	6	22	4	15	37	26	15	.....	2,105	1
1	.....	16	7	2	...	22	22	18	42	1	.....	41	83	2	11	18	28	8	11	20	24	2	1	1	6	65	274	3	4	20	8	10	1,291	0
2	2	16	6	5	...	1	14	6	17	5	10	65	13	8	8	5	22	2	5	3	4	9	2	...	4	5	8	517	954	14	1	4	2,879	2
.....	1	2	1	1	...	1	.....	1	3	1	1	3	6	.....	.....	.....	.....	1	.....	.....	.....	.....	...	.....	1	2	4	3	1	.....	198	0
10	5	20	12	4	5	18	9	7	13	6	.....	37	32	7	19	8	26	9	14	13	22	10	7	1	...	6	72	43	7	3	557	339	215	2,118	3
2,100	1,376	3,890	2,181	804	224	817	1,879	2,211	1,876	1,241	1,419	5,174	5,227	922	2,886	2,142	2,296	1,222	1,833	2,537	1,660	2,294	1,480	213	144	1,241	1,508	2,311	1,001	1,716	1,804	2,053	1,296	147,328	72

APPENDIX 4   LIBRARIES

Table 57. BOUND VOLUMES, JOURNAL SUBSCRIPTIONS, SEATING CAPACITIES, SALARY BUDGETS, AND PAID FULL-TIME STAFF, AT LIBRARIES OF 37 MEDICAL SCHOOLS, YEAR OF SURVEY

School No.	Bound volumes	Paid journal subscriptions	Seating capacity	Salary budget	Paid full-time staff
1	110,924	873	190	$25,464	5
3	89,354	720	250	39,714	13
4	34,000	No information	225	13,564	6
5	82,748	729	200	—	6
6	60,000	500	120	16,000	6
7	79,367	444	99	20,440	10
8	48,000	506	116	11,000	4
11	39,652	504	72	14,978	5
12	30,000	320	60	11,680	5
13	43,000	340	50	11,960	3
14	47,760	494	150	20,922	6
15	14,235	366	95	12,120	4
18	29,901	556	56	23,076	8
24	20,067	241	94	8,470	4
28	19,692	218	68	5,080	3
31	160,000	1,061	180	50,550	21
32	123,456	No information	138	28,437	13
33	55,795	535	59	9,765	3
35	158,705	544	188	46,380	20
36	71,200	551	51	17,870	8
37	157,000	800	152	34,514	13
38	15,020	177	100	3,878	2
39	60,000	948	203	35,520	15
41	16,000	105	44	8,640	3
42	118,150	659	150	21,480	7
48	118,500	1,029	128	24,760	11
51	53,634	556	95	15,740	5
54	35,154	251	55	5,280	2
57	16,346	208	75	7,540	3
61	23,514	233	100	16,000	3
64	18,025	198	40	5,000	2
65	14,155	175	40	7,800	3
66	11,059	174	70	5,600	2
68	43,770	432	80	9,358	3
71	9,060	156	60	7,560	3
73*	20,000	500	65	7,000	2
75*	7,000	270	18	2,880	1

* Two-year schools.
— Indicates budget not segregated from that of general university library.
Source: Figures supplied by librarians.

Table 58. EXPENDITURES ON LIBRARIES OF 37 MEDICAL SCHOOLS,
FISCAL YEAR 1950–51

School Number	1950–51 Expenditures	School Number	1950–51 Expenditures
1	$48,996*	36	$31,194
3	33,905	37	60,979
4	67,954	38	29,848
5	49,672	39	0
6	58,800	41	12,560
7	8,533	42	36,275
8	13,514	48	49,669
11	18,051	51	25,285
12	21,785	54	8,228
13	15,575	57	9,446
14	33,760	61	22,941
15	0	64	13,278
18	36,189	65	5,734
24	15,000	66	6,611
28	12,662	68	14,754
31	81,510	71	0
32	—	73†	28,500
33	23,895	75†	9,280
35	11,000		

* Estimated.
† Two-year schools.
— Indicates expenditures not segregated.
0 Indicates no expenditures from medical school budget.

APPENDIX 5   POSTGRADUATE
EDUCATION

Table 59. NUMBER OF POSTGRADUATE STUDENTS IN 26 MEDICAL SCHOOLS, 1948–49

Departments	Number of departments reporting	Number of students in 1948–49
Anatomy	16	673
Physiology	10	1,020
Pharmacology	10	470
Bacteriology	5	173
Pathology	15	933
Biochemistry	5	369
Medicine	17	3,958
Preventive medicine	5	147
Dermatology	5	180
Surgery	11	1,107
Orthopedics	5	233
Otolaryngology	10	461
Ophthalmology	12	628
Anesthesiology	5	179
Urology	2	50
Pediatrics	19	1,308
Obstetrics and gynecology	12	670
Psychiatry	16	1,121
Neurology	4	175
Radiology	11	876
Total		14,731

Source: Figures supplied by department heads.

348

APPENDIX 6   FINANCES

Finances

Amount of expenses for the fiscal year in which the medical school is surveyed.
Line items:

31. *Administration and General Expenses*	....
a. Share of expenses of university	....
b. Administration of medical school	....
c. Student health service	....
32. *Instruction and Research Expense*	....
a. Research budgeted separately	....
(1) Federal government grants (USPHS)	....
(2) Federal government contracts (Army, Navy, Veterans Administration)	
(3) Other research	....
b. Instructional activities, including research not budgeted separately	....
(1) U.S. Public Health Service grants	....
(2) All other	....
33. *Expense of Separately Organized Postgraduate Education*	....
34. *Libraries (Expense)*	....
35. *Physical Plant Operation and Maintenance*	....
36. *Expenses of Organized Activities Relating to Instructional Departments*	....
a. Hospital and clinics	....
b. All other	....
37. *Total Expense—Educational, Research, and General* (Items 31–36)	....

Table 61. FISCAL YEAR 1950-51,

School No.	Instruction All Except USPHS	USPHS	Total	Research Budgeted Separately Federal USPHS	Contracts	All Other	Total	Administration Medical School	Share of University	Total
										30 TAX-SUPPORTED
1	$1,320,055	$188,890	$1,508,945	$358,975	$ 145,902	$558,076	$1,062,953	$ 68,866	$338,449*	$407,315
2	1,574,055	32,001	1,606,056	375,854	1,030,695	125,184	1,531,733	71,600	17,619	89,219
3	1,535,035	0	1,535,035	302,773	79,978	280,714	663,465	50,541	165,845	216,386
4	1,330,843	22,071	1,352,914	182,468	102,102	287,943	572,513	73,336	124,953	198,289
5	1,118,345	0	1,118,345	195,531	195,026	385,604	776,161	51,625	185,837	237,462
6	985,705	18,000	1,003,705	$209,814		307,142	516,956	84,000	0	84,000
7	877,431	117,946	995,377	222,809		463,567	686,376	47,164	0	47,164
8	1,230,376	13,478	1,243,854	87,977	11,004	282,314	381,295	26,700	36,808	63,508
9	958,562	24,920	983,482	15,874	35,425	143,541	194,840	59,877	115,145	175,022
10	1,015,710	10,581	1,026,291	67,883	0	0	67,883	59,760	152,400	212,160
11	681,454	121,962	803,416	128,977	70,637	130,583	330,197	152,115	4,395	156,510
12	840,824	33,773	874,597	72,603	17,492	102,547	192,642	33,730	0	33,730
13	710,950	0	710,950	90,577	6,383	242,148	339,108	42,245	0	42,245
14	646,781	48,166	694,947	31,730	33,066	23,149	87,945	127,663	0	127,663
15	387,324	64,250	451,574	335,578	22,386	282,877	640,841	37,201	0	37,201
16	753,953	38,943	792,896	94,808	0	74,200	169,008	39,500	0	39,500
17	656,169	26,355	682,524	47,585	0	41,000	88,585	69,245	0	69,245
18	591,980	81,423	673,403	39,237	11,030	57,050	107,317	44,790	37,260	82,050
19	367,681	55,641	423,322	28,383	219,017	103,201	350,601	20,527	59,273	79,800
20	261,760	35,420	297,180	99,544	6,293	317,510	423,347	24,643	66,187	90,830
21	384,094	20,800	404,894	215,252	16,319	0	231,571	13,319	12,000	25,319
22	449,996	52,744	502,740	24,818	10,956	48,232	84,006	58,215	0	58,215
23	449,735	28,560	478,295	43,106	2,139	18,248	63,493	23,236	3,000	26,236
24	468,350	31,500	499,850	47,000	0	0	47,000	27,500	0	27,500
25	431,015	55,116	486,131	53,141	0	65,132	118,273	51,727	0	51,727
26	386,395	0	386,395	88,776	7,892	27,526	124,194	58,731	0	58,731
27	301,181	0	301,181	64,259	28,404	72,219	164,882	54,555	28,171	82,726
28	315,989	28,295	344,284	78,328	9,730	32,611	120,669	46,376	0	46,376
29	291,035	0	291,035	98,976	6,273	9,928	115,177	34,897	37,284	72,181
30	219,000	73,000	292,000	0	0	40,000	40,000	41,000	7,000	48,000
										41 PRIVATELY
31	1,780,606	24,894	1,805,500	782,250	529,851	993,844	2,305,945	88,889	328,509	417,398
32	2,230,138	67,275	2,297,413	0	1,051,534	775,190	1,826,724	—	—	483,328
33	727,587	0	727,587	206,437	1,623,387	498,416	2,328,240	126,010	40,667	166,627
34	931,486	79,347	1,010,833	447,393	375,002	705,997	1,528,392	108,537	0	108,537
35	994,547	0	994,547	441,236	178,436	958,766	1,578,438	144,372	100,620	244,992
36	823,795	42,423	866,218	198,820	114,991	503,785	817,596	62,643	140,730	203,373
37	986,322	93,024	1,079,346	315,408	304,009	498,871	1,118,288	56,728	233,266	289,994
38	730,900	66,401	797,301	375,688	286,524	960,415	1,622,627	50,903	82,350	133,253
39	675,248	62,616	737,864	249,981	215,072	864,701	1,329,754	93,467	149,075	242,542
40	588,714	0	588,714	379,627	96,497	731,522	1,207,646	187,615	0	187,615
41	670,598	59,858	730,456	157,994	525,252	383,181	1,066,427	86,657	85,930	172,587
42	487,008	25,000	512,008	173,986	100,344	442,690	717,020	53,915	92,328	146,243
43	562,860	70,735	633,595	203,994	75,376	232,016	511,386	30,203	65,369	95,572
44	626,606	47,588	674,194	91,871	30,490	166,866	289,227	161,536	0	161,536
45	547,010	55,664	602,674	93,162	54,587	92,237	239,986	43,405	109,959	153,364
46	668,037	50,000	718,037	200,000	50,000	83,010	333,010	51,880	0	51,880
47	776,610	0	776,610	92,154	0	162,966	255,120	21,900	0	21,900
48	644,461	17,152	661,613	113,076	0	160,643	273,719	40,752	0	40,752
49	516,241	0	516,241	20,922	56,653	281,975	359,550	32,898	75,410	108,308
50	691,609	0	691,609	64,634	6,364	14,320	85,318	88,484	0	88,484
51	452,734	34,806	487,540	101,002	2,022	126,240	229,264	76,935	26,801	103,736
52	266,147	0	266,147	109,225	14,481	274,525	398,231	35,308	26,819	62,127
53	462,918	23,181	486,099	6,528	1,109	57,853	65,490	96,195	0	96,195
54	340,285	0	340,285	107,548	29,354	283,252	420,154	30,412	13,545	43,957
55	427,588	50,300	477,888	32,110	9,500	43,069	84,679	62,457	35,000	97,457
56	266,731	48,136	314,867	97,263	44,068	202,123	343,454	30,356	53,082	83,438
57	344,862	84,122	428,984	81,403	24,191	103,490	209,084	52,190	63,032	115,222
58	423,416	39,000	462,416	49,828	29,090	35,610	114,528	66,365	0	66,365
59	474,486	64,084	538,570	44,564	2,640	11,555	58,759	51,322	35,482	86,804
60	303,804	23,484	327,288	19,855	25,910	115,353	161,118	91,199	0	91,199
61	408,941	11,893	420,834	30,338	9,658	108,458	148,454	60,731	0	60,731
62	427,443	0	427,443	44,269	33,348	67,112	144,729	69,468	0	69,468
63	199,305	0	199,305	115,420	0	141,068	256,488	—	—	130,825
64	272,492	0	272,492	94,029	0	82,357	176,386	66,238	0	66,238
65	406,937	0	406,937	4,569	125	37,224	41,918	84,766	0	84,766
66	201,777	0	201,777	112,917	0	99,989	212,906	51,696	0	51,696
67	270,670	0	270,670	16,908	4,029	14,016	34,953	54,562	60,008	114,570
68	211,387	0	211,387	55,570	0	66,872	122,442	64,253	0	64,253
69	182,229	28,313	210,542	5,886	4,718	21,018	31,622	48,367	68,029	116,396
70	195,016	56,206	251,222	6,836	53,841	5,132	65,809	28,334	0	28,334
71	226,996	0	226,996	70,665	0	1,048	71,713	48,862	0	48,862

* Estimated.
† Self-supporting—not in budget.
— Indicates expenditures not segregated but kept in total.
0 Indicates no expenditures from medical school budget.

EXPENDITURES OF 71 FOUR-YEAR MEDICAL SCHOOLS

Libraries	Postgraduate Education	Maintenance	Student Health	Other Expenditures	Hospitals and Clinics	Total	Total Exclusive of Hospitals and Clinics
SCHOOLS							
$48,996*	$523,849	$976,528*	—	0	$3,356,519	$7,885,105	$4,528,586
43,362	14,071	88,130	$ 21,824	0	2,449,097	5,843,492	3,394,395
33,905	42,363	579,909	18,369	$180,674	1,815,817	5,085,923	3,270,106
67,954	10,917	213,500	135,598	0	0	2,551,685	2,551,685
49,672	39,647	120,044	18,381	0	7,129,590	9,489,302	2,359,712
58,800	10,400	328,550	12,900	105,800	2,844,617	4,965,728	2,121,111
8,533	0	70,636	3,573	79,354	0	1,891,013	1,891,013
13,514	0	53,378	2,753	0	5,171,684	6,929,986	1,758,302
44,331	11,849	226,500	2,457	15,988	2,665,856	4,320,325	1,654,469
41,762	0	260,139	1,775	0	1,753,248	3,363,258	1,610,010
18,051	11,543	61,508	0	67,348	0	1,448,573	1,448,573
21,785	7,547	234,048	7,031	0	2,381,887	3,753,267	1,371,380
15,575	0	75,478	96,968	0	0†	1,280,324	1,280,324
33,760	12,895	259,497	0	20,823	701,410	1,938,940	1,237,530
0	0	0	0	0	0	1,129,616	1,129,616
0	10,200	82,240	0	0	0	1,093,844	1,093,844
13,753	0	117,339	4,147	22,756	0	998,349	998,349
36,189	6,400	60,760	3,600	0	20,250	989,969	969,719
21,435	23,823	35,340	0	24,342	4,042,948	5,001,611	958,663
9,519	0	21,750	0	4,448	23,696	870,770	847,074
12,429	3,679	63,000	5,000	29,370	0	775,262	775,262
26,648	0	78,967	9,331	13,153	0	773,060	773,060
18,487	0	84,041	1,509	93,499	759,503	1,525,063	765,560
15,000	6,000	152,000	4,150	0	39,250	790,750	751,500
36,252	0	51,181	4,343	0	25,487	773,394	747,907
23,761	54,227	40,857	5,580	9,567	0	703,312	703,312
12,280	7,103	94,984	7,160	0	23,760	694,076	670,316
12,662	0	62,116	0	2,117	192,551	780,775	588,224
18,123	16,047	31,839	0	13,741	0	558,143	558,143
23,000	0	46,000	8,000	0	0	457,000	457,000
SUPPORTED SCHOOLS							
81,510	95,840	293,353	8,245	0	0	5,007,791	5,007,791
—	0	—	—	0	4,106,140	8,713,605	4,607,465
23,895	0	66,181	6,426	129,760	3,701,282	7,150,048	3,448,766
38,956	111,096	378,520	0	0	0	3,176,334	3,176,334
11,000	0	66,644	44,508	8,000	30,185	2,978,314	2,948,129
31,194	23,205	110,958	15,065	827,486	0	2,895,095	2,895,095
60,979	14,500	220,218	3,227	41,128	129,375	2,957,055	2,827,680
29,848	0	168,409	0	0	0	2,751,438	2,751,438
0	0	191,125	9,380	0	0	2,510,665	2,510,665
17,171	15,506	106,540	2,500	122,878	364,349	2,612,919	2,248,570
12,560	1,560	174,334	5,928	53,502	0	2,217,354	2,217,354
36,275	21,987	173,666	10,000	0	306,247	1,923,446	1,617,199
25,330	18,506	139,409	5,720	16,260	32,741	1,478,519	1,445,778
53,600	0	234,724	6,776	0	0	1,420,057	1,420,057
34,203	0	99,526	6,799	82,076	208,992	1,427,620	1,218,628
19,718	—	71,000	0	0	3,000,000	4,193,645	1,193,645
24,535	0	102,000	4,990	0	0	1,185,155	1,185,155
49,669	4,581	36,901	0	0	192,487	1,259,722	1,067,235
6,448	0	75,385	0	0	115,049	1,180,981	1,065,932
23,652	0	72,280	3,952	9,928	0	975,223	975,223
25,285	0	53,591	1,560	10,029	9,406	920,411	911,005
3,770	49,740	45,942	6,105	65,322	5,589	902,973	897,384
42,725	25,940	127,311	0	21,925	5,033,454	5,899,139	865,685
8,228	0	37,397	0	0	0	850,021	850,021
14,488	2,405	91,853	4,321	71,209	0	844,300	844,300
9,960	10,215	63,475	14,002	0	0	839,411	839,411
9,446	—	71,656	0	0	0	834,392	834,392
26,691	28,300	120,891	3,000	0	67,560	889,751	822,191
23,401	0	37,076	49,599	0	0	794,209	794,209
8,774	23,165	101,853	2,750	46,592	210,058	972,797	762,739
22,941	1,442	48,222	13,920	35,003	57,791	809,338	751,547
1,470	0	88,229	4,920	0	0	736,259	736,259
22,461	0	110,927	0	0	0	720,006	720,006
13,278	0	0	3,426	185,971	0	717,791	717,791
5,734	0	39,079	6,354	89,261	0	674,049	674,049
6,611	0	29,470	3,298	61,632	268,556	835,946	567,390
13,896	0	35,118	2,368	0	0	471,575	471,575
14,754	0	40,622	0	11,467	24,813	489,738	464,925
13,168	0	50,169	0	0	0	421,897	421,897
—	0	39,441	0	31,750	86,378	502,934	416,556
0	0	40,991	397	26,886	0	415,845	415,845

Table 62. FISCAL YEAR 1947–48,

School No.	Instruction			Research Budgeted Separately				Administration		
	All Except USPHS	USPHS	Total	Federal		All Other	Total	Medical School	Share of University	Total
				USPHS	Contracts					

30 TAX-SUPPORTED

1	$ 971,129	$97,198	$1,068,327	$235,465	$ 77,525	$596,409	$ 909,399	$ 42,471	$349,225*	$391,696
2	1,080,048	3,834	1,083,882	81,323	0	303,018	384,341	59,147	225,000	284,147
3	1,301,148	0	1,301,148	37,484	81,705	173,527	292,716	45,259	151,499	196,758
4	728,848	0	728,848	90,704	66,026	0	156,730	71,367	61,299	132,666
5	799,423	0	799,423	170,846	22,793	212,386	406,025	41,178	134,232	175,410
6	813,166	4,562	817,728	31,292	74,077	143,190	248,559	225,513	0	225,513
7	512,603	4,650	517,253	139,744	0	303,580	443,324	37,124	0	37,124
8	1,079,190	0	1,079,190	9,917	16,079	125,687	151,683	14,043	31,972	46,015
9	564,425	8,318	572,743	11,818	2,699	30,891	45,408	136,779	128,864	265,643
10	663,688	10,172	673,860	33,839	15,707	48,667	98,213	52,008	105,118	157,126
11	327,172	0	327,172	93,119	65,679	76,054	234,852	72,380	4,395	76,775
12	211,504	0	211,504	24,459	8,581	12,931	45,971	14,345	0	14,345
13	484,024	0	484,024	28,799	0	162,923	191,722	40,454	25,420	65,874
14	416,915	2,433	419,348	6,057	8,917	77,673	92,647	95,477	0	95,477
15	282,735	6,511	289,246	159,390	11,319	136,365	307,074	19,263	21,625	40,888
16	482,469	6,202	488,671	44,957	0	61,814	106,771	36,000	0	36,000
17	356,500	24,927	381,427	81,246	0	68,450	149,696	29,500	0	29,500
18	321,220	0	321,220	4,409	28,746	32,289	65,444	32,560	61,922	94,482
19	342,732	0	342,732	11,228	97,402	42,099	150,729	13,814	37,614	51,428
20	338,218	8,558	346,776	20,021	0	3,695	23,716	23,114	19,579	42,693
21	272,759	24,800	297,559	24,227	40,112	21,792	86,131	5,800	11,952	17,752
22	224,198	8,166	232,364	0	0	0	0	45,214	0	45,214
23	304,657	3,047	307,704	6,327	0	17,316	23,643	66,406	12,000	78,406
24	288,450	0	288,450	9,748	0	0	9,748	25,050	0	25,050
25	251,096	0	251,096	14,614	0	19,247	33,861	58,211	0	58,211
26	266,460	0	266,460	25,115	0	23,346	48,461	42,248	0	42,248
27	322,715	0	322,715	2,200	9,440	22,461	34,101	18,254	26,287	44,541
28	233,565	0	233,565	46,431	0	33,143	79,574	24,016	0	24,016
29	284,276	4,069	288,345	1,798	0	24,949	26,747	15,994	27,889	43,883
30	240,704	0	240,704	0	6,200	800	7,000	38,610	5,361	43,971

41 PRIVATELY

31	2,293,888	11,097	2,304,985	291,528	266,350	62,000	619,878	99,061	392,420	491,481
32	1,339,870	16,816	1,356,686	176,467	213,652	716,989	1,107,108	30,090	160,838	190,928
33	948,028	0	948,028	133,352	1,225,771	81,821	1,440,944	93,770	92,504	186,274
34	1,587,926	10,869	1,598,795	223,558	300,403	0	523,961	52,710	0	52,710
35	1,042,179	0	1,042,179	273,867	87,818	554,184	915,869	101,569	45,080	146,649
36	779,418	1,620	781,038	129,823	26,626	349,565	506,014	70,816	53,355	124,171
37	775,083	25,000	800,083	114,239	0	502,683	616,922	54,115	202,834	256,949
38	776,114	14,654	790,768	121,474	145,441	217,888	484,803	32,691	69,618	102,309
39	565,459	0	565,459	227,270	7,793	731,424	966,487	114,620	43,922	158,542
40	561,949	0	561,949	170,418	82,492	585,427	838,337	109,849	0	109,849
41	627,234	0	627,234	88,562	206,526	278,619	573,707	45,973	31,951	77,924
42	398,391	0	398,391	144,178	67,322	342,572	554,072	52,161	81,839	134,000
43	505,506	0	505,506	76,151	113,716	47,059	236,926	37,667	61,607	99,274
44	432,935	0	432,935	31,953	15,868	42,553	90,374	152,119	—	152,119
45	409,688	0	409,688	102,095	12,308	132,665	247,068	38,032	91,639	129,671
46	679,810	19,535	699,345	32,017	9,069	180,015	221,101	31,934	19,234	51,168
47	325,633	0	325,633	21,747	0	59,525	81,272	26,621	17,830	44,451
48	472,471	0	472,471	14,247	40,862	314,492	369,601	25,888	41,508	67,396
49	281,771	0	281,771	0	0	60,013	60,013	23,983	46,449	70,432
50	340,842	0	340,842	23,470	0	68,318	91,788	205,659	0	205,659
51	371,486	23,491	394,977	40,167	4,088	155,648	199,903	47,766	25,816	73,582
52	211,266	4,664	215,930	24,252	0	105,209	129,461	7,250	20,194	27,444
53	306,920	0	306,920	4,093	0	64,617	68,710	85,255	0	85,255
54	376,050	0	376,050	17,730	0	33,035	50,765	29,016	8,395	37,411
55	211,698	0	211,698	4,418	0	16,518	20,936	44,873	0	44,873
56	250,524	0	250,524	51,309	41,745	36,057	129,111	16,711	65,500	82,211
57	190,326	38,381	228,707	15,602	56,769	48,660	121,031	25,628	51,811	77,439
58	304,148	0	304,148	30,053	0	80,315	110,368	43,650	5,000	48,650
59	375,615	7,730	383,345	2,837	0	7,652	10,489	37,837	20,771	58,608
60	278,128	0	278,128	3,734	88,523	63,065	155,322	83,804	0	83,804
61	280,167	10,171	290,338	17,994	0	91,181	109,175	31,130	124,374	155,504
62	243,850	0	243,850	9,172	0	11,805	20,977	42,074	0	42,074
63	389,298	16,375	405,673	31,475	408	26,465	58,348	46,074	0	46,074
64	108,710	0	108,710	6,591	0	18,215	24,806	40,756	0	40,756
65	211,526	0	211,526	0	0	0	0	61,880	0	61,880
66	263,348	0	263,348	3,731	0	48,540	52,271	36,343	0	36,343
67	136,284	239	136,523	1,162	4,375	16,634	22,171	55,524	19,317	74,841
68	161,883	10,343	172,226	13,541	0	8,673	22,214	33,672	9,023	42,695
69	125,382	0	125,382	2,251	3,153	3,794	9,198	15,053	25,694	40,747
70	212,173	6,922	219,095	15,701	15,304	0	31,005	29,258	34,123	63,381
71	148,083	0	148,083	2,750	0	8,262	11,012	43,940	0	43,940

Source: Figures supplied by the Surgeon General's Committee on Medical School Grants and Finances.
* Estimated.
— Indicates expenditures not segregated but kept in total.
0 Indicates no expenditures from medical school budget.

EXPENDITURES OF 71 FOUR-YEAR MEDICAL SCHOOLS

Libraries	Postgraduate Education	Maintenance	Student Health	Other Expenditures	Hospitals and Clinics	Total	Total Exclusive of Hospitals and Clinics
SCHOOLS							
$37,480*	$600,849	$844,866*	$26,597	$ 48,238	$2,812,833	$6,740,285	$3,927,452
26,667	0	103,259	0	19,004	2,194,785	4,096,085	1,901,300
27,349	36,626	527,732	0	116,023	1,683,007	4,181,359	2,498,352
49,040	0	81,733	5,407	0	0	1,154,424	1,154,424
34,990	45,954	88,536	12,090	584,260	5,264,577	7,411,265	2,146,688
41,887	10,861	132,353	9,828	22,121	2,223,036	3,731,886	1,508,850
41,881	0	67,297	3,016	6,257	0	1,116,152	1,116,152
13,087	17,843	147,704	1,077	9,251	0	1,465,850	1,465,850
22,654	7,126	75,705	1,017	946,711	2,216,567	4,153,574	1,937,007
21,044	0	160,572	2,661	7,892	1,460,838	2,582,206	1,121,368
16,223	12,690	69,010	0	57,642	0	794,364	794,364
17,279	22,298	63,867	6,489	1,800	1,979,062	2,362,615	383,553
16,250	0	46,166	57,814	0	0	861,850	861,850
24,552	60,859	119,708	3,849	190,677	490,501	1,497,618	1,007,117
3,807	0	28,661	557	14,488	0	684,721	684,721
27,000	0	92,752	0	1,460	0	752,654	752,654
8,750	0	91,750	3,500	138,566	0	803,189	803,189
23,810	5,971	42,204	2,633	54,085	0	609,849	609,849
10,655	11,756	26,687	0	19,647	0	613,634	613,634
16,012	0	20,152	0	45,421	13,012	507,782	494,770
10,695	10,389	62,802	4,789	10,682	0	500,799	500,799
22,799	0	30,009	0	36,796	0	367,182	367,182
12,686	0	72,396	0	209,596	344,223	1,048,654	704,431
17,000	6,000	155,000	0	0	15,000	516,248	501,248
50,910	0	19,796	1,530	204,412	74,151	693,967	619,816
18,064	0	26,988	0	8,284	0	410,505	410,505
17,768	3,573	108,507	3,638	15,247	2,349,735	2,899,825	550,090
5,766	0	63,581	0	27,810	76,675	510,987	434,312
13,051	0	33,055	22	12,368	8,094	425,565	417,471
24,539	0	50,402	5,380	32,000	0	403,996	403,996
SUPPORTED SCHOOLS							
54,915	137,396	227,324	7,469	87,532	0	3,930,980	3,930,980
78,906	0	289,131	—	34,298	3,541,883	6,598,940	3,057,057
19,729	0	84,047	7,655	51,057	2,660,063	5,397,797	2,737,734
35,252	117,318	284,694	0	214,087	0	2,826,817	2,826,817
11,000	0	62,280	0	183,026	236,684	2,597,687	2,361,003
24,234	22,998	111,121	13,614	473,443	0	2,056,633	2,056,633
44,040	0	234,665	0	94,330	176,375	2,223,364	2,046,989
19,430	0	95,278	0	3,100	0	1,495,688	1,495,688
21,938	119,754	225,239	0	5,986	0	2,063,405	2,063,405
15,716	39,086	126,570	2,566	137,243	294,529	2,125,845	1,831,316
9,594	0	212,872	0	34,311	0	1,535,642	1,535,642
37,953	0	218,492	0	48,896	269,864	1,661,668	1,391,804
21,957	0	131,933	0	27,703	13,943	1,037,242	1,023,299
8,151	0	74,328	0	77,479	0	835,386	835,386
43,622	11,751	78,115	4,748	36,188	66,700	1,027,551	960,851
16,716	0	41,764	7,942	14,883	230,777	1,283,696	1,052,919
4,722	20,395	67,107	0	630	0	544,210	544,210
13,392	0	47,713	0	4,427	1,161,298	2,136,298	975,000
7,796	0	81,187	430	24,830	144,406	670,865	526,459
12,153	16,050	60,427	3,199	115,671	0	845,789	845,789
20,781	0	55,846	4,401	0	1,294,072	2,043,562	749,490
4,335	122,829	46,147	3,313	32,202	81,170	662,831	581,661
19,088	30,342	211,310	0	968,097	3,046,216	4,735,938	1,689,722
6,805	0	28,097	276	26,797	0	526,201	526,201
9,500	0	30,657	6,120	207,598	0	531,382	531,382
10,900	49,192	60,400	28,100	22,350	90,000	722,788	632,788
7,745	0	45,489	—	8,252	0	488,663	488,663
18,398	0	71,812	0	15,650	—	569,026	569,026
15,904	0	32,136	1,897	6,431	0	508,810	508,810
8,927	29,616	78,718	3,807	28,943	152,366	819,631	667,265
12,349	0	42,803	4,036	1,309	856,592	1,472,106	615,514
7,057	0	42,955	685	1,965	0	359,563	359,563
18,500	0	47,366	4,576	8,100	0	588,637	588,637
10,297	0	13,108	1,500	86,347	66,030	351,554	285,524
10,248	0	30,128	0	27,872	59,888	401,542	341,654
6,173	0	19,707	0	63,310	0	441,152	441,152
7,472	0	32,759	1,678	160,097	100,350	535,891	435,541
12,651	0	47,025	2,043	0	15,915	314,769	298,854
7,824	0	62,144	2,692	0	0	247,987	247,987
8,984	0	28,636	0	0	0	351,101	351,101
5,970	0	36,883	3,529	9,290	0	258,707	258,707

Table 63. FISCAL YEAR 1940–41, EXPENDITURES OF 65 FOUR-YEAR MEDICAL SCHOOLS

27 TAX-SUPPORTED SCHOOLS

School No.	Instruction			Research Budgeted Separately				Administration			Libraries	Post-graduate Education	Maintenance	Student Health	Other Expenditures	Hospitals and Clinics	Total	Total Exclusive of Hospitals and Clinics
	All Except USPHS	USPHS	Total	Federal USPHS	Federal Contracts	All Other	Total	Medical School	Share of University	Total								
1	$376,636	$15,685	$392,321	0	0	$132,672	$132,672	$24,074	$125,393	$149,467	$13,457	$340,243	$303,358	$13,950	$18,312	$1,027,969	$2,391,749	$1,363,780
2	464,582	0	464,582	0	0	105,550	105,550	8,272		8,272	16,760	0	50,354	0	6,750	826,363	1,478,631	652,268
3	561,049	0	561,049	0	0	59,072	59,072	19,865	25,695	45,560	17,175	0	148,332	0	536	0	831,724	831,724
5	449,476	0	449,476	0	0	125,280	125,280	18,341	82,052	100,393	24,464	16,094	38,503	8,871	130,908	2,074,644	2,968,633	893,989
6	281,149	0	281,149	0	0	0	0	54,008		54,008	8,565	0	37,312	2,460	465	547,769	931,728	383,959
7	370,077	0	370,077	0	0	143,953	143,953	25,311		25,311	20,325	0	42,821	0	4,000	0	606,487	606,487
8	346,651	0	346,651	0	0	101,935	101,935	10,922	12,361	23,283	6,721	0	59,741	903	571	0	539,805	539,805
9	214,318	0	214,318	0	0	17,501	17,501	87,422	75,101	162,523	3,962	4,376	37,240	0	260,261	910,498	1,610,679	700,181
10	282,969	0	282,969	0	0	21,452	21,452	22,827	63,024	85,851	0	0	96,502	2,000	1,003	431,863	921,640	489,777
11	120,881	0	120,881	0	0	0	0	4,500		4,500	7,873	0	7,585	35,586	40,542	0	216,967	216,967
12	77,746	0	77,746	0	0	0	0	9,217		9,217	6,884	0	41,990	0	0	567,398	703,235	135,837
13	303,992	0	303,992	0	0	54,522	54,522	28,372	13,980	42,352	11,090	0	40,818	37,574	0	0	490,348	490,348
14	165,916	0	165,916	0	0	17,464	17,464	25,723		25,723	12,051	0	56,366	0	43,087	233,024	553,631	320,607
15	49,679	0	49,679	0	0	2,003	2,003	1,145	5,695	6,840	0	0	7,104	125	0	0	65,751	65,751
16	233,998	0	233,998	0	0	26,343	26,343	24,900		24,900	0	0	49,505	0	0	0	334,746	334,746
17	158,421	0	158,421	0	0	16,374	16,374	13,725		13,725	7,557	0	20,136	2,765	53,747	0	272,725	272,725
18	249,907	0	249,907	0	0	782	782	17,228		17,228	14,303	3,410	20,601	4,067	3,869	0	314,167	314,167
19	130,148	0	130,148	0	0	11,942	11,942	3,264	20,289	23,553	8,721	0	11,250	0	0	0	185,614	185,614
20	181,776	0	181,776	0	0	3,745	3,745	8,374	5,853	14,227	7,345	0	3,892	0	17,312	470	228,767	228,297
21	193,898	0	193,898	0	0	8,343	8,343	Not available		78,406	0	0	0	—	0	0	202,941	202,941
22	130,807	0	130,807	0	0	19,357	19,357	25,897		25,897	4,455	0	14,125	0	20,135	0	214,776	214,776
23	124,656	0	124,656	0	0	0	0	32,533	5,000	37,533	4,941	0	53,212	0	87,601	144,258	452,201	307,943
24				No information												15,000	242,373	227,373
27	196,096	0	196,096	0	0	12,672	12,672	4,875	37,114	41,989	6,420	0	20,874	2,537	9,065	541,281	830,934	289,653
28	110,009	0	110,009	0	0	17,252	17,252	10,341		10,341	3,416	0	22,254	0	9,613	12,000	184,885	172,885
29	133,785	0	133,785	0	0	1,904	1,904	9,129		9,129	2,399	0	11,300	0	5,000	0	163,517	163,517
30	68,730	0	68,730	0	0	0	0	19,650	6,476	26,126	8,826	0	23,120	4,729	12,000	0	143,531	143,531

38 PRIVATELY SUPPORTED SCHOOLS

School	1	2	3	4	5	6	7	8	9	10	11	12	13	14	15	16	17	18	19
31	1,711,050	0	0	0	0	295,409	300,500	30,446	240,050	270,496	27,986	0	130,242	0	4,140	102,273	0	2,246,187	2,246,187
32	889,710	0	0	$5,091	0	0	4,474	1,941	113,067	115,008	74,953	0	154,733	0	—	0	1,751,365	3,286,269	1,534,904
33	642,281	0	0	0	$4,474	357,473	377,411	45,363	20,604	65,967	16,155	0	19,829	0	3,466	8,413	1,220,553	1,981,138	760,585
35	567,203	0	0	0	19,938	190,494	190,494	55,765	31,583	87,348	10,000	0	40,232	0	0	34,418	220,066	1,336,678	1,116,612
36	434,110	0	0	0	0	389,419	389,419	35,783	9,736	45,519	12,608	0	48,155	0	3,504	424,953	0	1,159,343	1,159,343
37	590,531	0	0	0	0	118,538	118,538	45,966	28,920	74,886	23,773	0	138,350	0	—	19,691	146,003	1,382,653	1,236,650
38	559,718	0	0	0	0	197,551	197,551	22,081	29,942	52,023	8,367	0	35,875	0	0	1,361	0	775,882	775,882
39	396,678	0	0	0	0	279,493	279,493	69,034	26,370	95,404	10,084	0	126,775	0	0	0	0	834,613	834,613
40	440,002	0	0	0	0	129,618	132,392	64,091	0	64,091	11,975	0	65,207	0	8,121	0	251,080	1,125,924	874,844
41	220,656	0	0	0	2,774	94,755	94,755	16,240	23,762	40,002	2,037	261	89,263	0	0	14,076	0	492,185	492,185
42	250,460	0	0	0	0	985	985	27,440	52,475	79,915	21,823	0	84,992	0	0	7,574	167,642	729,696	562,054
43	341,587	0	0	0	0	0	0	50,737	0	50,737	9,188	0	51,180	0	0	30,109	0	470,331	470,331
44	181,117	0	0	0	0	3,035	3,035	84,639	0	84,639	6,009	0	27,686	0	0	16,654	0	339,626	339,626
45	124,891	0	0	0	0	102,264	102,264	8,954	29,908	38,862	7,279	0	13,060	0	1,296	40,175	0	188,423	188,423
46	428,645	0	0	0	0	0	0	17,834	9,101	26,935	8,165	6,331	—	0	4,508	0	309,893	880,410	570,517
47	147,348	0	0	0	0	83,555	83,555	18,887	13,044	31,931	3,740	0	29,258	0	0	8,500	0	227,108	227,108
48	365,426	0	0	0	0	31,454	31,454	10,495	26,288	36,783	16,332	0	25,614	0	0	1,359	526,933	1,056,002	529,069
49	169,397	0	0	0	0	0	0	13,674	35,438	49,112	5,370	0	36,499	0	639	27,426	60,945	380,842	319,897
50	264,999	0	0	0	0	143,280	143,280	55,875	0	55,875	6,678	0	32,257	0	3,435	3,809	0	367,050	367,053
51	306,170	0	0	0	0	59,546	59,546	38,095	17,567	38,095	6,682	0	38,378	0	0	0	543,630	1,076,235	532,605
52	142,255	0	0	0	0	0	0	4,382	0	21,949	2,172	0	23,339	0	62	14,533	45,249	309,105	263,856
53	155,338	0	0	0	0	0	0	35,768	14,977	35,768	14,087	0	35,183	0	0	374,997	1,346,032	1,961,405	615,373
54	116,299	0	0	0	0	0	0	8,639	0	33,616	5,579	0	17,388	0	0	9,756	0	182,638	182,638
55	134,984	0	0	0	0	0	0	20,773	0	20,773	4,288	0	12,929	0	0	176,001	0	348,975	348,975
56	142,352	0	0	0	0	4,720	4,720	19,959	7,360	22,319	8,050	10,607	27,800	0	19,200	0	0	240,048	240,048
57	89,665	0	0	0	0	4,472	4,472	32,765	32,373	45,138	2,938	0	9,130	0	—	7,810	0	159,153	159,153
58	269,925	0	0	0	0	9,540	9,540	17,614	5,000	22,614	12,232	0	24,126	0	0	3,847	0	342,284	342,284
59	166,198	0	0	0	0	0	0	14,216	10,273	24,489	8,110	0	8,285	0	555	2,205	—	209,842	209,842
60	187,825	0	0	0	0	8,196	8,196	12,230	0	45,420	5,039	4,372	34,480	0	0	39,804	67,684	392,820	325,136
61	110,069	0	0	0	0	20,482	20,482	26,400	48,505	60,735	3,421	0	16,816	0	1,943	810	427,944	642,220	214,276
63	229,961	0	0	0	0	0	0	21,399	0	26,400	4,000	0	38,250	0	0	0	0	294,611	294,611
64	62,382	0	0	0	0	40,439	40,439	21,399	0	19,375	7,979	0	9,939	0	1,250	8,048	43,585	189,018	145,433
65	44,245	0	0	0	0	0	0	32,226	11,868	21,399	2,476	0	13,753	0	0	4,491	29,000	120,867	91,867
67	125,739	0	0	0	0	12,778	12,778	18,717	9,044	44,094	6,809	0	32,336	0	918	0	100,350	318,691	218,341
68	89,602	0	0	0	0	3,495	3,495	—	6,412	27,761	4,384	0	15,647	0	1,830	55,966	9,947	211,057	201,110
69	82,443	0	0	0	0	739	739	—	6,412	6,412	—	0	17,350	0	2,656	0	0	113,984	113,984
70	86,747	0	0	0	0	0	0	7,148	0	7,148	—	0	8,810	0	0	0	0	102,705	102,705
71	87,114	0	0	0	0	0	0	20,008	0	20,008	3,112	0	11,523	0	0	10,646	0	132,403	132,403

Source: Figures supplied by the Surgeon General's Committee on Medical School Grants and Finances.
— Indicates that expenditures not segregated but kept in total.
0 Indicates no expenditures from medical school budget.
No information on schools 4, 25, 26, 34, 62, and 66.

Table 64. EXPENDITURES OF TWO-YEAR MEDICAL SCHOOLS IN FISCAL YEARS 1940–41, 1947–48, AND 1950–51

School No.	Instruction — All Except USPHS	Instruction — USPHS	Instruction — Total	Research Budgeted Separately — Federal USPHS	Research — Federal Contracts	Research — All Other	Research — Total	Administration — Medical School	Administration — Share of University	Administration — Total	Libraries	Separately Organized Postgrad. Education	Maintenance	Student Health	All Other Expenditures	Hospitals and Clinics	Total	Total Exclusive of Hospitals and Clinics
1940–41*																		
72	$ 21,500	0	$ 21,500	0	0	0	0	$ 7,500	$ 5,000	$12,500	$ 1,000	0	$10,000	0	0	0	$ 45,000	$ 45,000
73	68,866	0	68,866	0	0	$10,106	$10,106	3,677	2,555	6,232	1,214	$ 2,839	20,000	$ 1,215	$ 409	0	110,881	110,881
74	42,727	0	42,727	0	0	0	0	4,364	2,164	6,528	0	0	0	137	0	0	49,392	49,392
75	29,354	0	29,354	0	0	0	0	2,546	3,120	5,666	1,560	0	5,504	450	0	0	42,534	42,534
76	50,900	0	50,900	0	0	0	0	3,826	6,500	10,326	5,000	0	8,248	1,650	0	0	76,124	76,124
77	57,686	0	57,686	0	0	0	0	5,200	751	5,951	546	0	2,016	162	0	0	66,361	66,361
1947–48*																		
72	49,400	0	49,400	0	0	0	0	5,000	5,000	10,000	1,050	0	20,000	0	0	0	80,450	80,450
73	165,688	0	165,688	$15,258	0	7,501	22,759	9,041	5,056	14,097	4,283	6,937	30,000	1,660	150	0	245,574	245,574
74	149,836	0	149,836	0	0	0	0	15,429	16,893	32,322	6,260	0	18,889	886	0	0	208,193	208,193
75	93,443	0	93,443	0	$ 2,689	1,357	4,046	12,911	7,395	20,306	8,000	0	10,670	685	4,450	0	141,600	141,600
76	80,476	0	80,476	0	0	0	0	9,157	9,000	18,157	8,000	22,285	23,622	2,400	0	0	154,940	154,940
77	97,953	0	97,953	0	0	0	0	12,900	4,182	17,082	2,695	0	10,128	569	0	0	128,427	128,427
1950–51																		
72	294,107	$ 5,000	299,107	18,376	26,000	37,572	81,948	25,670	9,356	35,026	23,000	0	0	12,592	7,500	0	459,173	459,173
73	262,615	5,000	267,615	59,850	0	16,950	76,800	—	—	—	28,500	0	38,166	0	0	0	411,081	411,081
74	152,397	0	152,397	25,880	0	14	25,894	16,334	27,097	43,431	10,456	0	27,212	0	5,196	0	264,586	264,586
75	141,869	10,000	151,869	17,344	0	18,328	35,672	14,580	0	14,580	9,280	0	—	3,300	0	$3,850	218,551	214,701
76	83,451	0	83,451	4,910	400	3,410	8,720	10,808	12,000	22,808	8,000	44,035	19,348	2,600	0	0	188,962	188,962
77	71,590	5,000	76,590	7,300	0	0	7,300	17,750	0	17,750	—	—	—	0	0	0	101,640	101,640

* 1940–41 and 1947–48 figures supplied by the Surgeon General's Committee on Medical School Grants and Finances.
— Indicate expenditures not segregated but kept in total.
0 Indicates no expenditures from medical school budget.

Table 65. THE SURVEY'S QUESTIONNAIRE TO ALL MEDICAL SCHOOLS REGARD-
ING INCOME

Finances	
Amount of income for the fiscal year in which the medical school is surveyed. Line items:	
19. *Tuition and Fees*	. . . .
a. Undergraduate (medical)	. . . .
b. Postgraduate (medical)	. . . .
c. All other tuition fees received by the medical school	. . . .
20. *All Income from Endowment Investments*	. . . .
a. Specifically designated for the medical school	. . . .
b. General university	. . . .
21. *Governmental Appropriations and Grants*	. . . .
a. Federal	. . . .
(1*a*) Research	. . . .
(1*b*) Instructional	. . . .
b. State	. . . .
c. County or city	. . . .
22. *Gifts and Grants from Private Sources*	. . . .
a. Research	. . . .
b. Instructional or nonrestricted	. . . .
23. *Income Received from Organized Activities Relating to Instructional Depart-* *ments*	. . . .
a. Hospitals and clinics	. . . .
b. All other	. . . .
24. *All Other Income Including Educational and Noneducational*	. . . .
(Specify type and source)	. . . .
25. *Total Income—Educational, Research, and General* (Items 19–24)	. . . .

Table 66. FISCAL YEAR 1950–51,

School No.	Tuition and Fees				Endowment			Governmental		
	Medical Under-graduate	Medical Post-graduate	All Other	Total	Medical School	University Used for Medical School	Total	Federal		Tota
								Research	Instruc-tion	
30 TAX-SUPPORTED										
1	$236,800	$ 53,757	0	$290,557	$ 185,232	0	$ 185,232	$ 666,061	$119,091	$ 785,152
2	Not itemized			71,300	96,987	0	96,987	1,539,247	46,000	1,585,247
3	221,317	35,022	0	256,339	1,489	0	1,489	321,572	61,178	382,750
4	91,234	0	0	91,234	3,951	$ 47,140	51,091	284,570	22,071	306,641
5	191,119	37,536	0	228,655	104,491	243,640	348,131	421,041	0	421,041
6	10,838	11,417	$ 79,202	101,457	43,989	0	43,989	209,814	25,000	234,814
7	230,058	0	4,610	234,668	0	180,056	180,056	222,809	117,946	340,755
8	92,858	5,283	0	98,141	5,867	0	5,867	85,196	24,964	110,160
9	159,092	12,460	10,240	181,792	7,036	1,477	8,513	69,450	34,700	104,150
10	Not available				?	?	16,449	112,888	27,700	140,588
11	211,422	28,764	22,832	263,018	0	0	0	236,628	109,704	346,332
12	106,229	0	0	106,229	0	0	0	127,497	50,980	178,477
13	Not available				6,839	0	6,839	103,160	0	103,160
14	109,627	12,960	19,413	142,000	20,192	0	20,192	71,859	38,941	110,800
15	77,851	—	—	77,851	0	34,732	34,732	811,782	17,178	828,960
16	131,250	18,270	0	149,520	0	0	0	94,808	38,943	133,751
17	209,076	0	52,238	261,314	0	0	0	47,585	39,621	87,206
18	77,069	3,275	19,839	100,183	0	14,831	14,831	50,267	81,423	131,690
19	170,811	2,516	18,412	191,739	3,498	949	4,447	247,401	55,641	303,042
20	228,677	—	275	228,952	5,229	0	5,229	97,350	20,400	117,750
21	130,563	3,679	0	134,242	10,763	0	10,763	215,252	37,119	252,371
22	93,313	0	0	93,313	"A con-siderable sum"	0	?	37,771	54,975	92,746
23	129,200	0	5,757	134,957	0	0	0	39,149	24,996	64,145
24	120,898	0	0	120,898	0	0	0	47,000	31,500	78,500
25	111,281	0	12,100	123,381	0	0	0	91,163	54,000	145,163
26	93,611	5,020	0	98,631	0	0	0	35,431	51,225	86,656
27	226,328	2,560	14,650	243,538	0	0	0	66,800	21,250	88,050
28	155,278	0	0	155,278	12,785	0	12,785	99,857	41,417	141,274
29	107,221	47,760	0	154,981	5,984	1,282	7,266	89,047	35,385	124,432
30	175,000	0	0	175,000	1,000	?	1,000	0	73,000	73,000
41 PRIVATELY										
31	353,638	95,840	62,612	512,090	375,651	1,326,206	1,701,857	1,294,301	24,894	1,319,195
32	177,840	0	368,640	546,480	1,402,616	0	1,402,616	1,051,534	67,275	1,118,809
33	175,351	0	0	175,351	857,548	50,116	907,664	1,838,394	6,000	1,844,394
34	429,226	119,124	11,799	560,149	856,271	70,135	926,406	822,395	79,347	901,742
35	241,652	10,530	3,670	255,852	828,404	0	828,404	619,672	0	619,672
36	345,957	31,853	0	377,810	765,020	144,000	909,020	351,009	45,843	396,852
37	218,539	3,000	0	221,539	494,472	0	494,472	631,365	96,549	727,914
38	329,978	0	12,890	342,868	404,959	2,000	406,959	662,212	66,401	728,613
39	366,225	0	25,088	391,313	178,279	0	178,279	527,669	0	527,669
40	277,193	6,488	6,365	290,046	482,660	0	482,660	410,046	57,000	467,046
41	255,457	10,634	2,461	268,552	402,890	0	402,890	628,424	59,858	688,282
42	460,645	8,533	40,466	509,644	319,700	123,284	442,984	295,901	25,000	320,901
43	332,867	54,052	0	386,919	336,910	0	336,910	279,370	70,735	350,105
44	451,500	12,480	8,373	472,353	78,046	0	78,046	129,840	50,633	180,473
45	168,705	0	0	168,705	147,734	172,252	319,986	147,749	55,664	203,413
46	217,500	20,000	15,500	253,000	0	464,810	464,810	250,000	50,000	300,000
47	340,800	0	0	340,800	143,255	69,575	212,830	59,782	40,232	100,014
48	194,570	12,535	77	207,182	83,564	599,693	683,257	113,076	17,151	130,227
49	170,032	3,985	0	174,017	67,415	0	67,415	77,575	0	77,575
50	265,753	3,050	0	268,803	117,400	0	117,400	56,279	15,819	72,098
51	124,492	2,765	16,760	144,017	512,983	0	512,983	103,023	56,755	159,778
52	326,101	24,293	0	350,394	23,783	0	23,783	123,706	0	123,706
53	264,292	31,000	0	295,292	0	0	0	8,120	25,000	33,120
54	182,236	3,794	0	186,030	1,200	0	1,200	136,902	0	136,902
55	261,000	3,384	0	264,384	2,510	0	2,510	41,610	50,300	91,910
56	220,379	10,215	32,557	263,151	2,400	2,786	5,186	141,331	48,136	189,467
57	220,012	0	9,295	229,307	33,562	0	33,562	105,594	84,122	189,716
58	384,170	3,800	14,897	402,867	162,989	6,138	169,127	79,118	39,000	118,118
59	101,781	0	0	101,781	23,971	712	24,683	47,204	565,560	612,764
60	379,941	25,214	0	405,155	19,662	100,876	120,538	47,440	25,000	72,440
61	170,117	3,410	4,559	178,086	21,985	0	21,985	66,504	48,855	115,359
62	221,381	0	0	221,381	0	3,406	3,406	58,474	19,143	77,617
63	381,399	3,750	1,275	386,424	0	0	0	105,653	39,019	144,672
64	161,967	2,426	0	164,393	40,339	0	40,339	55,889	37,448	93,337
65	214,042	0	0	214,042	4,375	0	4,375	6,254	43,525	49,779
66	135,737	9,006	0	144,743	120,712	0	120,712	76,096	46,755	122,851
67	235,872	0	0	235,872	6,878	0	6,878	22,179	53,607	75,786
68	255,709	2,588	19,270	277,567	47,563	0	47,563	22,611	43,406	66,017
69	208,900	0	0	208,900	13,557	0	13,557	15,919	36,810	52,729
70	117,325	100	4,628	122,053	0	0	0	65,810	56,206	122,016
71	120,150	3,500	0	123,650	39,780	0	39,780	17,469	63,818	81,287

— Indicates income not segregated but kept in total.
0 Indicates no income.

INCOME OF 71 FOUR-YEAR MEDICAL SCHOOLS

Appropriations			Gifts and Grants from Private Sources			Other Income	Hospitals and Clinics	Total	Total Exclusive of Hospitals and Clinics
State	City or County	Total Government	For Research	Nonrestricted	Total				
SCHOOLS									
$2,375,228	$762,255	$3,922,635	$512,580	$521,744	$1,034,324	$ 89,715	$1,302,439	$6,824,902	$5,522,463
87,147	0	1,672,394	218,596	17,585	236,181	0	1,660,268	3,737,130	2,076,862
3,977,495	0	4,360,245	269,901	0	269,901	30,886	167,062	5,085,922	4,918,860
1,821,061	0	2,127,702	287,943	36,140	324,083	0	0	2,594,110	2,594,110
941,937	0	1,362,978	366,040	29,592	395,632	67,622	7,191,211	9,594,229	2,403,018
1,400,000	0	1,634,814	253,962	157,965	411,927	0	2,887,000	5,079,187	2,192,187
0	Incl. under Univ.	340,755	327,062	84,388	411,450	724,085	0	1,891,014	1,891,014
1,041,771	0	1,151,931	171,065	0	171,065	2,885	5,407,167	6,837,056	1,429,889
1,040,595	0	1,144,745	150,630	27,567	178,197	134,352	2,750,154	4,397,753	1,647,599
1,918,198	0	2,058,786	0	0	0	1,344	1,286,679	3,363,258	2,076,579
441,948	0	788,280	140,387	226,498	366,885	11,752	0	1,429,935	1,429,935
1,067,500	0	1,245,977	108,525	78,000	186,525	100,000	2,057,255	3,695,986	1,638,731
867,378	0	970,538	196,909	0	196,909	0	0	1,174,286	1,174,286
828,218	0	939,018	75,616	46,786	122,402	49,725	723,264	1,996,601	1,273,337
360,748	0	1,189,708	208,485	0	208,485	5,685	0	1,516,461	1,516,461
43,213	668,040	845,004	74,200	0	74,200	0	25,100	1,093,824	1,068,724
545,795	0	633,001	34,100	9,490	43,590	60,444	0	998,349	998,349
765,539	0	897,229	46,050	1,080	47,130	0	20,250	1,079,623	1,059,373
243,811	0	546,853	86,986	23,823	110,809	104,815	4,042,948	5,001,611	958,663
125,000	125,000	367,750	79,607	13,002	92,609	42,484	23,847	760,871	737,024
325,132	0	577,503	31,550	1,204	32,754	20,000	0	775,262	775,262
500,000	0	592,746	47,888	50,680	98,568	3,674	0	788,301	788,301
1,201,210	0	1,265,355	14,800	0	14,800	98,420	163,921	1,677,453	1,513,532
525,602	0	604,102	26,500	0	26,500	0	39,250	790,750	751,500
650,430	0	795,593	38,409	15,000	53,409	43,082	0	1,015,465	1,015,465
408,722	0	495,378	10,282	47,663	57,945	4,784	0	656,738	656,738
304,380	0	392,430	103,730	19,338	123,068	7,656	0	766,692	766,692
475,000	7,500	623,774	37,352	0	37,352	847	14,925	844,961	830,036
202,399	3,100	329,931	12,405	11,086	23,491	1,155	24,435	541,259	516,824
163,000	0	236,000	40,000	0	40,000	0	0	452,000	452,000
SUPPORTED SCHOOLS									
17,800	37,396	1,374,391	$1,419,453		1,419,453	0	0	5,007,791	5,007,791
0	0	1,118,809	784,106		784,106	0	5,209,333	9,061,344	3,852,011
39,764	0	1,884,158	419,592	51,839	471,431	148,677	3,589,982	7,177,263	3,587,281
0	0	901,742	733,800	23,493	757,293	374,520	31,531	3,551,641	3,520,110
15,983	0	635,655	691,326	92,421	783,747	90,767	112,560	2,706,985	2,594,425
0	0	396,852	436,313		436,313	1,015,984	0	3,135,979	3,135,979
0	0	727,914	517,785	14,900	532,685	316,224	68,681	2,361,515	2,292,834
126,056	0	854,669	456,714	111,116	567,830	204,506	0	2,376,832	2,376,832
0	0	527,669	864,701	2	864,703	148,701	0	2,110,665	2,110,665
0	0	467,046	828,666	86,765	915,431	133,714	444,105	2,733,002	2,288,897
0	0	688,282	424,645	356,131	780,776	76,853	0	2,217,353	2,217,353
0	0	320,901	338,328	85,668	423,996	72,964	152,957	1,923,446	1,770,489
27,840	0	377,945	200,769	147,087	347,856	48,036	6,285	1,503,951	1,497,666
438,000	0	618,473	69,838	73,600	143,438	33,737	103,962	1,450,009	1,346,047
0	0	203,413	92,237	299,706	391,943	82,076	261,497	1,427,620	1,166,123
16,200	0	316,200	50,000	0	50,000	1,375	3,108,260	4,193,645	1,085,385
460,000	0	560,014	26,000	0	26,000	0	0	1,139,644	1,139,644
0	0	130,227	160,643	78,413	239,056	0	0	1,259,722	1,259,722
478,156	0	555,731	248,791	40,200	288,991	4,609	90,218	1,180,981	1,090,763
597,120	0	669,218	30,283	0	30,283	42,891	0	1,128,595	1,128,595
0	0	159,778	126,240	2,861	129,101	18,303	0	964,182	964,182
0	5,386	129,092	264,621	48,914	313,535	61,420	0	878,224	878,224
0	0	33,120	30,312	216,778	247,090	253,250	5,112,891	5,941,643	828,752
226,646	0	363,548	56,606	0	56,606	86,287	0	693,671	693,671
350,000	0	441,910	36,500	46,673	83,173	25,116	0	817,093	817,093
0	0	189,467	202,123	10,815	212,938	0	0	670,742	670,742
0	0	189,716	103,490	47,234	150,724	5,060	0	608,369	608,369
23,500	1,505	143,123	5,760	24,236	29,996	2,500	0	747,613	747,613
0	0	612,764	11,555	0	11,555	43,426	0	794,209	794,209
0	0	72,440	121,935	0	121,935	48,487	188,108	956,663	768,555
606,579	4,609	726,547	121,176	930	122,106	32,023	10,703	1,091,450	1,080,747
0	0	77,617	67,112	354,931	422,043	86,150	0	810,597	810,597
0	0	144,672	176,821	0	176,821	64,164	0	772,081	772,081
15,314	0	108,651	71,646	12,288	83,934	218,836	83,508	699,731	616,153
0	12,800	62,579	9,950	394,500	404,450	2,872	0	688,318	688,318
0	0	122,851	103,357	16,547	119,904	35,488	265,693	809,391	543,698
0	0	75,786	13,205	133,159	146,364	1,713	0	466,613	466,613
0	0	66,017	90,890	14,833	105,723	36,426	7,683	540,979	533,296
0	0	52,729	17,380	12,069	29,449	0	3,167	307,802	304,635
153,000	0	275,016	0	58,111	58,111	31,750	86,378	573,308	486,930
125,000	0	206,287	446	148,954	149,400	1,551	0	520,668	520,668

Table 67. FISCAL YEAR 1947–48, INCOME OF 71 FOUR-YEAR MEDICAL SCHOOLS

School No.	Tuition and Fees—Medical Students			Endowment	Governmental Appropriations and Grants				Gifts and Grants from Private Sources	Other Income	Hospitals and Clinics	Total	Total Exclusive of Hospitals and Clinics
	Undergraduate	Postgraduate	Total		Federal	State	City or County	Total					
						30 TAX-SUPPORTED SCHOOLS							
1	$201,099	$71,322	$272,421	$120,984	$472,963	$2,000,686	0	$2,473,649	$1,000,298	$83,871	$2,827,521	$6,778,744	$3,951,223
2			88,574	85,776	217,845	1,147,485	0	1,365,330	232,398	778,377	1,433,880	3,984,335	2,550,455
3	179,960	64,284	244,244	894	119,189	1,124,684	0	1,243,873	185,939	823,402	1,683,007	4,181,359	2,498,352
4	67,293		67,293	3,783	161,124	877,276	0	1,038,400	65,102	248,908		1,423,486	1,423,486
5	199,819	60,014	259,833	46,831	185,674	539,774	0	725,448	175,399	604,737	5,299,530	7,111,778	1,812,248
6	181,030	11,446	192,476	1,956	67,254	1,195,724	$1,200	1,264,178	102,062	18,728	2,049,067	3,628,467	1,579,400
7	171,881	1,045	172,926	190,990	235,164	0	*	235,164	488,177	6,257		1,093,514	1,093,514
8	59,658	10,950	70,608	6,581	30,633	787,220	0	817,853	105,915	593,483		1,594,440	1,594,440
9	135,000	6,060	141,060	32,322	27,076	30,000	0	57,076	77,517	1,915,522	1,981,236	4,204,733	2,223,497
10				15,403	65,306	1,306,753	0	1,372,059	55,092	1,230	1,137,963	2,581,747	1,443,784
11	109,954	49,821	159,775	3,723	165,755	324,042	0	489,797	104,466	18,591	23,000	799,352	776,352
12	123,459	22,298	145,757		33,040	675,051	0	708,091	12,931	247,756	1,248,080	2,362,615	1,114,535
13	85,000		85,000	5,853	45,507	571,407	0	616,914	113,465	880		822,112	822,112
14	108,928	46,624	155,552	24,099	14,575	1,093,825	9,579	1,117,979	211,457	169,080	134,272	1,812,439	1,678,167
15	78,713		78,713		186,957	282,500	0	469,457	153,542	41,359		743,071	743,071
16	122,725	6,797	129,522		57,026	0	476,739	533,765	52,560	15,113		730,960	730,960
17	185,931	24,729	210,660		109,673	272,000	0	381,673	64,950	161,903		819,186	819,186
18	53,244	995	54,239		34,332	371,040	0	405,372	22,536	65,781		547,928	547,928
19	151,774	3,577	155,351	4,607	238,240	182,167	0	420,407	70,039	36,750		687,154	687,154
20	236,058	1,775	237,833		28,579	0	0	28,579	15,503	47,721	13,113	342,749	329,636
21	128,179	10,389	138,568	10,025	99,528	228,788	0	328,316	21,792			498,701	498,701
22	122,579	3,475	126,054	1,730	20,000	0	0	20,000	187,425	43,981		379,190	379,190
23	100,342	350	100,692		76,423	759,998	36,000	872,421	16,548	120,566	60,572	1,170,799	1,110,227
24	113,315	8,000	121,315		37,734	367,685	0	405,419	0	2,500	15,000	544,234	529,234
25	53,167	21,783	74,950		6,507	425,000	0	431,507	31,684	216,602		754,743	754,743
26	61,561	2,850	64,411		31,393	290,000	0	321,393	21,202	11,181		418,187	418,187
27	192,832	2,746	195,578		11,640	395,548	0	407,188	20,478	14,280	2,523,210	3,160,734	637,524
28	93,229		93,229	3,068	40,099	298,100	5,000	343,199	24,669	31,650		495,815	495,815
29	100,388	11,203	111,591	4,098	5,867	100,000	10,100	115,967	30,960	29,930		292,546	292,546
30	136,000		136,000	1,000	23,800	170,000	0	193,800	41,100	37,380		409,280	409,280

41 PRIVATELY SUPPORTED SCHOOLS

31	277,599	137,396	414,995	402,321	568,975	62,000	630,975	1,023,812	87,532	3,010,971	2,559,635	2,559,635
32	142,436	—	132,400	980,943	413,694	0	413,694	655,324	856,549	2,708,352	6,049,881	3,038,910
33	286,750	0	142,456	643,088	1,539,203	36,801	1,576,004	402,324	106,800	0	5,579,004	2,870,652
34	188,886	116,926	403,676	708,289	578,914	0	578,914	576,619	371,196	96,756	2,638,694	2,638,694
35	234,699	18,230	207,116	821,273	368,548	0	368,548	664,098	528,190	0	2,685,981	2,589,225
36	181,922	78,600	313,299	592,400	158,069	0	158,069	352,171	728,181	0	1,613,681	2,144,120
37	229,881	45,784	227,706	391,939	139,239	0	139,239	360,777	494,020	0	1,120,811	1,613,681
38	335,856	0	229,881	279,301	281,569	33,406	314,975	283,785	12,869	0	1,564,721	1,120,811
39	244,480	148,702	484,558	87,920	235,063	0	235,063	667,783	89,397	319,138	2,291,445	1,564,721
40	191,839	57,509	301,989	474,735	294,435	0	294,435	632,038	269,110	0	1,517,642	1,972,307
41	250,796	9,356	201,195	302,822	295,088	0	295,088	642,171	76,366	155,367	1,398,898	1,517,642
42	262,315	125,521	376,317	255,383	228,717	0	228,717	304,796	78,318	13,943	948,518	1,243,531
43	283,349	42,363	304,678	249,517	189,867	0	189,867	92,781	97,732	71,090	877,074	934,575
44	110,887	0	283,349	99,531	49,575	294,000	343,575	79,529	0	0	629,601	805,984
45	158,585	13,980	124,867	110,185	133,419	0	133,419	261,130	34,525	0	695,828	629,601
46	241,425	95,220	253,805	0	111,134	0	111,134	296,364	630	0	348,637	695,828
47	146,025	25,310	266,735	15,951	21,747	0	21,747	43,574	4,497	942,641	1,491,242	348,637
48	126,923	0	146,025	100,872	65,664	0	65,664	231,543	349,020	120,150	670,865	548,601
49	266,457	9,640	136,563	5,795	0	0	0	59,337	66,934	0	914,138	550,715
50	101,744	23,002	289,459	105,418	56,877	0	56,877	395,450	9,466	1,216,801	1,875,860	914,138
51	244,855	8,177	109,921	316,278	67,767	0	67,767	155,627	13,286	41,004	665,469	659,059
52	182,384	157,112	401,967	30,916	48,983	0	52,101	126,195	1,531,468	2,738,882	4,732,890	624,465
53	142,820	38,392	220,776		4,093	3,118	4,093	237,671	194,261	0	408,555	1,994,008
54	255,149	4,255	147,075	1,200	22,010	0	23,212	42,807	27,591	0	564,638	408,555
55	207,280	0	255,149	10,383	44,027	1,112	251,777	19,738	0	0	390,921	564,638
56	137,293	49,272	256,552	3,073	93,054	0	93,054	38,242	18,377	0	342,574	390,921
57	294,167	0	137,293	27,492	110,752	0	110,752	48,660	62,733	0	486,695	342,574
58	89,916	0	294,167	79,155	21,505	0	21,505	29,135	6,431	0	508,810	486,695
59	336,192	36,312	89,916	21,000	383,811	0	383,811	7,652	23,361	136,778	785,464	508,810
60	259,947	1,416	372,504	98,099	101,205	0	101,205	53,517	14,025	820,609	1,194,160	648,686
61	137,354	2,635	261,363	31,996	37,860	0	37,860	28,307	12,089	0	429,019	373,551
62	260,614	2,392	139,989	1,286	13,828	0	13,828	261,827	10,150	0	457,477	429,019
63	99,803	0	263,006	1,089	70,657	0	70,657	112,575	101,756	68,530	352,870	457,477
64	178,413	0	99,803	39,610	8,500	0	8,500	34,671	10,546	0	480,963	284,340
65	86,869	44,975	178,413		0	0	0	292,004	211,672	0	673,502	480,963
66	156,786	0	131,844	123,429	9,800	0	9,800	196,757	3,041	100,350	366,669	673,502
67	211,073	3,550	156,786	1,252	10,577	0	10,577	94,663	10,567	7,957	349,893	266,319
68	144,329	0	214,623	52,011	41,307	0	41,307	23,428	116	0	277,757	341,936
69	93,253	3,510	144,329	2,772	3,731	0	3,731	126,809	0	0	403,461	277,757
70	104,361		93,253	70,241	103,787	4,800	108,587	131,380	9,716	0		403,461
71			107,871	30,669	6,295	82,500	88,795	47,209			284,260	284,260

Source: Figures supplied by the Surgeon General's Committee on Medical School Grants and Finances.
* Included in endowment figure.
0 Indicates no income.
— Indicates income not segregated but kept in total.

Table 68. FISCAL YEAR 1940–41, INCOME OF 64 FOUR-YEAR MEDICAL SCHOOLS

26 TAX-SUPPORTED SCHOOLS

School No.	Tuition and Fees—Medical Students			Endowment	Governmental Appropriations and Grants				Gifts and Grants from Private Sources	Other Income	Hospitals and Clinics	Total	Total Exclusive of Hospitals and Clinics
	Undergraduate	Postgraduate	Total		Federal	State	City or County	Total					
1	$119,144	—	$119,144	$109,517	0	$761,922	0	$761,922	$472,062	$34,885	$922,123	$2,419,653	$1,497,530
2	—	—	56,196	66,872	0	522,813	0	522,813	62,751	210,497	620,677	1,539,806	919,129
3	169,135	0	169,135	259	0	386,959	0	386,959	58,813	216,558	0	831,724	831,724
5	144,037	$4,280	148,317	50,655	0	329,813	0	329,813	116,057	51,615	2,391,152	3,087,609	696,457
6	52,623	0	52,623	498	0	305,000	0	305,000	150	9,759	559,252	927,282	368,030
7	148,551	1,440	149,991	160,470	0	0	0	0	134,563	4,000	0	449,024	449,024
8	56,000	0	56,000	6,790	0	377,481	0	377,481	31,055	76,019	0	547,345	547,345
9	0	6,122	6,122	5,777	0	0	0	0	29,832	672,504	901,463	1,615,698	714,235
10	Not available	Not available		13,493	0	631,752	0	631,752	7,917	875	267,603	921,640	654,037
11	58,378	0	58,378	0	0	122,810	0	122,810	39,868	546	21,120	242,722	221,602
12	54,355	0	54,355	0	0	195,000	0	195,000	0	66,465	387,415	703,235	315,820
13	Not available	Not available		824	0	391,377	0	391,377	40,900	0	0	433,101	433,101
14	112,758	0	112,758	7,483	0	314,599	$23,006	337,605	38,550	32,797	25,004	554,197	529,193
15	14,296	0	14,296	0	0	31,655	0	31,655	0	5,820	0	51,771	51,771
16	84,500	0	84,500	0	0	0	223,902	223,902	45,547	0	0	353,949	353,949
17	124,753	1,200	125,953	0	0	85,330	0	85,330	16,374	58,474	0	286,131	286,131
18	71,169	526	71,695	0	0	232,444	0	232,444	782	9,245	0	314,166	314,166
19	119,362	0	119,362	354	0	54,310	0	54,310	16,172	0	0	190,198	190,198
20	155,896	0	155,896	0	0	0	0	0	12,947	19,752	4,025	192,620	188,595
21	79,387	0	79,387	6,575	0	114,511	0	114,511	8,343	700	0	209,516	209,516
23	92,519	0	92,519	0	0	300,000	42,398	342,398	1,204	33,904	9,154	479,179	470,025
24	48,500	0	48,500	0	0	163,712	0	163,712	0	0	15,000	227,212	212,212
27	217,310	0	217,310	0	0	45,559	0	45,559	12,772	24,278	549,973	849,892	299,919
28	40,725	0	40,725	1,800	0	147,518	5,000	152,518	23,101	5,442	0	223,586	223,586
29	46,802	0	46,802	3,814	0	60,000	7,400	67,400	3,010	11,009	0	132,035	132,035
30	83,413	0	83,413	1,000	0	49,587	0	49,587	2,000	12,000	0	148,000	148,000

38 PRIVATELY SUPPORTED SCHOOLS

School													
31	224,341	0	224,341	368,272	0	0	0	0	613,341	102,273	0	1,308,227	1,308,227
32	—	—	117,150	715,096	$ 5,091	0	0	5,091	221,961	336,077	1,312,056	2,707,431	1,395,375
33	96,801	0	96,801	516,475	5,369	375	0	5,744	224,752	1,360	1,143,471	1,988,603	845,132
35	171,254	0	171,254	667,038	20,000	0	0	20,000	361,281	93,271	16,488	1,329,332	1,312,844
36	172,617	126	172,743	251,518	0	0	0	0	195,746	428,357	0	1,048,364	1,048,364
37	109,640	0	109,640	305,111	0	0	0	0	329,468	279,774	0	1,023,993	1,023,993
38	183,183	0	183,183	205,926	0	54,500	0	54,500	191,031	10,234	0	644,874	644,874
39	331,363	0	331,363	73,396	0	0	0	0	252,414	51,437	0	708,610	708,610
40	164,619	0	164,619	421,277	0	0	0	0	251,080	74,163	230,974	1,142,113	911,139
41	115,762	0	115,762	200,483	0	0	0	0	139,807	11,474	0	467,526	467,526
42	217,149	3,615	220,764	199,303	0	0	0	0	10,096	74,541	57,705	562,409	504,704
43	258,308	0	258,308	166,663	0	0	0	0	48,050	19,154	0	492,175	492,175
44	205,391	0	205,391	71,331	0	62,500	0	62,500	0	0	0	339,222	339,222
45	—	—	76,045	34,626	0	0	0	0	22,182	0	0	132,853	132,853
46	115,245	0	115,245	0	0	0	0	0	102,133	5,671	0	223,049	223,049
47	167,439	7,125	174,564	800	0	0	0	0	0	0	0	175,364	175,364
48	102,698	0	102,698	17,059	0	0	0	0	73,683	8,855	410,913	613,208	202,295
49	135,112	0	135,112	11,033	0	0	0	0	27,824	160,705	46,168	380,842	334,674
50	221,735	0	221,735	98,273	0	0	0	0	39,778	20,327	0	380,113	380,113
51	80,000	0	80,000	334,914	2,499	0	0	2,499	140,781	11,357	553,181	1,122,732	569,551
52	197,185	205	197,390	787	0	0	2,764	2,764	131,757	3,091	16,582	352,371	335,789
53	128,486	0	128,486	0	0	0	0	0	54,278	600,011	1,211,291	1,994,066	782,775
54	135,087	3,023	138,110	1,200	0	0	0	0	0	42,520	0	181,830	181,830
55	272,116	0	272,116	11,204	0	50,000	0	50,000	0	14,326	0	347,646	347,646
56	150,397	10,607	161,004	2,845	4,720	0	0	4,720	680	7,500	0	176,749	176,749
57	89,485	0	89,485	7,222	0	0	0	0	9,605	2,878	0	109,190	109,190
58	254,274	0	254,274	46,432	0	0	0	0	12,140	18,612	0	331,458	331,458
59	37,113	0	37,113	17,898	152,626	0	0	152,626	0	2,205	0	209,842	209,842
60	208,504	6,190	214,694	60,344	0	0	0	0	9,975	11,175	57,659	353,847	296,188
61	98,518	0	98,518	23,297	0	0	0	0	300	3,778	413,443	539,336	125,893
63	163,500	0	163,500	31,000	0	0	0	0	4,500	95,611	0	294,611	294,611
64	56,048	1,281	57,329	36,431	0	0	0	0	10,185	35,475	43,585	183,005	139,420
65	119,026	0	119,026	0	0	0	0	0	0	5,342	17,729	142,097	124,368
67	141,675	0	141,675	0	0	0	0	0	0	2,775	100,350	244,800	144,450
68	140,428	0	140,428	65,288	0	0	0	0	8,344	4,871	5,275	224,206	218,931
69	82,673	0	82,673	0	0	0	0	0	43,692	16	0	126,381	126,381
70	56,114	0	56,114	0	0	0	0	0	0	46,591	0	102,705	102,705
71	47,314	0	47,314	26,926	0	50,000	0	50,000	582	6,096	0	130,918	130,918

Source: Figures supplied by the Surgeon General's Committee on Medical School Grants and Finances.

0 Indicates no income.

— Indicates income not segregated but kept in total.

No information on schools 4, 22, 25, 26, 34, 62, and 66.

Table 69. INCOME OF TWO-YEAR MEDICAL SCHOOLS IN FISCAL YEARS 1940–41, 1947–48, AND 1950–51

1940–41*

School No.	Tuition and Fees—Medical			Endowment	Governmental Appropriations and Grants				Gifts and Grants from Private Sources	Other Income	Hospitals and Clinics	Total	Total Exclusive of Hospitals and Clinics
	Undergrad.	Postgrad.	Total		Federal	State	City or County	Total					
72	$ 4,015	0	$ 4,015	0	0	$ 40,985	0	$ 40,985	0	$ 0	0	$ 45,000	$ 45,000
73	22,858	$2,839	25,697	$8,478	0	64,601	0	64,601	$13,775	254	0	112,805	112,805
74	7,976	255	8,231	0	0	0	0	0	0	0	0	8,231	8,231
75	8,400	0	8,400	0	0	34,134	0	34,134	0	0	0	42,534	42,534
76	18,500	0	18,500	1,607	0	0	0	0	0	56,017	0	76,124	76,124
77	12,954	0	12,954	0	0	49,932	0	49,932	0	0	0	62,886	62,886

1947–48*

School No.	Tuition and Fees—Medical			Endowment	Governmental Appropriations and Grants				Gifts and Grants from Private Sources	Other Income	Hospitals and Clinics	Total	Total Exclusive of Hospitals and Clinics
	Undergrad.	Postgrad.	Total		Federal	State	City or County	Total					
72	7,313	0	7,313	0	0	73,137	0	73,137	0	2,000	0	82,450	82,450
73	35,746	7,548	43,294	7,713	$16,252	171,620	0	187,872	10,350	177	0	249,406	249,406
74	28,375	0	28,375	0	4,000	100,000	0	104,000	0	0	0	132,375	132,375
75	22,000	0	22,000	0	2,400	111,393	0	113,793	1,357	4,450	0	141,600	141,600
76	26,225	2,725	28,950	1,631	0	1,200	0	1,200	10,850	112,309	0	154,940	154,940
77	21,632	0	21,632	0	0	89,221	0	89,221	0	0	0	110,853	110,853

1950–51

School No.	Tuition and Fees				Endowment			Governmental Appropriations and Grants						Gifts and Grants—Private			Other Income	Hospitals and Clinics	Total	Total Exclusive of Hospitals and Clinics
	Medical		Other	Total	Medical School	University (for M.S.)	Total	Federal			State	City or County	Total Gov't.	Research	Non-restr.	Total				
	Undergrad.	Postgrad.						Research	Instruction	Total Federal										
72	$ 9,356	0	0	$ 9,356	$61,574	0	$61,574	$60,948	$5,000	$65,948	$312,377	0	$378,325	$83,480	$7,500	$90,980	$12,516	0	$552,751	$552,751
73	31,162	0	$1,500	32,662	0	$10,150	10,150	59,850	5,000	64,850	248,303	0	313,153	16,950	0	16,950	0	0	372,915	372,915
74	43,694	0	0	43,694	0	0	0	15,647	14,848	30,495	195,000	0	225,495	0	0	0	10,002	0	279,191	279,191
75	24,000	0	0	24,000	0	0	0	0	0	0	140,000	0	140,100	8,328	0	8,328	5,927	0	178,355	178,355
76	16,200	$20,918	633	37,751	4,657	0	4,657	6,900	0	6,900	1,420	0	8,320	11,606	0	11,606	1,118	$39,242	102,694	63,452
77	14,698	0	900	15,598	0	0	0	7,400	5,000	12,400	184,400	0	196,800	0	0	0	0	0	212,398	212,398

* 1940–41 and 1947–48 figures supplied by the Surgeon General's Committee on Medical School Grants and Finances.
0 Indicates no income.

Table 70. BUDGETS OF FIVE MAJOR CLINICAL DEPARTMENTS FOR FISCAL YEARS 1940-41,* 1948-49,* AND 1950-51, IN 36 FOUR-YEAR MEDICAL SCHOOLS

School No.	Medicine 1940-41	Medicine 1948-49	Medicine 1950-51 Dept. Budget	Medicine 1950-51 Special Funds	Surgery 1940-41	Surgery 1948-49	Surgery 1950-51 Dept. Budget	Surgery 1950-51 Special Funds	Pediatrics 1940-41	Pediatrics 1948-49	Pediatrics 1950-51 Dept. Budget	Pediatrics 1950-51 Special Funds	Obstetrics and Gynecology 1940-41	Obstetrics and Gynecology 1948-49	Obstetrics and Gynecology 1950-51 Dept. Budget	Obstetrics and Gynecology 1950-51 Special Funds	Psychiatry or Neuropsychiatry 1940-41	Psychiatry or Neuropsychiatry 1948-49	Psychiatry or Neuropsychiatry 1950-51 Dept. Budget	Psychiatry or Neuropsychiatry 1950-51 Special Funds
15 TAX-SUPPORTED SCHOOLS																				
13	$70,399	$131,705	$155,175	$31,000	$54,815	$96,600	$106,680	$3,877	See Medicine				$12,830	$19,900	$20,500	$0	$9,833	$21,900	$28,300	$5,000
11	41,509	46,361	46,361	102,147	41,337	105,012	25,450	27,400	23,862	23,862	23,862	48,669	—	16,920	31,714	9,000	19,950	60,900	60,900	39,008
3	16,926	137,879	141,618	28,786	15,536	47,300	109,895	0	16,998	47,775	53,405	13,455	26,056	36,189	13,100	6,000	See Medicine	149,464	159,163	150,326
28	34,020	37,660	42,360	31,960	28,500	32,410	57,400	44,345	4,854	11,400	11,700	0	8,832	12,600	34,210	3,000	See Medicine			
18	—	47,125	49,535	25,680	—	19,650	32,540	7,000	7,504	39,200	38,200	23,575	17,580	33,670	14,300	1,100	—	8,097	19,020	10,000
24	10,650	25,000	23,000	11,600	16,300	52,780	23,550	46,902	—	16,500	15,900	—	—	12,800	28,168	—	—	See Medicine		
12	59,890	28,112	38,430	0	62,902	99,098	86,932	35,200	2,660	17,570	13,200	103,200	9,750	20,630	36,867	—	1,050	9,520	21,600	11,800
5	—	120,956	178,706	261,633	—	121,463	104,344	81,103	11,780	39,479	46,143	18,257	9,901	28,317	5,240	16,510	4,695	8,500	10,000	16,490
7	—	178,830	71,075	144,687	—	101,305	100,570	0	—	20,318	18,890†	269,000†	—	6,500‡	19,990	—	—	63,961	38,900	108,900
15	33,821	34,700	36,800	147,843	23,325	27,400	27,725	10,425	—	27,300	31,200	—	—	20,100	20,100	—	6,680	21,600	23,186	67,325
6	48,040	87,075	102,000	36,050	29,710	111,045	122,840	9,000	6,696	58,559	78,000	13,400	12,425	37,535	34,265	—	—	27,040	55,960	—
1	38,547	105,766	122,039	10,000	37,030	120,923	134,870	201,000	21,500	59,267	88,878	85,558	42,872	39,256	42,872	13,370	6,680	62,845	73,425	34,333
8	—	149,315	156,337	89,716	—	69,366	93,924	94,089	24,406	69,959	42,000	35,000	30,955	87,048	56,287	29,200	15,630	44,020	53,110	28,380
14	14,795	62,213	17,379	53,972	10,455	31,923	54,439	26,853	—	—	20,340	—	5,180	12,769	16,029	—	See Medicine			
4	—	43,391	118,000	125,000	—	—	109,093	38,852	15,220	35,738	63,755	—	—	11,080	48,650	15,000	834	36,681	36,681	60,505
21 PRIVATELY SUPPORTED SCHOOLS																				
61	8,100	53,400	55,700	283,456	—	—	7,250	300	1,750	14,400	17,496	0	9,000	10,540	23,830	5,500	2,000	2,000	No Department	0
32	283,487	553,382	689,786	485,300	176,749	377,897	231,771	272,400	61,758	105,134	101,791	86,585	78,637	108,230	110,850	62,875	51,026	88,995	See Medicine	—
68	5,152	10,904	10,904	10,000	—	—	3,710	0	—	—	—	2,960	0	—	9,000	—	0	See Medicine	See Medicine	
65	—	—	74,000	—	—	—	24,600	0	0	—	1,800	0	0	—	—	6,800	—	—	—	—
71	—	19,947	19,947	17,700	—	13,540	12,000	0	—	7,185	7,665	4,890	0	11,895	11,455	1,500	—	—	—	0
56	18,590	53,545	34,670	68,850	3,462	24,100	21,490	35,834	2,050	7,500	8,175	—	6,150	20,620	21,850	30,498	1,850	2,800	2,800	9,900
37	53,545	99,144	113,652	14,032	73,342	125,306	125,934	170,261	36,660	46,196	45,615	27,248	25,720	27,986	28,521	—	27,183	69,640	61,700	10,000
54	99,144	16,312	16,312	1,000	3,000	36,015	35,210	55,450	1,000	25,066	18,466	141,113	—	8,200	4,461	—	6,250	21,025	24,850	79,000
64	27,325	18,650	19,850	43,200	2,000	7,000	7,800	4,700	—	1,100	1,260	2,200	350	600	300	—	1,000	7,300	8,800	2,000
66	—	31,000	105,170	1,000	—	9,800	287,440	3,613	4,375	12,900	37,200	16,755	—	11,400	59,400	—	—	38,200	41,750	10,000
70	5,000	105,170	53,000	51,150	12,765	47,630	55,500	16,200	25,802	37,230	2,400	22,900	2,200†	18,100	24,520	—	—	See Medicine	See Medicine	18,300
2	—	53,000	96,419	206,871	54,651	65,977	85,259	317,000	95,610	41,000	50,558	—	34,061	38,130	41,937	7,860	3,450	4,540	35,500	35,382
31	55,100	83,164	179,140	402,480	197,975	180,235	85,332	93,540	16,000	103,240	119,330	61,536	60,474	79,440	60,740	23,400	26,850	29,900	35,390	176,241
48	197,195	202,459	123,166	92,150	52,510	68,289	91,393	109,836	—	27,682	40,800	55,520	17,120	26,402	43,392	—	—	See Medicine	See Medicine	
57	72,392	87,401	21,842	35,040	5,136	27,905	29,300	10,000	950	750	750	—	2,560	5,628	7,820	9,593	2,525	12,600	43,834	62,509
41	15,634	22,041	73,985	240,185	21,735	31,433	37,200	73,832	14,626	43,908	37,150	21,970	11,826	11,891	50,209	800	—	52,733	36,840	47,500
39	39,845	77,823	72,895	98,188	20,810	34,890	58,850	116,880	18,138	31,770	40,000	200,000	16,130	34,575	34,485	—	7,050	29,775	61,225	54,850
51	51,810	59,562	46,710	387,819	47,645	46,470	47,040	—	22,485	32,868	37,000	4,212	19,805	24,470	26,950	31,232	—	13,724	14,410	57,540
35	49,182	47,110	173,685	299,418	43,411	13,607	223,565	125,240	43,971	77,516	108,679	54,434	42,353	58,150	56,705	24,641	59,274	114,618	151,365	151,565
38	82,407	173,685	145,580	97,320	—	14,430	116,060	204,087	—	28,425	26,300†	426,000†	—	24,380	60,650	9,390	—	800	4,200	87,886
42	35,308	21,970	47,000	—	4,948	1,500	5,805	73,588	2,980	2,450	1,800	—	—	3,730	9,800	—	5,645	13,515	12,332	26,804

The budgets of the five major clinical departments presented in this table are the figures reported to the Survey by the department heads. They do not reflect the organization of the various departments or the extent of their activities. The departments may or may not include the medical and surgical specialties, and the budgets may or may not include such items as faculty earnings or contributions by teaching hospitals. In no case is allowance made for the value of the time contributed by volunteer faculty members. The figures are of interest in showing the growth of the departmental budgets over a decade and the relative size of medical school funds and special funds in 1950-51. Special funds are usually research funds although some teaching grants are probably included. Departmental budgets were not obtained from all the medical schools and departments studied.

* 1940-41 and 1948-49 figures supplied by the Surgeon General's Committee on Medical School Grants and Finances.
‡ Large department financed almost entirely by private gifts or research funds.
† Obstetrics only.
— Indicates figure not obtained.

Table 71. BUDGETS FOR MEDICAL BASIC SCIENCE DEPARTMENTS FOR

School No.	Anatomy		1950-51		Biochemistry		1950-51		Physiology		1950-51	
	1940-41	1948-49	Medical School	Special Funds	1940-41	1948-49	Medical School	Special Funds	1940-41	1948-49	Medical School	Special Funds
												15 TAX-SUPPORTED
13	$ 29,250	$ 57,100	$ 60,120	$15,435	$15,375	$31,830	$41,220	$ 20,500	$27,314	$ 45,250	$ 54,604	$ 26,725
11	—	55,093	55,093	41,144	—	69,503	79,380	18,550	—	56,389‡	56,390‡	42,158‡
3	42,542	86,451	88,782	7,000	29,340	78,858	81,108	4,500	37,558	104,963	115,467	80,000
28	17,158	33,254	34,822	0	10,924	20,200	23,300	5,768	14,004‡	37,720‡	26,000	8,400
18	36,460	40,220	56,240	5,200	15,733	21,640	33,511	0	18,683	24,560	31,460	0
24	—	36,600	39,010	11,500	—	18,280	20,780	2,000	—	26,340	29,580	5,120
12	—	—	64,010	25,500	—	—	32,964	20,380	—	—	54,997	11,320
5	57,360	109,350	129,302	19,486	26,331	55,690	77,380	11,400	31,688	60,740	77,430	12,976
7	—	38,929	51,315	8,907	—	46,270	47,014	53,892	—	26,923	27,216	3,500
15	12,750	31,210	32,595	11,264	6,950	31,600	33,050	68,291	9,701‡	29,300	31,400	28,700
6	31,156	69,480	97,180	600	15,424	45,547	72,720	3,500	14,673	54,810	48,100	13,000
1	48,748	70,666	89,995	60,006	—	34,950	38,468	130,974	51,430	60,601	85,500	75,000
8	32,070	75,760	85,882	22,180	7,782	45,580	62,179	9,000	22,990	58,252	81,454	51,386
14	16,199	38,011	42,347	25,793	15,971	25,829	27,466	30,108	12,665	26,493	31,524	25,933
4	—	57,608	85,325	67,991	—	17,634	88,000	43,600	—	50,455¶	103,889¶	84,595¶
												22 PRIVATELY
61	19,260	34,100	44,550	0	9,686	34,260	25,000	9,000	13,810	40,400	49,350	32,150
32	31,059	70,631	84,369	62,065	13,604	20,393	72,497	52,400	14,648	37,139	78,159	125,125
68	18,932	26,614	39,576	18,800	12,927	19,369	27,710	10,387	12,783	18,948	23,561	0
65	13,906	74,660	78,300	1,125	8,849	34,000	36,600	0	12,087‡	57,500‡	44,900‡	5,100‡
71	—	15,150	27,570	3,545	—	4,870	17,620	90	—	16,240	17,740	1,500
56	11,161	19,850	22,750	7,500	16,899	26,620	26,520	10,688	16,652	23,650	26,050	10,000
37	42,085	58,334	56,594	67,130	33,600	56,840	66,580	37,882	68,260	52,060	59,056	74,790
54	23,197	40,105	41,176	333	14,098	23,440	23,140	0	18,549	34,587	32,062	2,100
64	23,000	33,680	38,000	5,500	17,190	32,480	38,040	0	21,980‡	33,120‡	36,650‡	52,813‡
66	—	23,075	18,500	1,750	—	18,180	32,800	21,800	—	30,900‡	37,800‡	46,825‡
70	3,720	20,500	18,250	0	5,060	39,636	34,911	15,397	6,905‡	21,800‡	40,700‡	0
33	35,481	43,350	44,062	16,500	28,332	30,750	35,300	43,000	37,232	42,000	64,888	94,966
31	104,427	113,040	142,230	4,000	76,958	61,866	78,640	151,334	72,093	102,171	108,700	40,258
48	42,540	59,927	63,350	29,816	—	—	17,500	55,000	31,020	44,132	53,150	18,507
57	16,035	40,020	55,065	10,000	6,593	21,410	24,050	21,600	10,154	28,830	29,770	21,000
41	40,798	59,436	63,000	78,382	14,740	62,950	61,200	74,680	21,730	39,041	42,760	88,281
39	36,330	53,561	68,340	0	32,780	45,760	50,730	57,350	35,310	44,210	57,105	29,862
51	26,860	28,260	29,060	13,024	19,668	20,400	44,660	35,350	21,455	28,000	29,900	9,700
35	50,591	66,155	65,918	8,295	28,933	46,918	49,331	22,629	30,350	49,255	49,295	9,200
38	—	96,660	97,600	33,180	—	56,464	67,209	103,519	—	67,100	73,017	26,208
34	—	58,966	50,000	58,000	—	87,918	69,000	14,000	—	42,196	54,868	17,300
42	36,212	54,530	62,840	36,474	16,291	30,625	41,575	38,242	60,640‡	54,125	59,310	1,500
												3 TWO-YEAR
75	7,463	19,675	24,494	3,820	5,000	19,040	24,750	1,800	7,667‡	26,525‡	25,263‡	8,025‡
78	16,661	23,458	26,043	300	9,169	13,773	15,560	10,000	16,620‡	35,795‡	43,100‡	0‡
73	13,394	29,355	45,815	33,000	8,131	18,100	28,420	5,950	22,903	23,750	28,500	35,700

Departmental budgets were not obtained from all the schools and departments studied.
* 1940-41 and 1948-49 figures supplied by the Surgeon General's Committee on Medical School Grants and Finances.
† Bacteriology and pathology.
‡ Pharmacology and physiology.
§ Bacteriology and preventive medicine.
¶ Physiology and biophysics.
— Indicates figures not obtained.

APPENDIX 4   LIBRARIES

Table 57. BOUND VOLUMES, JOURNAL SUBSCRIPTIONS, SEATING CAPACITIES, SALARY BUDGETS, AND PAID FULL-TIME STAFF, AT LIBRARIES OF 37 MEDICAL SCHOOLS, YEAR OF SURVEY

School No.	Bound volumes	Paid journal subscriptions	Seating capacity	Salary budget	Paid full-time staff
1	110,924	873	190	$25,464	5
3	89,354	720	250	39,714	13
4	34,000	No information	225	13,564	6
5	82,748	729	200	—	6
6	60,000	500	120	16,000	6
7	79,367	444	99	20,440	10
8	48,000	506	116	11,000	4
11	39,652	504	72	14,978	5
12	30,000	320	60	11,680	5
13	43,000	340	50	11,960	3
14	47,760	494	150	20,922	6
15	14,235	366	95	12,120	4
18	29,901	556	56	23,076	8
24	20,067	241	94	8,470	4
28	19,692	218	68	5,080	3
31	160,000	1,061	180	50,550	21
32	123,456	No information	138	28,437	13
33	55,795	535	59	9,765	3
35	158,705	544	188	46,380	20
36	71,200	551	51	17,870	8
37	157,000	800	152	34,514	13
38	15,020	177	100	3,878	2
39	60,000	948	203	35,520	15
41	16,000	105	44	8,640	3
42	118,150	659	150	21,480	7
48	118,500	1,029	128	24,760	11
51	53,634	556	95	15,740	5
54	35,154	251	55	5,280	2
57	16,346	208	75	7,540	3
61	23,514	233	100	16,000	3
64	18,025	198	40	5,000	2
65	14,155	175	40	7,800	3
66	11,059	174	70	5,600	2
68	43,770	432	80	9,358	3
71	9,060	156	60	7,560	3
73*	20,000	500	65	7,000	2
75*	7,000	270	18	2,880	1

* Two-year schools.
— Indicates budget not segregated from that of general university library.
Source: Figures supplied by librarians.

Table 58. EXPENDITURES ON LIBRARIES OF 37 MEDICAL SCHOOLS, FISCAL YEAR 1950–51

School Number	1950–51 Expenditures	School Number	1950–51 Expenditures
1	$48,996*	36	$31,194
3	33,905	37	60,979
4	67,954	38	29,848
5	49,672	39	0
6	58,800	41	12,560
7	8,533	42	36,275
8	13,514	48	49,669
11	18,051	51	25,285
12	21,785	54	8,228
13	15,575	57	9,446
14	33,760	61	22,941
15	0	64	13,278
18	36,189	65	5,734
24	15,000	66	6,611
28	12,662	68	14,754
31	81,510	71	0
32	—	73†	28,500
33	23,895	75†	9,280
35	11,000		

* Estimated.
† Two-year schools.
— Indicates expenditures not segregated.
0 Indicates no expenditures from medical school budget.

APPENDIX 5   POSTGRADUATE
EDUCATION

Table 59. NUMBER OF POSTGRADUATE STUDENTS IN 26 MEDICAL SCHOOLS, 1948–49

Departments	Number of departments reporting	Number of students in 1948–49
Anatomy..................	16	673
Physiology................	10	1,020
Pharmacology.............	10	470
Bacteriology..............	5	173
Pathology................	15	933
Biochemistry.............	5	369
Medicine.................	17	3,958
Preventive medicine.........	5	147
Dermatology..............	5	180
Surgery..................	11	1,107
Orthopedics..............	5	233
Otolaryngology...........	10	461
Ophthalmology...........	12	628
Anesthesiology............	5	179
Urology..................	2	50
Pediatrics................	19	1,308
Obstetrics and gynecology....	12	670
Psychiatry................	16	1,121
Neurology................	4	175
Radiology................	11	876
Total.................		14,731

Source: Figures supplied by department heads.

APPENDIX 6   FINANCES

Table 60. THE SURVEY'S QUESTIONNAIRE TO ALL MEDICAL SCHOOLS REGARD-
ING EXPENDITURES

Finances

Amount of expenses for the fiscal year in which the medical school is surveyed.
Line items:

31. *Administration and General Expenses*	. . . .
a. Share of expenses of university	. . . .
b. Administration of medical school	. . . .
c. Student health service	. . . .
32. *Instruction and Research Expense*	. . . .
a. Research budgeted separately	. . . .
(1) Federal government grants (USPHS)	. . . .
(2) Federal government contracts (Army, Navy, Veterans Administration)	
(3) Other research	. . . .
b. Instructional activities, including research not budgeted separately	. . . .
(1) U.S. Public Health Service grants	. . . .
(2) All other	. . . .
33. *Expense of Separately Organized Postgraduate Education*	. . . .
34. *Libraries (Expense)*	. . . .
35. *Physical Plant Operation and Maintenance*	. . . .
36. *Expenses of Organized Activities Relating to Instructional Departments*	. . . .
a. Hospital and clinics	. . . .
b. All other	. . . .
37. *Total Expense—Educational, Research, and General* (Items 31–36)	. . . .

Table 61. FISCAL YEAR 1950–51,

School No.	Instruction			Research Budgeted Separately				Administration		
	All Except USPHS	USPHS	Total	Federal		All Other	Total	Medical School	Share of University	Total
				USPHS	Contracts					
										30 TAX-SUPPORTED
1	$1,320,055	$188,890	$1,508,945	$358,975	$ 145,902	$558,076	$1,062,953	$ 68,866	$338,449*	$407,315
2	1,574,055	32,001	1,606,056	375,854	1,030,695	125,184	1,531,733	71,600	17,619	89,219
3	1,535,035	0	1,535,035	302,773	79,978	280,714	663,465	50,541	165,845	216,386
4	1,330,843	22,071	1,352,914	182,468	102,102	287,943	572,513	73,336	124,953	198,289
5	1,118,345	0	1,118,345	195,531	195,026	385,604	776,161	51,625	185,837	237,462
6	985,705	18,000	1,003,705	$209,814		307,142	516,956	84,000	0	84,000
7	877,431	117,946	995,377	222,809		463,567	686,376	47,164	0	47,164
8	1,230,376	13,478	1,243,854	87,977	11,004	282,314	381,295	26,700	36,808	63,508
9	958,562	24,920	983,482	15,874	35,425	143,541	194,840	59,877	115,145	175,022
10	1,015,710	10,581	1,026,291	67,883	0	0	67,883	59,760	152,400	212,160
11	681,454	121,962	803,416	128,977	70,637	130,583	330,197	152,115	4,395	156,510
12	840,824	33,773	874,597	72,603	17,492	102,547	192,642	33,730	0	33,730
13	710,950	0	710,950	90,577	6,383	242,148	339,108	42,245	0	42,245
14	646,781	48,166	694,947	31,730	33,066	23,149	87,945	127,663	0	127,663
15	387,324	64,250	451,574	335,578	22,386	282,877	640,841	37,201	0	37,201
16	753,953	38,943	792,896	94,808	0	74,200	169,008	39,500	0	39,500
17	656,169	26,355	682,524	47,585	0	41,000	88,585	69,245	0	69,245
18	591,980	81,423	673,403	39,237	11,030	57,050	107,317	44,790	37,260	82,050
19	367,681	55,641	423,322	28,383	219,017	103,201	350,601	20,527	59,273	79,800
20	261,760	35,420	297,180	99,544	6,293	317,510	423,347	24,643	66,187	90,830
21	384,094	20,800	404,894	215,252	16,319	0	231,571	13,319	12,000	25,319
22	449,996	52,744	502,740	24,818	10,956	48,232	84,006	58,215	0	58,215
23	449,735	28,560	478,295	43,106	2,139	18,248	63,493	23,236	3,000	26,236
24	468,350	31,500	499,850	47,000	0	0	47,000	27,500	0	27,500
25	431,015	55,116	486,131	53,141	0	65,132	118,273	51,727	0	51,727
26	386,395	0	386,395	88,776	7,892	27,526	124,194	58,731	0	58,731
27	301,181	0	301,181	64,259	28,404	72,219	164,882	54,555	28,171	82,726
28	315,989	28,295	344,284	78,328	9,730	32,611	120,669	46,376	0	46,376
29	291,035	0	291,035	98,976	6,273	9,928	115,177	34,897	37,284	72,181
30	219,000	73,000	292,000	0	0	40,000	40,000	41,000	7,000	48,000
										41 PRIVATELY
31	1,780,606	24,894	1,805,500	782,250	529,851	993,844	2,305,945	88,889	328,509	417,398
32	2,230,138	67,275	2,297,413	0	1,051,534	775,190	1,826,724	—	—	483,328
33	727,587	0	727,587	206,437	1,623,387	498,416	2,328,240	126,010	40,667	166,677
34	931,486	79,347	1,010,833	447,393	375,002	705,997	1,528,392	108,537	0	108,537
35	994,547	0	994,547	441,236	178,436	958,766	1,578,438	144,372	100,620	244,992
36	823,795	42,423	866,218	198,820	114,991	503,785	817,596	62,643	140,730	203,373
37	986,322	93,024	1,079,346	315,408	304,009	498,871	1,118,288	56,728	233,266	289,994
38	730,900	66,401	797,301	375,688	286,524	960,415	1,622,627	50,903	82,350	133,253
39	675,248	62,616	737,864	249,981	215,072	864,701	1,329,754	93,467	149,075	242,542
40	588,714	0	588,714	379,627	96,497	731,522	1,207,646	187,615	0	187,615
41	670,598	59,858	730,456	157,994	525,252	383,181	1,066,427	86,657	85,930	172,587
42	487,008	25,000	512,008	173,986	100,344	442,690	717,020	53,915	92,328	146,243
43	562,860	70,735	633,595	203,994	75,376	232,016	511,386	30,203	65,369	95,572
44	626,606	47,588	674,194	91,871	30,490	166,866	289,227	161,536	0	161,536
45	547,010	55,664	602,674	93,162	54,587	92,237	239,986	43,405	109,959	153,364
46	668,037	50,000	718,037	200,000	50,000	83,010	333,010	51,880	0	51,880
47	776,610	0	776,610	92,154	0	162,966	255,120	21,900	0	21,900
48	644,461	17,152	661,613	113,076	0	160,643	273,719	40,752	0	40,752
49	516,241	0	516,241	20,922	56,653	281,975	359,550	32,898	75,410	108,308
50	691,609	0	691,609	64,634	6,364	14,320	85,318	88,484	0	88,484
51	452,734	34,806	487,540	101,002	2,022	126,240	229,264	76,935	26,801	103,736
52	266,147	0	266,147	109,225	14,481	274,525	398,231	35,308	26,819	62,127
53	462,918	23,181	486,099	6,528	1,109	57,853	65,490	96,195	0	96,195
54	340,285	0	340,285	107,548	29,354	283,252	420,154	30,412	13,545	43,957
55	427,588	50,300	477,888	32,110	9,500	43,069	84,679	62,457	35,000	97,457
56	266,731	48,136	314,867	97,263	44,068	202,123	343,454	30,356	53,082	83,438
57	344,862	84,122	428,984	81,403	24,191	103,490	209,084	52,190	63,032	115,222
58	423,416	39,000	462,416	49,828	29,090	35,610	114,528	66,365	0	66,365
59	474,486	64,084	538,570	44,564	2,640	11,555	58,759	51,322	35,482	86,804
60	303,804	23,484	327,288	19,855	25,910	115,353	161,118	91,199	0	91,199
61	408,941	11,893	420,834	30,338	9,658	108,458	148,454	60,731	0	60,731
62	427,443	0	427,443	44,269	33,348	67,112	144,729	69,468	0	69,468
63	199,305	0	199,305	115,420	0	141,068	256,488	—	—	130,825
64	272,492	0	272,492	94,029	0	82,357	176,386	66,238	0	66,238
65	406,937	0	406,937	4,569	125	37,224	41,918	84,766	0	84,766
66	201,777	0	201,777	112,917	0	99,989	212,906	51,696	0	51,696
67	270,670	0	270,670	16,908	4,029	14,016	34,953	54,562	60,008	114,570
68	211,387	0	211,387	55,570	0	66,872	122,442	64,253	0	64,253
69	182,229	28,313	210,542	5,886	4,718	21,018	31,622	48,367	68,029	116,396
70	195,016	56,206	251,222	6,836	53,841	5,132	65,809	28,334	0	28,334
71	226,996	0	226,996	70,665	0	1,048	71,713	48,862	0	48,862

* Estimated.
† Self-supporting—not in budget.
— Indicates expenditures not segregated but kept in total.
0 Indicates no expenditures from medical school budget.

EXPENDITURES OF 71 FOUR-YEAR MEDICAL SCHOOLS

Libraries	Postgraduate Education	Maintenance	Student Health	Other Expenditures	Hospitals and Clinics	Total	Total Exclusive of Hospitals and Clinics
SCHOOLS							
$48,996*	$523,849	$976,528*	—	0	$3,356,519	$7,885,105	$4,528,586
43,362	14,071	88,130	$ 21,824	0	2,449,097	5,843,492	3,394,395
33,905	42,363	579,909	18,369	$180,674	1,815,817	5,085,923	3,270,106
67,954	10,917	213,500	135,598	0	0	2,551,685	2,551,685
49,672	39,647	120,044	18,381	0	7,129,590	9,489,302	2,359,712
58,800	10,400	328,550	12,900	105,800	2,844,617	4,965,728	2,121,111
8,533	0	70,636	3,573	79,354	0	1,891,013	1,891,013
13,514	0	53,378	2,753	0	5,171,684	6,929,986	1,758,302
44,331	11,849	226,500	2,457	15,988	2,665,856	4,320,325	1,654,469
41,762	0	260,139	1,775	0	1,753,248	3,363,258	1,610,010
18,051	11,543	61,508	0	67,348	0	1,448,573	1,448,573
21,785	7,547	234,048	7,031	0	2,381,887	3,753,267	1,371,380
15,575	0	75,478	96,968	0	0†	1,280,324	1,280,324
33,760	12,895	259,497	0	20,823	701,410	1,938,940	1,237,530
0	0	0	0	0	0	1,129,616	1,129,616
0	10,200	82,240	0	0	0	1,093,844	1,093,844
13,753	0	117,339	4,147	22,756	0	998,349	998,349
36,189	6,400	60,760	3,600	0	20,250	989,969	969,719
21,435	23,823	35,340	0	24,342	4,042,948	5,001,611	958,663
9,519	0	21,750	0	4,448	23,696	870,770	847,074
12,429	3,679	63,000	5,000	29,370	0	775,262	775,262
26,648	0	78,967	9,331	13,153	0	773,060	773,060
18,487	0	84,041	1,509	93,499	759,503	1,525,063	765,560
15,000	6,000	152,000	4,150	0	39,250	790,750	751,500
36,252	0	51,181	4,343	0	25,487	773,394	747,907
23,761	54,227	40,857	5,580	9,567	0	703,312	703,312
12,280	7,103	94,984	7,160	0	23,760	694,076	670,316
12,662	0	62,116	0	2,117	192,551	780,775	588,224
18,123	16,047	31,839	0	13,741	0	558,143	558,143
23,000	0	46,000	8,000	0	0	457,000	457,000
SUPPORTED SCHOOLS							
81,510	95,840	293,353	8,245	0	0	5,007,791	5,007,791
—	0	—	—	0	4,106,140	8,713,605	4,607,465
23,895	0	66,181	6,426	129,760	3,701,282	7,150,048	3,448,766
38,956	111,096	378,520	0	0	0	3,176,334	3,176,334
11,000	0	66,644	44,508	8,000	30,185	2,978,314	2,948,129
31,194	23,205	110,958	15,065	827,486	0	2,895,095	2,895,095
60,979	14,500	220,218	3,227	41,128	129,375	2,957,055	2,827,680
29,848	0	168,409	0	0	0	2,751,438	2,751,438
0	0	191,125	9,380	0	0	2,510,665	2,510,665
17,171	15,506	106,540	2,500	122,878	364,349	2,612,919	2,248,570
12,560	1,560	174,334	5,928	53,502	0	2,217,354	2,217,354
36,275	21,987	173,666	10,000	0	306,247	1,923,446	1,617,199
25,330	18,506	139,409	5,720	16,260	32,741	1,478,519	1,445,778
53,600	0	234,724	6,776	0	0	1,420,057	1,420,057
34,203	0	99,526	6,799	82,076	208,992	1,427,620	1,218,628
19,718	—	71,000	0	0	3,000,000	4,193,645	1,193,645
24,535	0	102,000	4,990	0	0	1,185,155	1,185,155
49,669	4,581	36,901	0	0	192,487	1,259,722	1,067,235
6,448	0	75,385	0	0	115,049	1,180,981	1,065,932
23,652	0	72,280	3,952	9,928	0	975,223	975,223
25,285	0	53,591	1,560	10,029	9,406	920,411	911,005
3,770	49,740	45,942	6,105	65,322	5,589	902,973	897,384
42,725	25,940	127,311	0	21,925	5,033,454	5,899,139	865,685
8,228	0	37,397	0	0	0	850,021	850,021
14,488	2,405	91,853	4,321	71,209	0	844,300	844,300
9,960	10,215	63,475	14,002	0	0	839,411	839,411
9,446	—	71,656	0	0	0	834,392	834,392
26,691	28,300	120,891	3,000	0	67,560	889,751	822,191
23,401	0	37,076	49,599	0	0	794,209	794,209
8,774	23,165	101,853	2,750	46,592	210,058	972,797	762,739
22,941	1,442	48,222	13,920	35,003	57,791	809,338	751,547
1,470	0	88,229	4,920	0	0	736,259	736,259
22,461	0	110,927	0	0	0	720,006	720,006
13,278	0	0	3,426	185,971	0	717,791	717,791
5,734	0	39,079	6,354	89,261	0	674,049	674,049
6,611	0	29,470	3,298	61,632	268,556	835,946	567,390
13,896	0	35,118	2,368	0	0	471,575	471,575
14,754	0	40,622	0	11,467	24,813	489,738	464,925
13,168	0	50,169	0	0	0	421,897	421,897
—	0	39,441	0	31,750	86,378	502,934	416,556
0	0	40,991	397	26,886	0	415,845	415,845

Table 62. FISCAL YEAR 1947–48,

School No.	Instruction — All Except USPHS	Instruction — USPHS	Instruction — Total	Research Budgeted Separately — Federal USPHS	Research Budgeted Separately — Federal Contracts	Research Budgeted Separately — All Other	Research Budgeted Separately — Total	Administration — Medical School	Administration — Share of University	Administration — Total
									30 TAX-SUPPORTED	
1	$ 971,129	$97,198	$1,068,327	$235,465	$ 77,525	$596,409	$ 909,399	$ 42,471	$349,225*	$391,696
2	1,080,048	3,834	1,083,882	81,323	0	303,018	384,341	59,147	225,000	284,147
3	1,301,148	0	1,301,148	37,484	81,705	173,527	292,716	45,259	151,499	196,758
4	728,848	0	728,848	90,704	66,026	0	156,730	71,367	61,299	132,666
5	799,423	0	799,423	170,846	22,793	212,386	406,025	41,178	134,232	175,410
6	813,166	4,562	817,728	31,292	74,077	143,190	248,559	225,513	0	225,513
7	512,603	4,650	517,253	139,744	0	303,580	443,324	37,124	0	37,124
8	1,079,190	0	1,079,190	9,917	16,079	125,687	151,683	14,043	31,972	46,015
9	564,425	8,318	572,743	11,818	2,699	30,891	45,408	136,779	128,864	265,643
10	663,688	10,172	673,860	33,839	15,707	48,667	98,213	52,008	105,118	157,126
11	327,172	0	327,172	93,119	65,679	76,054	234,852	72,380	4,395	76,775
12	211,504	0	211,504	24,459	8,581	12,931	45,971	14,345	0	14,345
13	484,024	0	484,024	28,799	0	162,923	191,722	40,454	25,420	65,874
14	416,915	2,433	419,348	6,057	8,917	77,673	92,647	95,477	0	95,477
15	282,735	6,511	289,246	159,390	11,319	136,365	307,074	19,263	21,625	40,888
16	482,469	6,202	488,671	44,957	0	61,814	106,771	36,000	0	36,000
17	356,500	24,927	381,427	81,246	0	68,450	149,696	29,500	0	29,500
18	321,220	0	321,220	4,409	28,746	32,289	65,444	32,560	61,922	94,482
19	342,732	0	342,732	11,228	97,402	42,099	150,729	13,814	37,614	51,428
20	338,218	8,558	346,776	20,021	0	3,695	23,716	23,114	19,579	42,693
21	272,759	24,800	297,559	24,227	40,112	21,792	86,131	5,800	11,952	17,752
22	224,198	8,166	232,364	0	0	0	0	45,214	0	45,214
23	304,657	3,047	307,704	6,327	0	17,316	23,643	66,406	12,000	78,406
24	288,450	0	288,450	9,748	0	0	9,748	25,050	0	25,050
25	251,096	0	251,096	14,614	0	19,247	33,861	58,211	0	58,211
26	266,460	0	266,460	25,115	0	23,346	48,461	42,248	0	42,248
27	322,715	0	322,715	2,200	9,440	22,461	34,101	18,254	26,287	44,541
28	233,565	0	233,565	46,431	0	33,143	79,574	24,016	0	24,016
29	284,276	4,069	288,345	1,798	0	24,949	26,747	15,994	27,889	43,883
30	240,704	0	240,704	0	6,200	800	7,000	38,610	5,361	43,971
									41 PRIVATELY	
31	2,293,888	11,097	2,304,985	291,528	266,350	62,000	619,878	99,061	392,420	491,481
32	1,339,870	16,816	1,356,686	176,467	213,652	716,989	1,107,108	30,090	160,838	190,928
33	948,028	0	948,028	133,352	1,225,771	81,821	1,440,944	93,770	92,504	186,274
34	1,587,926	10,869	1,598,795	223,558	300,403	0	523,961	52,710	0	52,710
35	1,042,179	0	1,042,179	273,867	87,818	554,184	915,869	101,569	45,080	146,649
36	779,418	1,620	781,038	129,823	26,626	349,565	506,014	70,816	53,355	124,171
37	775,083	25,000	800,083	114,239	0	502,683	616,922	54,115	202,834	256,949
38	776,114	14,654	790,768	121,474	145,441	217,888	484,803	32,691	69,618	102,309
39	565,459	0	565,459	227,270	7,793	731,424	966,487	114,620	43,922	158,542
40	561,949	0	561,949	170,418	82,492	585,427	838,337	109,849	0	109,849
41	627,234	0	627,234	88,562	206,526	278,619	573,707	45,973	31,951	77,924
42	398,391	0	398,391	144,178	67,322	342,572	554,072	52,161	81,839	134,000
43	505,506	0	505,506	76,151	113,716	47,059	236,926	37,667	61,607	99,274
44	432,935	0	432,935	31,953	15,868	42,553	90,374	152,119	—	152,119
45	409,688	0	409,688	102,095	12,308	132,665	247,068	38,032	91,639	129,671
46	679,810	19,535	699,345	32,017	9,069	180,015	221,101	31,934	19,234	51,168
47	325,633	0	325,633	21,747	0	59,525	81,272	26,621	17,830	44,451
48	472,471	0	472,471	14,247	40,862	314,492	369,601	25,888	41,508	67,396
49	281,771	0	281,771	0	0	60,013	60,013	23,983	46,449	70,432
50	340,842	0	340,842	23,470	0	68,318	91,788	205,659	0	205,659
51	371,486	23,491	394,977	40,167	4,088	155,648	199,903	47,766	25,816	73,582
52	211,266	4,664	215,930	24,252	0	105,209	129,461	7,250	20,194	27,444
53	306,920	0	306,920	4,093	0	64,617	68,710	85,255	0	85,255
54	376,050	0	376,050	17,730	0	33,035	50,765	29,016	8,395	37,411
55	211,698	0	211,698	4,418	0	16,518	20,936	44,873	0	44,873
56	250,524	0	250,524	51,309	41,745	36,057	129,111	16,711	65,500	82,211
57	190,326	38,381	228,707	15,602	56,769	48,660	121,031	25,628	51,811	77,439
58	304,148	0	304,148	30,053	0	80,315	110,368	43,650	5,000	48,650
59	375,615	7,730	383,345	2,837	0	7,652	10,489	37,837	20,771	58,608
60	278,128	0	278,128	3,734	88,523	63,065	155,322	83,804	0	83,804
61	280,167	10,171	290,338	17,994	0	91,181	109,175	31,130	124,374	155,504
62	243,850	0	243,850	9,172	0	11,805	20,977	42,074	0	42,074
63	389,298	16,375	405,673	31,475	408	26,465	58,348	46,074	0	46,074
64	108,710	0	108,710	6,591	0	18,215	24,806	40,756	0	40,756
65	211,526	0	211,526	0	0	0	0	61,880	0	61,880
66	263,348	0	263,348	3,731	0	48,540	52,271	36,343	0	36,343
67	136,284	239	136,523	1,162	4,375	16,634	22,171	55,524	19,317	74,841
68	161,883	10,343	172,226	13,541	0	8,673	22,214	33,672	9,023	42,695
69	125,382	0	125,382	2,251	3,153	3,794	9,198	15,053	25,694	40,747
70	212,173	6,922	219,095	15,701	15,304	0	31,005	29,258	34,123	63,381
71	148,083	0	148,083	2,750	0	8,262	11,012	43,940	0	43,940

Source: Figures supplied by the Surgeon General's Committee on Medical School Grants and Finances.
* Estimated.
— Indicates expenditures not segregated but kept in total.
0 Indicates no expenditures from medical school budget.

EXPENDITURES OF 71 FOUR-YEAR MEDICAL SCHOOLS

Libraries	Postgraduate Education	Maintenance	Student Health	Other Expenditures	Hospitals and Clinics	Total	Total Exclusive of Hospitals and Clinics
SCHOOLS							
$37,480*	$600,849	$844,866*	$26,597	$ 48,238	$2,812,833	$6,740,285	$3,927,452
26,667	0	103,259	0	19,004	2,194,785	4,096,085	1,901,300
27,349	36,626	527,732	0	116,023	1,683,007	4,181,359	2,498,352
49,040	0	81,733	5,407	0	0	1,154,424	1,154,424
34,990	45,954	88,536	12,090	584,260	5,264,577	7,411,265	2,146,688
41,887	10,861	132,353	9,828	22,121	2,223,036	3,731,886	1,508,850
41,881	0	67,297	3,016	6,257	0	1,116,152	1,116,152
13,087	17,843	147,704	1,077	9,251	0	1,465,850	1,465,850
22,654	7,126	75,705	1,017	946,711	2,216,567	4,153,574	1,937,007
21,044	0	160,572	2,661	7,892	1,460,838	2,582,206	1,121,368
16,223	12,690	69,010	0	57,642	0	794,364	794,364
17,279	22,298	63,867	6,489	1,800	1,979,062	2,362,615	383,553
16,250	0	46,166	57,814	0	0	861,850	861,850
24,552	60,859	119,708	3,849	190,677	490,501	1,497,618	1,007,117
3,807	0	28,661	557	14,488	0	684,721	684,721
27,000	0	92,752	0	1,460	0	752,654	752,654
8,750	0	91,750	3,500	138,566	0	803,189	803,189
23,810	5,971	42,204	2,633	54,085	0	609,849	609,849
10,655	11,756	26,687	0	19,647	0	613,634	613,634
16,012	0	20,152	0	45,421	13,012	507,782	494,770
10,695	10,389	62,802	4,789	10,682	0	500,799	500,799
22,799	0	30,009	0	36,796	0	367,182	367,182
12,686	0	72,396	0	209,596	344,223	1,048,654	704,431
17,000	6,000	155,000	0	0	15,000	516,248	501,248
50,910	0	19,796	1,530	204,412	74,151	693,967	619,816
18,064	0	26,988	0	8,284	0	410,505	410,505
17,768	3,573	108,507	3,638	15,247	2,349,735	2,899,825	550,090
5,766	0	63,581	0	27,810	76,675	510,987	434,312
13,051	0	33,055	22	12,368	8,094	425,565	417,471
24,539	0	50,402	5,380	32,000	0	403,996	403,996
SUPPORTED SCHOOLS							
54,915	137,396	227,324	7,469	87,532	0	3,930,980	3,930,980
78,906	0	289,131	—	34,298	3,541,883	6,598,940	3,057,057
19,729	0	84,047	7,655	51,057	2,660,063	5,397,797	2,737,734
35,252	117,318	284,694	0	214,087	0	2,826,817	2,826,817
11,000	0	62,280	0	183,026	236,684	2,597,687	2,361,003
24,234	22,998	111,121	13,614	473,443	0	2,056,633	2,056,633
44,040	0	234,665	0	94,330	176,375	2,223,364	2,046,989
19,430	0	95,278	0	3,100	0	1,495,688	1,495,688
21,938	119,754	225,239	0	5,986	0	2,063,405	2,063,405
15,716	39,086	126,570	2,566	137,243	294,529	2,125,845	1,831,316
9,594	0	212,872	0	34,311	0	1,535,642	1,535,642
37,953	0	218,492	0	48,896	269,864	1,661,668	1,391,804
21,957	0	131,933	0	27,703	13,943	1,037,242	1,023,299
8,151	0	74,328	0	77,479	0	835,386	835,386
43,622	11,751	78,115	4,748	36,188	66,700	1,027,551	960,851
16,716	0	41,764	7,942	14,883	230,777	1,283,696	1,052,919
4,722	20,395	67,107	0	630	0	544,210	544,210
13,392	0	47,713	0	4,427	1,161,298	2,136,298	975,000
7,796	0	81,187	430	24,830	144,406	670,865	526,459
12,153	16,050	60,427	3,199	115,671	0	845,789	845,789
20,781	0	55,846	4,401	0	1,294,072	2,043,562	749,490
4,335	122,829	46,147	3,313	32,202	81,170	662,831	581,661
19,088	30,342	211,310	0	968,097	3,046,216	4,735,938	1,689,722
6,805	0	28,097	276	26,797	0	526,201	526,201
9,500	0	30,657	6,120	207,598	0	531,382	531,382
10,900	49,192	60,400	28,100	22,350	90,000	722,788	632,788
7,745	0	45,489	—	8,252	0	488,663	488,663
18,398	0	71,812	0	15,650	—	569,026	569,026
15,904	0	32,136	1,897	6,431	0	508,810	508,810
8,927	29,616	78,718	3,807	28,943	152,366	819,631	667,265
12,349	0	42,803	4,036	1,309	856,592	1,472,106	615,514
7,057	0	42,955	685	1,965	0	359,563	359,563
18,500	0	47,366	4,576	8,100	0	588,637	588,637
10,297	0	13,108	1,500	86,347	66,030	351,554	285,524
10,248	0	30,128	0	27,872	59,888	401,542	341,654
6,173	0	19,707	0	63,310	0	441,152	441,152
7,472	0	32,759	1,678	160,097	100,350	535,891	435,541
12,651	0	47,025	2,043	0	15,915	314,769	298,854
7,824	0	62,144	2,692	0	0	247,987	247,987
8,984	0	28,636	0	0	0	351,101	351,101
5,970	0	36,883	3,529	9,290	0	258,707	258,707

Table 63. FISCAL YEAR 1940–41, EXPENDITURES OF 65 FOUR-YEAR MEDICAL SCHOOLS

School No.	Instruction — All Except USPHS	Instruction — USPHS	Instruction — Total	Research Budgeted Separately — Federal USPHS	Federal Contracts	All Other	Research Total	Administration — Medical School	Share of University	Administration Total	Libraries	Post-graduate Education	Maintenance	Student Health	Other Expenditures	Hospitals and Clinics	Total	Total Exclusive of Hospitals and Clinics
1	$376,636	$15,685	$392,321	0	0	$132,672	$132,672	$24,074	$125,393	$149,467	$13,457	$340,243	$303,358	$13,950	$18,312	$1,027,969	$2,391,749	$1,363,780
2	464,582	0	464,582	0	0	105,550	105,550	8,272	0	8,272	16,760	0	50,354	0	6,750	826,363	1,478,631	652,268

27 TAX-SUPPORTED SCHOOLS

School No.	Instruction — All Except USPHS	Instruction — USPHS	Instruction — Total	Federal USPHS	Federal Contracts	All Other	Research Total	Medical School	Share of University	Administration Total	Libraries	Post-graduate Education	Maintenance	Student Health	Other Expenditures	Hospitals and Clinics	Total	Total Exclusive
5	561,049	0	561,049	0	0	59,072	59,072	19,865	25,695	45,560	17,175	16,094	148,332	8,871	536	0	831,724	831,724
6	449,476	0	449,476	0	0	125,280	125,280	18,341	82,052	100,393	24,464	0	38,503	2,460	130,908	2,074,644	2,968,633	893,989
7	281,149	0	281,149	0	0	0		54,008	0	54,008	8,565	0	37,312	0	465	547,769	931,728	383,959
8	370,077	0	370,077	0	0	143,953	143,953	10,922	12,361	25,311	6,721	0	42,821	903	4,000	0	606,487	606,487
9	346,651	0	346,651	0	0	101,935	101,935	87,422	75,101	23,283	3,962	0	59,741	0	571	0	539,805	539,805
10	214,318	0	214,318	0	0	17,501	17,501	22,827	63,024	162,523	6,721	4,376	37,240	2,000	260,261	910,498	1,610,679	700,181
11	282,969	0	282,969	0	0	21,452	21,452	4,500	0	85,851	0	0	96,502	35,586	1,003	431,863	921,640	489,777
12	120,881	0	120,881	0	0	0		9,217	0	4,500	7,873	0	7,585	0	40,542	0	216,967	216,967
13	77,746	0	77,746	0	0	0		28,372	13,980	9,217	6,884	0	41,990	37,574	0	567,398	703,235	135,837
14	303,992	0	303,992	0	0	54,522	54,522	25,723	0	42,352	11,090	0	40,818	0	0	0	490,348	490,348
15	165,916	0	165,916	0	0	17,464	17,464	1,145	5,695	25,723	12,051	0	56,366	0	43,087	233,024	553,631	320,607
16	49,679	0	49,679	0	0	2,003	2,003	24,900	0	6,840	0	0	7,104	125	0	0	65,751	65,751
17	233,998	0	233,998	0	0	26,343	26,343	13,725	0	24,900	0	0	49,505	0	53,747	0	334,746	334,746
18	158,421	0	158,421	0	0	16,374	16,374	17,228	0	13,725	7,557	3,410	20,136	2,765	3,869	0	272,725	272,725
19	249,907	0	249,907	0	0	782	782	3,264	20,289	17,228	14,303	0	20,601	4,067	0	0	314,167	314,167
20	130,148	0	130,148	0	0	11,942	11,942	8,374	5,853	23,553	8,721	0	11,250	0	17,312	0	185,614	185,614
21	181,776	0	181,776	0	0	3,745	3,745	Not available	—	14,227	7,345	0	3,892	0	700	470	228,767	228,297
22	193,898	0	193,898	0	0	8,343	8,343	25,897	20,289	78,406	4,455	0	14,125	—	0	0	202,941	202,941
23	130,807	0	130,807	0	0	19,357	19,357	25,897	5,853	25,897	4,941	0	53,212	0	20,135	0	214,776	214,776
24	124,656	0	124,656	0	0	0		32,533	5,000	37,533		0		0	87,601	144,258	452,201	307,943
	No information			No information		No information		No information								15,000	242,373	227,373
27	196,096	0	196,096	0	0	12,672	12,672	4,875	37,114	41,989	6,420	0	20,874	2,537	9,065	541,281	830,934	289,653
28	110,009	0	110,009	0	0	17,252	17,252	10,341	0	10,341	3,416	0	22,254	0	9,613	12,000	184,885	172,885
29	133,785	0	133,785	0	0	1,904	1,904	9,129	0	9,129	2,399	0	11,300	0	5,000	0	163,517	163,517
30	68,730	0	68,730	0	0	0		19,650	6,476	26,126	8,826	0	23,120	4,729	12,000	0	143,531	143,531

38 PRIVATELY SUPPORTED SCHOOLS

No.			$5.09														Total	Total
31	1,711,050	0	0	0	295,409	0	30,446	240,050	270,496	27,986	0	4,140	130,242	102,273	1,751,365	2,246,187	2,246,187
32	889,710	0	$4,474	300,500	295,409	0	1,941	113,067	115,008	74,953	0	3,466	154,733	8,413	1,220,553	3,286,269	1,534,904
33	642,281	0	19,938	4,474	357,473	377,411	45,363	20,604	65,967	16,155	0	0	19,829	34,418	220,066	1,981,138	760,585
34	567,203	0	0	377,411	190,494	190,494	55,765	31,583	87,348	10,000	0	3,504	40,232	424,953	—	1,336,678	1,116,612
35	434,110	0	0	190,494	389,419	389,419	35,783	9,736	45,519	12,608	0	0	48,155	19,691	146,003	1,159,343	1,159,343
36	590,531	0	0	389,419	118,538	118,538	45,966	28,920	74,886	23,773	0	0	138,350	1,361	0	1,382,653	1,236,650
37	559,718	0	0	118,538	197,551	197,551	22,081	29,942	52,023	8,367	0	0	35,875	8,121	0	775,882	775,882
38	396,678	0	0	197,551	279,493	279,493	69,034	26,370	95,404	10,084	0	0	126,775	14,076	251,080	834,613	834,613
39	440,002	0	0	279,493	129,618	132,392	64,091	—	64,091	11,975	261	0	65,207	7,574	0	1,125,924	874,844
40	220,656	0	2,774	132,392	94,755	94,755	16,240	23,762	40,002	2,037	0	0	89,263	30,109	167,642	492,185	492,185
41	250,460	0	0	94,755	985	985	27,440	52,475	79,915	21,823	0	0	84,992	16,654	0	729,696	562,054
42	341,587	0	0	985			50,737		50,737	9,188	0	0	51,180	40,175	0	470,331	470,331
43	181,117	0	0				84,639		84,639	6,009	0	0	27,686		0	339,626	339,626
44	124,891	0	0		3,035	3,035	8,954	29,908	38,862	7,279	0	1,296	13,060		309,893	188,423	188,423
45	428,645	0	0	3,035	102,264	102,264	17,834	9,101	26,935	8,165	0	4,508	—		0	880,410	570,517
46	147,348	0	0	102,264			18,887	13,044	31,931	3,740	6,331	0	29,258	8,500	0	227,108	227,108
47	365,426	0	0		83,555	83,555	10,495	26,288	36,783	16,332	0	639	25,614	1,359	526,933	1,056,002	529,069
48	169,397	0	0	83,555	31,454	31,454	13,674	35,438	49,112	5,370	0	3,435	36,499	27,426	60,945	380,842	319,897
49	264,999	0	0	31,454			55,875		55,875	6,678	0	0	32,257	3,809	0	367,053	367,053
50	306,170	0	0		143,280	143,280	38,095	17,567	38,095	6,682	0	62	38,278		543,630	1,076,235	532,605
51	142,255	0	0	143,280	59,546	59,546	4,382		21,949	2,172	0	0	23,339	14,533	45,249	309,105	263,856
52	155,338	0	0	59,546			35,768	14,977	35,768	14,087	0	0	35,183	374,997	1,346,032	1,961,405	615,373
53	116,299	0	0				18,639		33,616	5,579	0	0	17,388	9,756	0	182,638	182,638
54	134,984	0	0				20,773		20,773	4,288	0	0	12,929	176,001	0	348,975	348,975
55	142,352	0	0		4,720	4,720	19,959	7,360	27,319	8,050	10,607	0	27,800		0	240,048	240,048
56	89,665	0	0	4,720	4,472	4,472	12,765	32,373	45,138	2,938	0	19,200	9,130	7,810	0	159,153	159,153
57	269,925	0	0	4,472	9,540	9,540	17,614	5,000	22,614	12,232	0	0	24,126	3,847	0	342,284	342,284
58	166,198	0	0	9,540			14,216	10,273	24,489	8,110	0	555	8,285	2,205	0	209,842	209,842
59	187,825	0	0		8,196	8,196	45,420		45,420	5,039	4,372	1,943	34,480	39,804	67,684	392,820	325,136
60	110,069	0	0	8,196	20,482	20,482	12,230	48,505	60,735	3,421	0	0	16,816	810	427,944	642,220	214,276
61	229,961	0	0	20,482			26,400		26,400	4,000	0	1,250	38,250		0	294,611	294,611
63	62,382	0	0		40,439	40,439	19,375		19,375	7,979	0	0	9,939	8,048	43,585	189,018	145,433
64	44,245	0	0	40,439			21,399		21,399	2,476	0	918	13,753	4,491	29,000	120,867	91,867
65	125,739	0	0		12,778	12,778	32,226	11,868	44,094	6,809	0	1,830	32,336		100,350	318,691	218,341
66	89,602	0	0	12,778	3,495	3,495	18,717	9,044	27,761	4,384	0	2,656	15,647	55,966	9,947	211,057	201,110
67	82,443	0	0	3,495	739	739		6,412	6,412		0	0	17,350		0	113,984	113,984
68	86,747	0	0	739			7,148		7,148		0	0	8,810	0	0	102,705	102,705
69	87,114	0	0				20,008	6,412	20,008	3,112	0	0	11,523	10,646	0	132,403	132,403

Source: Figures supplied by the Surgeon General's Committee on Medical School Grants and Finances.
— Indicates that expenditures not segregated but kept in total.
0 Indicates no expenditures from medical school budget.
No information on schools 4, 25, 26, 34, 62, and 66.

Table 64. EXPENDITURES OF TWO-YEAR MEDICAL SCHOOLS IN FISCAL YEARS 1940–41, 1947–48, AND 1950–51

School No.	Instruction All Except USPHS	Instruction USPHS	Instruction Total	Research Federal USPHS	Research Federal Contracts	Research All Other	Research Total	Admin. Medical School	Admin. Share of University	Admin. Total	Libraries	Separately Organized Postgrad. Education	Maintenance	Student Health	All Other Expenditures	Hospitals and Clinics	Total	Total Exclusive of Hospitals and Clinics
1940–41*																		
72	$ 21,500	0	$ 21,500	0	0	0	0	$ 7,500	$ 5,000	$12,500	$ 1,000	0	$10,000	0	0	0	$ 45,000	$ 45,000
73	68,866	0	68,866	0	0	$10,106	$10,106	3,677	2,555	6,232	1,214	$ 2,839	20,000	$ 1,215	$ 409	0	110,881	110,881
74	42,727	0	42,727	0	0	0	0	4,364	2,164	6,528	0	0	0	137	0	0	49,392	49,392
75	29,354	0	29,354	0	0	0	0	2,546	3,120	5,666	1,560	0	5,504	450	0	0	42,534	42,534
76	50,900	0	50,900	0	0	0	0	3,826	6,500	10,326	5,000	0	8,248	1,650	0	0	76,124	76,124
77	57,686	0	57,686	0	0	0	0	5,200	751	5,951	546	0	2,016	162	0	0	66,361	66,361
1947–48*																		
72	49,400	0	49,400	0	0	0	0	5,000	5,000	10,000	1,050	0	20,000	0	0	0	80,450	80,450
73	165,688	0	165,688	$15,258	0	7,501	22,759	9,041	5,056	14,097	4,283	6,937	30,000	1,660	150	0	245,574	245,574
74	149,836	0	149,836	0	0	0	0	15,429	16,893	32,322	6,260	0	18,889	886	0	0	208,193	208,193
75	93,443	0	93,443	0	$ 2,689	1,357	4,046	12,911	7,395	20,306	8,000	0	10,670	685	4,450	0	141,600	141,600
76	80,476	0	80,476	0	0	0	0	9,157	9,000	18,157	8,000	22,285	23,622	2,400	0	0	154,940	154,940
77	97,953	0	97,953	0	0	0	0	12,900	4,182	17,082	2,695	0	10,128	569	0	0	128,427	128,427
1950–51																		
72	294,107	$ 5,000	299,107	18,376	0	37,572	81,948	25,670	9,356	35,026	23,000	0	0	12,592	7,500	0	459,173	459,173
73	262,615	5,000	267,615	59,850	0	16,950	76,800	—	—	—	28,500	0	38,166	0	0	0	411,081	411,081
74	152,397	0	152,397	25,880	0	14	25,894	16,334	27,097	43,431	10,456	0	27,212	0	5,196	0	264,586	264,586
75	141,869	10,000	151,869	17,344	0	18,328	35,672	14,580	0	14,580	9,280	0	0	3,300	0	$3,850	218,551	214,701
76	83,451	0	83,451	4,910	400	3,410	8,720	10,808	12,000	22,808	8,000	44,035	19,348	2,600	0	0	188,962	188,962
77	71,590	5,000	76,590	7,300	0	0	7,300	17,750	0	17,750	—	—	—	0	0	0	101,640	101,640

* 1940–41 and 1947–48 figures supplied by the Surgeon General's Committee on Medical School Grants and Finances.
— Indicate expenditures not segregated but kept in total.
0 Indicates no expenditures from medical school budget.

Table 65. THE SURVEY'S QUESTIONNAIRE TO ALL MEDICAL SCHOOLS REGARD-
ING INCOME

Finances	
Amount of income for the fiscal year in which the medical school is surveyed. Line items:	
19. *Tuition and Fees*	. . . .
a. Undergraduate (medical)	. . . .
b. Postgraduate (medical)	. . . .
c. All other tuition fees received by the medical school	. . . .
20. *All Income from Endowment Investments*	. . . .
a. Specifically designated for the medical school	. . . .
b. General university	. . . .
21. *Governmental Appropriations and Grants*	. . . .
a. Federal	. . . .
(1*a*) Research	. . . .
(1*b*) Instructional	. . . .
b. State	. . . .
c. County or city	. . . .
22. *Gifts and Grants from Private Sources*	. . . .
a. Research	. . . .
b. Instructional or nonrestricted	. . . .
23. *Income Received from Organized Activities Relating to Instructional Depart-ments*	. . . .
a. Hospitals and clinics	. . . .
b. All other	. . . .
24. *All Other Income Including Educational and Noneducational* (Specify type and source)	. . . .
25. *Total Income—Educational, Research, and General* (Items 19–24)	. . . .

Table 66. FISCAL YEAR 1950–51,

School No.	Tuition and Fees				Endowment			Governmenta[l]		
	Medical Under-graduate	Medical Post-graduate	All Other	Total	Medical School	University Used for Medical School	Total	Federal		Tota[l]
								Research	Instruction	
30 TAX-SUPPORTED										
1	$236,800	$53,757	0	$290,557	$185,232	0	$185,232	$666,061	$119,091	$785,152
2	Not itemized			71,300	96,987	0	96,987	1,539,247	46,000	1,585,247
3	221,317	35,022	0	256,339	1,489	0	1,489	321,572	61,178	382,750
4	91,234	0	0	91,234	3,951	$47,140	51,091	284,570	22,071	306,641
5	191,119	37,536	0	228,655	104,491	243,640	348,131	421,041	0	421,041
6	10,838	11,417	$79,202	101,457	43,989	0	43,989	209,814	25,000	234,814
7	230,058	0	4,610	234,668	0	180,056	180,056	222,809	117,946	340,755
8	92,858	5,283	0	98,141	5,867	0	5,867	85,196	24,964	110,160
9	159,092	12,460	10,240	181,792	7,036	1,477	8,513	69,450	34,700	104,150
10	Not available				?	?	16,449	112,888	27,700	140,588
11	211,422	28,764	22,832	263,018	0	0	0	236,628	109,704	346,332
12	106,229	0	0	106,229	0	0	0	127,497	50,980	178,477
13	Not available				6,839	0	6,839	103,160	0	103,160
14	109,627	12,960	19,413	142,000	20,192	0	20,192	71,859	38,941	110,800
15	77,851	—	—	77,851	0	34,732	34,732	811,782	17,178	828,960
16	131,250	18,270	0	149,520	0	0	0	94,808	38,943	133,751
17	209,076	0	52,238	261,314	0	0	0	47,585	39,621	87,206
18	77,069	3,275	19,839	100,183	0	14,831	14,831	50,267	81,423	131,690
19	170,811	2,516	18,412	191,739	3,498	949	4,447	247,401	55,641	303,042
20	228,677	—	275	228,952	5,229	0	5,229	97,350	20,400	117,750
21	130,563	3,679	0	134,242	10,763	0	10,763	215,252	37,119	252,371
22	93,313	0	0	93,313	"A considerable sum"		?	37,771	54,975	92,746
23	129,200	0	5,757	134,957	0	0	0	39,149	24,996	64,145
24	120,898	0	0	120,898	0	0	0	47,000	31,500	78,500
25	111,281	0	12,100	123,381	0	0	0	91,163	54,000	145,163
26	93,611	5,020	0	98,631	0	0	0	35,431	51,225	86,656
27	226,328	2,560	14,650	243,538	0	0	0	66,800	21,250	88,050
28	155,278	0	0	155,278	12,785	0	12,785	99,857	41,417	141,274
29	107,221	47,760	0	154,981	5,984	1,282	7,266	89,047	35,385	124,432
30	175,000	0	0	175,000	1,000	?	1,000	0	73,000	73,000
41 PRIVATELY										
31	353,638	95,840	62,612	512,090	375,651	1,326,206	1,701,857	1,294,301	24,894	1,319,195
32	177,840	0	368,640	546,480	1,402,616	0	1,402,616	1,051,534	67,275	1,118,809
33	175,351	0	0	175,351	857,548	50,116	907,664	1,838,394	6,000	1,844,394
34	429,226	119,124	11,799	560,149	856,271	70,135	926,406	822,395	79,347	901,742
35	241,652	10,530	3,670	255,852	828,404	0	828,404	619,672	0	619,672
36	345,957	31,853	0	377,810	765,020	144,000	909,020	351,009	45,843	396,852
37	218,539	3,000	0	221,539	494,472	0	494,472	631,365	96,549	727,914
38	329,978	0	12,890	342,868	404,959	2,000	406,959	662,212	66,401	728,613
39	366,225	0	25,088	391,313	178,279	0	178,279	527,669	0	527,669
40	277,193	6,488	6,365	290,046	482,660	0	482,660	410,046	57,000	467,046
41	255,457	10,634	2,461	268,552	402,890	0	402,890	628,424	59,858	688,282
42	460,645	8,533	40,466	509,644	319,700	123,284	442,984	295,901	25,000	320,901
43	332,867	54,052	0	386,919	336,910	0	336,910	279,370	70,735	350,105
44	451,500	12,480	8,373	472,353	78,046	0	78,046	129,840	50,633	180,473
45	168,705	0	0	168,705	147,734	172,252	319,986	147,749	55,664	203,413
46	217,500	20,000	15,500	253,000	0	464,810	464,810	250,000	50,000	300,000
47	340,800	0	0	340,800	143,255	69,575	212,830	59,782	40,232	100,014
48	194,570	12,535	77	207,182	83,564	599,693	683,257	113,076	17,151	130,227
49	170,032	3,985	0	174,017	67,415	0	67,415	77,575	0	77,575
50	265,753	3,050	0	268,803	117,400	0	117,400	56,279	15,819	72,098
51	124,492	2,765	16,760	144,017	512,983	0	512,983	103,023	56,755	159,778
52	326,101	24,293	0	350,394	23,783	0	23,783	123,706	0	123,706
53	264,292	31,000	0	295,292	0	0	0	8,120	25,000	33,120
54	182,236	3,794	0	186,030	1,200	0	1,200	136,902	0	136,902
55	261,000	3,384	0	264,384	2,510	0	2,510	41,610	50,300	91,910
56	220,379	10,215	32,557	263,151	2,400	2,786	5,186	141,331	48,136	189,467
57	220,012	0	9,295	229,307	33,562	0	33,562	105,594	84,122	189,716
58	384,170	3,800	14,897	402,867	162,989	6,138	169,127	79,118	39,000	118,118
59	101,781	0	0	101,781	23,971	712	24,683	47,204	565,560	612,764
60	379,941	25,214	0	405,155	19,662	100,876	120,538	47,440	25,000	72,440
61	170,117	3,410	4,559	178,086	21,985	0	21,985	66,504	48,855	115,359
62	221,381	0	0	221,381	0	3,406	3,406	58,474	19,143	77,617
63	381,399	3,750	1,275	386,424	0	0	0	105,653	39,019	144,672
64	161,967	2,426	0	164,393	40,339	0	40,339	55,889	37,448	93,337
65	214,042	0	0	214,042	4,375	0	4,375	6,254	43,525	49,779
66	135,737	9,006	0	144,743	120,712	0	120,712	76,096	46,755	122,851
67	235,872	0	0	235,872	6,878	0	6,878	22,179	53,607	75,786
68	255,709	2,588	19,270	277,567	47,563	0	47,563	22,611	43,406	66,017
69	208,900	0	0	208,900	13,557	0	13,557	15,919	36,810	52,729
70	117,325	100	4,628	122,053	0	0	0	65,810	56,206	122,016
71	120,150	3,500	0	123,650	39,780	0	39,780	17,469	63,818	81,287

— Indicates income not segregated but kept in total.
0 Indicates no income.

INCOME OF 71 FOUR-YEAR MEDICAL SCHOOLS

Appropriations			Gifts and Grants from Private Sources			Other Income	Hospitals and Clinics	Total	Total Exclusive of Hospitals and Clinics
State	City or County	Total Government	For Research	Nonrestricted	Total				
SCHOOLS									
$2,375,228	$762,255	$3,922,635	$512,580	$521,744	$1,034,324	$89,715	$1,302,439	$6,824,902	$5,522,463
87,147	0	1,672,394	218,596	17,585	236,181	0	1,660,268	3,737,130	2,076,862
3,977,495	0	4,360,245	269,901	0	269,901	30,886	167,062	5,085,922	4,918,860
1,821,061	0	2,127,702	287,943	36,140	324,083	0	0	2,594,110	2,594,110
941,937	0	1,362,978	366,040	29,592	395,632	67,622	7,191,211	9,594,229	2,403,018
1,400,000	0	1,634,814	253,962	157,965	411,927	0	2,887,000	5,079,187	2,192,187
0	Incl. under Univ.	340,755	327,062	84,388	411,450	724,085	0	1,891,014	1,891,014
1,041,771	0	1,151,931	171,065	0	171,065	2,885	5,407,167	6,837,056	1,429,889
1,040,595	0	1,144,745	150,630	27,567	178,197	134,352	2,750,154	4,397,753	1,647,599
1,918,198	0	2,058,786	0	0	0	1,344	1,286,679	3,363,258	2,076,579
441,948	0	788,280	140,387	226,498	366,885	11,752	0	1,429,935	1,429,935
1,067,500	0	1,245,977	108,525	78,000	186,525	100,000	2,057,255	3,695,986	1,638,731
867,378	0	970,538	196,909	0	196,909	0	0	1,174,286	1,174,286
828,218	0	939,018	75,616	46,786	122,402	49,725	723,264	1,996,601	1,273,337
360,748	0	1,189,708	208,485	0	208,485	5,685	0	1,516,461	1,516,461
43,213	668,040	845,004	74,200	0	74,200	0	25,100	1,093,824	1,068,724
545,795	0	633,001	34,100	9,490	43,590	60,444	0	998,349	998,349
765,539	0	897,229	46,050	1,080	47,130	0	20,250	1,079,623	1,059,373
243,811	0	546,853	86,986	23,823	110,809	104,815	4,042,948	5,001,611	958,663
125,000	125,000	367,750	79,607	13,002	92,609	42,484	23,847	760,871	737,024
325,132	0	577,503	31,550	1,204	32,754	20,000	0	775,262	775,262
500,000	0	592,746	47,888	50,680	98,568	3,674	0	788,301	788,301
1,201,210	0	1,265,355	14,800	0	14,800	98,420	163,921	1,677,453	1,513,532
525,602	0	604,102	26,500	0	26,500	0	39,250	790,750	751,500
650,430	0	795,593	38,409	15,000	53,409	43,082	0	1,015,465	1,015,465
408,722	0	495,378	10,282	47,663	57,945	4,784	0	656,738	656,738
304,380	0	392,430	103,730	19,338	123,068	7,656	0	766,692	766,692
475,000	7,500	623,774	37,352	0	37,352	847	14,925	844,961	830,036
202,399	3,100	329,931	12,405	11,086	23,491	1,155	24,435	541,259	516,824
163,000	0	236,000	40,000	0	40,000	0	0	452,000	452,000
SUPPORTED SCHOOLS									
17,800	37,396	1,374,391	$1,419,453		1,419,453	0	0	5,007,791	5,007,791
0	0	1,118,809	784,106		784,106	0	5,209,333	9,061,344	3,852,011
39,764	0	1,884,158	419,592	51,839	471,431	148,677	3,589,982	7,177,263	3,587,281
0	0	901,742	733,800	23,493	757,293	374,520	31,531	3,551,641	3,520,110
15,983	0	635,655	691,326	92,421	783,747	90,767	112,560	2,706,985	2,594,425
0	0	396,852	436,313		436,313	1,015,984	0	3,135,979	3,135,979
0	0	727,914	517,785	14,900	532,685	316,224	68,681	2,361,515	2,292,834
126,056	0	854,669	456,714	111,116	567,830	204,506	0	2,376,832	2,376,832
0	0	527,669	864,701	2	864,703	148,701	0	2,110,665	2,110,665
0	0	467,046	828,666	86,765	915,431	133,714	444,105	2,733,002	2,288,897
0	0	688,282	424,645	356,131	780,776	76,853	0	2,217,353	2,217,353
0	0	320,901	338,328	85,668	423,996	72,964	152,957	1,923,446	1,770,489
27,840	0	377,945	200,769	147,087	347,856	48,036	6,285	1,503,951	1,497,666
438,000	0	618,473	69,838	73,600	143,438	33,737	103,962	1,450,009	1,346,047
0	0	203,413	92,237	299,706	391,943	82,076	261,497	1,427,620	1,166,123
16,200	0	316,200	50,000	0	50,000	1,375	3,108,260	4,193,645	1,085,385
460,000	0	560,014	26,000	0	26,000	0	0	1,139,644	1,139,644
0	0	130,227	160,643	78,413	239,056	0	0	1,259,722	1,259,722
478,156	0	555,731	248,791	40,200	288,991	4,609	90,218	1,180,981	1,090,763
597,120	0	669,218	30,283	0	30,283	42,891	0	1,128,595	1,128,595
0	0	159,778	126,240	2,861	129,101	18,303	0	964,182	964,182
0	5,386	129,092	264,621	48,914	313,535	61,420	0	878,224	878,224
0	0	33,120	30,312	216,778	247,090	253,250	5,112,891	5,941,643	828,752
226,646	0	363,548	56,606	0	56,606	86,287	0	693,671	693,671
350,000	0	441,910	36,500	46,673	83,173	25,116	0	817,093	817,093
0	0	189,467	202,123	10,815	212,938	0	0	670,742	670,742
0	0	189,716	103,490	47,234	150,724	5,060	0	608,369	608,369
23,500	1,505	143,123	5,760	24,236	29,996	2,500	0	747,613	747,613
0	0	612,764	11,555	0	11,555	43,426	0	794,209	794,209
0	0	72,440	121,935	0	121,935	48,487	188,108	956,663	768,555
606,579	4,609	726,547	121,176	930	122,106	32,023	10,703	1,091,450	1,080,747
0	0	77,617	67,112	354,931	422,043	86,150	0	810,597	810,597
0	0	144,672	176,821	0	176,821	64,164	0	772,081	772,081
15,314	0	108,651	71,646	12,288	83,934	218,836	83,578	699,731	616,153
0	12,800	62,579	9,950	394,500	404,450	2,872	0	688,318	688,318
0	0	122,851	103,357	16,547	119,904	35,488	265,693	809,391	543,698
0	0	75,786	13,205	133,159	146,364	1,713	0	466,613	466,613
0	0	66,017	90,890	14,833	105,723	36,426	7,683	540,979	533,296
0	0	52,729	17,380	12,069	29,449	0	3,167	307,802	304,635
153,000	0	275,016	0	58,111	58,111	31,750	86,378	573,308	486,930
125,000	0	206,287	446	148,954	149,400	1,551	0	520,668	520,668

Table 67. FISCAL YEAR 1947–48, INCOME OF 71 FOUR-YEAR MEDICAL SCHOOLS

School No.	Tuition and Fees—Medical Students			Endowment	Governmental Appropriations and Grants				Gifts and Grants from Private Sources	Other Income	Hospitals and Clinics	Total	Total Exclusive of Hospitals and Clinics
	Undergraduate	Postgraduate	Total		Federal	State	City or County	Total					
						30 TAX-SUPPORTED SCHOOLS							
1	$201,099	$71,322	$272,421	$120,984	$472,963	$2,000,686	0	$2,473,649	$1,000,298	$83,871	$2,827,521	$6,778,744	$3,951,223
2	—	—	88,574	85,776	217,845	1,147,485	0	1,365,330	232,398	778,377	1,433,880	3,984,335	2,550,455
3	179,960	64,284	244,244	894	119,189	1,124,684	0	1,243,873	185,939	823,402	1,683,007	4,181,359	2,498,352
4	67,293	0	67,293	3,783	161,124	877,276	0	1,038,400	65,102	248,908	0	1,423,486	1,423,486
5	199,819	60,014	259,833	46,831	185,674	539,774	0	725,448	175,399	604,737	5,299,530	7,111,778	1,812,248
6	181,030	11,446	192,476	1,956	67,254	1,195,724	$1,200	1,264,178	102,062	18,728	2,049,067	3,628,467	1,579,400
7	171,881	1,045	172,926	190,990	235,164	*	0	235,164	488,177	6,257	0	1,093,514	1,093,514
8	59,658	10,950	70,608	6,581	30,633	787,220	0	817,853	105,915	593,483	0	1,594,440	1,594,440
9	135,000	6,060	141,060	32,322	27,076	30,000	0	57,076	77,517	1,915,522	1,981,236	4,204,733	2,223,497
10	—	—	—	15,403	65,306	1,306,753	0	1,372,059	55,092	1,230	1,137,963	2,581,747	1,443,784
11	109,954	49,821	159,775	3,723	165,755	324,042	0	489,797	104,466	18,591	23,000	799,352	776,352
12	123,459	22,298	145,757	0	33,040	675,051	0	708,091	12,931	247,256	1,248,080	2,362,615	1,114,535
13	85,000	0	85,000	0	45,507	571,407	0	616,914	113,465	880	0	822,112	822,112
14	108,928	46,624	155,552	5,853	14,575	1,093,825	9,579	1,117,979	211,457	169,080	134,272	1,812,439	1,678,167
15	78,713	0	78,713	24,099	186,957	282,500	0	469,457	153,542	41,359	0	743,071	743,071
16	122,725	6,797	129,522	0	57,026	0	476,739	533,765	52,560	15,113	0	730,960	730,960
17	185,931	24,729	210,660	0	109,673	272,000	0	381,673	64,950	161,903	0	819,186	819,186
18	53,244	995	54,239	0	34,332	371,040	0	405,372	22,536	65,781	0	547,928	547,928
19	151,774	3,577	155,351	4,607	238,240	182,167	0	420,407	70,039	36,750	0	687,154	687,154
20	236,058	1,775	237,833	0	28,579	0	0	28,579	15,503	47,721	13,113	342,749	329,636
21	128,179	10,389	138,568	0	99,528	228,788	0	328,316	21,792	0	0	498,701	498,701
22	122,579	3,475	126,054	10,025	20,000	0	0	20,000	187,425	43,981	0	379,190	379,190
23	100,342	350	100,692	1,730	76,423	759,998	36,000	872,421	16,548	120,566	60,572	1,170,799	1,110,227
24	113,315	8,000	121,315	0	37,734	367,685	0	405,419	0	2,500	15,000	544,234	529,234
25	53,167	21,783	74,950	0	6,507	425,000	0	431,507	31,684	216,602	0	754,743	754,743
26	61,561	2,850	64,411	0	31,393	290,000	0	321,393	21,202	11,181	0	418,187	418,187
27	192,832	2,746	195,578	0	11,640	395,548	0	407,188	20,478	14,280	2,523,210	3,160,734	637,524
28	93,229	0	93,229	3,068	40,199	298,100	5,000	343,199	24,669	31,650	0	495,815	495,815
29	100,388	11,203	111,591	4,098	5,867	100,000	10,100	115,967	30,960	29,930	0	292,546	292,546
30	136,000	0	136,000	1,000	23,800	170,000	0	193,800	41,100	37,380	0	409,280	409,280

41 PRIVATELY SUPPORTED SCHOOLS

#													
31	277,599	137,396	414,995	402,321	62,000	568,975	0	630,975	1,023,812	87,532	3,010,971	2,559,635	2,559,635
32	142,436	—	132,400	980,943	0	413,694	0	413,694	655,324	856,549	2,708,352	6,049,881	3,038,910
33	286,750	116,926	142,436	643,088	36,801	1,539,203	0	1,576,004	402,324	106,800	0	5,579,004	2,870,652
34	207,116	18,230	403,676	708,289	0	578,914	0	578,914	576,619	371,196	96,756	2,638,694	2,638,694
35	188,886	78,600	207,116	821,273	0	368,548	0	368,548	664,098	528,181	0	2,685,981	2,589,225
36	234,699	45,784	313,299	592,400	0	158,069	0	158,069	352,171	728,181	0	2,144,120	2,144,120
37	181,922	0	227,706	391,939	0	139,239	0	139,239	360,777	494,020	0	1,613,681	1,613,681
38	229,881	148,702	229,881	279,301	33,406	281,569	0	314,975	283,785	12,869	0	1,120,811	1,120,811
39	335,856	57,509	484,558	87,920	0	235,063	0	235,063	667,783	89,397	319,138	1,564,721	1,564,721
40	244,480	9,356	301,989	474,735	0	294,435	0	294,435	632,038	269,110	0	2,291,445	1,972,307
41	191,839	125,521	201,195	302,822	0	295,088	0	295,088	642,171	76,366	155,367	1,517,642	1,517,642
42	250,796	42,363	376,317	255,383	0	228,717	0	228,717	304,796	78,318	13,943	1,398,898	1,243,531
43	262,315		304,678	249,517	0	189,867	0	189,867	92,281	97,732	71,090	948,518	934,575
44	283,349	13,980	283,349	99,531	294,000	49,575	0	343,575	79,529	0	0	877,074	805,984
45	110,887	95,220	124,867	110,185	0	133,419	0	133,419	261,130	34,525	0	629,601	629,601
46	158,585	25,310	253,805	0	0	111,134	0	111,134	296,364	630	0	695,828	695,828
47	241,425		266,735	15,951	0	21,747	0	21,747	43,574	4,497	942,641	348,637	348,637
48	146,025	9,640	146,025	100,872	0	65,664	0	65,664	231,543	349,020	120,150	1,491,242	548,601
49	126,923	23,002	136,563	5,795	0		3,118		59,337	66,934	0	670,865	550,715
50	266,457	8,177	289,459	105,418	0	56,877	0	56,877	395,450	9,466	1,216,801	914,138	914,138
51	101,744	157,112	109,921	316,278	0	67,767	0	67,767	155,627	13,286	41,004	1,875,860	659,059
52	244,855	38,392	401,967	30,916	0	48,983	0	52,101	126,195	1,531,468	2,738,882	665,469	624,465
53	182,384	4,255	220,776		0	4,093	0	4,093	237,671	194,261	0	4,732,890	1,994,008
54	142,820		147,075	1,200	0	22,100	0	23,212	42,807	27,591	0	408,555	408,555
55	255,149	49,272	255,149	10,383	207,750	44,027	0	251,777	19,738	18,377	0	564,638	564,638
56	207,280		256,552	3,073	0	93,054	1,112	93,054	38,242	62,733	0	390,921	390,921
57	137,293		137,293	27,492	0	110,752	0	110,752	48,660	6,431	0	342,574	342,574
58	294,167		294,167	79,155	0	21,505	0	21,505	29,135	23,361	0	486,695	486,695
59	89,916		89,916	21,000	0	383,811	0	383,811	7,652	14,025	136,778	508,810	508,810
60	336,192	36,312	372,504	98,099	0	101,205	0	101,205	53,517	12,089	820,609	785,464	648,686
61	259,947	1,416	261,363	31,996	0	37,860	0	37,860	28,307	10,150	0	1,194,160	373,551
62	137,354	2,635	139,989	1,286	0	13,828	0	13,828	261,827	101,756	0	429,019	429,019
63	260,614	2,392	263,006	1,089	0	70,657	0	70,657	112,575	10,546	68,530	457,477	457,477
64	99,803		99,803	39,610	0	8,500	0	8,500	34,671	211,672	0	352,870	284,340
65	178,413		178,413		0		0		292,004	3,041	0	480,963	480,963
66	86,869	44,975	131,844	123,429	0	9,800	0	9,800	196,757	10,567	100,350	673,502	673,502
67	156,786		156,786	1,252	0	10,577	0	10,577	94,663	116	7,957	366,669	266,319
68	211,073	3,550	214,623	52,011	0	41,307	0	41,307	23,428	9,716	0	349,893	341,936
69	144,329		144,329	2,772	0	3,731	0	3,731	126,809		0	277,757	277,757
70	93,253	0	93,253	70,241	4,800	103,787	0	108,587	131,380		0	403,461	403,461
71	104,361	3,510	107,871	30,669	82,500	6,295	0	88,795	47,209	9,716	0	284,260	284,260

Source: Figures supplied by the Surgeon General's Committee on Medical School Grants and Finances.

* Included in endowment figure.

0 Indicates no income.

— Indicates income not segregated but kept in total.

Table 68. FISCAL YEAR 1940–41, INCOME OF 64 FOUR-YEAR MEDICAL SCHOOLS

School No.	Tuition and Fees—Medical Students			Endowment	Governmental Appropriations and Grants				Gifts and Grants from Private Sources	Other Income	Hospitals and Clinics	Total	Total Exclusive of Hospitals and Clinics
	Undergraduate	Postgraduate	Total		Federal	State	City or County	Total					
						26 TAX-SUPPORTED SCHOOLS							
1	$119,144	—	$119,144	$109,517	0	$761,922	0	$761,922	$472,062	$34,885	$ 922,123	$2,419,653	$1,497,530
2	56,196	—	56,196	66,872	0	522,813	0	522,813	62,751	210,497	620,677	1,539,806	919,129
5	169,135	0	169,135	259	0	386,959	0	386,959	58,813	216,558	0	831,724	831,724
6	144,037	$ 4,280	148,317	50,655	0	329,813	0	329,813	116,057	51,615	2,391,152	3,087,609	696,457
7	52,623	0	52,623	498	0	305,000	0	305,000	150	9,759	559,252	927,282	368,030
8	148,551	1,440	149,991	160,470	0	0	0	0	134,563	4,000	0	449,024	449,024
9	56,000	0	56,000	6,790	0	377,481	0	377,481	31,055	76,019	0	547,345	547,345
10	0	6,122	6,122	5,777	0	0	0	0	29,832	672,504	901,463	1,615,698	714,235
11	Not available	Not available	Not available	13,493	0	631,752	0	631,752	7,917	875	267,603	921,640	654,037
12	58,378	0	58,378	0	0	122,810	0	122,810	39,868	546	21,120	242,722	221,602
13	54,355	0	54,355	0	0	195,000	0	195,000	0	66,465	387,415	703,235	315,820
14	Not available	Not available	Not available	824	0	391,377	0	391,377	40,900	0	0	433,101	433,101
15	112,758	0	112,758	7,483	0	314,599	$ 23,006	337,605	38,550	32,797	25,004	554,197	529,193
16	14,296	0	14,296	0	0	31,655	0	31,655	0	5,820	0	51,771	51,771
17	84,500	0	84,500	0	0	0	223,902	223,902	45,547	0	0	353,949	353,949
18	124,753	1,200	125,953	0	0	85,330	0	85,330	16,374	58,474	0	286,131	286,131
19	71,169	526	71,695	0	0	232,444	0	232,444	782	9,245	0	314,166	314,166
20	119,362	0	119,362	354	0	54,310	0	54,310	16,172	0	0	190,198	190,198
21	155,896	0	155,896	0	0	0	0	0	12,947	19,752	4,025	192,620	188,595
23	79,387	0	79,387	6,575	0	114,511	0	114,511	8,343	700	0	209,516	209,516
24	92,519	0	92,519	0	0	300,000	42,398	342,398	1,204	33,904	9,154	479,179	470,025
25	48,500	0	48,500	0	0	163,712	0	163,712	0	0	15,000	227,212	212,212
27	217,310	0	217,310	0	0	45,559	0	45,559	12,772	24,278	549,973	849,892	299,919
28	40,725	0	40,725	1,800	0	147,518	5,000	152,518	23,101	5,442	0	223,586	223,586
29	46,802	0	46,802	3,814	0	60,000	7,400	67,400	3,010	11,009	0	132,035	132,035
30	83,413	0	83,413	1,000	0	49,587	0	49,587	2,000	12,000	0	148,000	148,000

38 PRIVATELY SUPPORTED SCHOOLS

School											Subtotal	Total
31	0	224,341	368,272				0	613,341	102,273	0	1,308,227	1,308,227
32	—	117,150	715,096	$ 5,091			5,091	221,961	336,077	1,312,056	1,395,375	2,707,431
33	0	96,801	516,475	5,369	375		5,744	224,752	1,360	1,143,471	845,132	1,988,603
35	126	171,254	667,038	20,000			20,000	361,281	93,271	16,488	1,312,844	1,329,332
36	0	172,743	251,518				0	195,746	428,357	0	1,048,364	1,048,364
37	0	109,640	305,111				0	329,468	279,774	0	1,023,993	1,023,993
38	0	183,183	205,926		54,500		54,500	191,031	10,234	0	644,874	644,874
39	0	331,363	73,396				0	252,414	51,437	0	708,610	708,610
40	0	164,619	421,277				0	251,080	74,163	230,974	911,139	1,142,113
41	0	115,762	200,483				0	139,807	11,474	0	467,526	467,526
42	3,615	220,764	199,303				0	10,096	74,541	57,705	504,704	562,409
43	0	258,308	166,663				0	48,050	19,154	0	492,175	492,175
44	0	205,391	71,331		62,500		62,500	0	0	0	339,222	339,222
45	—	76,045	34,626				0	22,182	0	0	132,853	132,853
46	7,125	115,245	0				0	102,133	5,671	0	223,049	223,049
47	0	167,439	800				0	0	7,125	0	175,364	175,364
48	0	102,698	17,059				0	73,683	8,855	410,913	202,295	613,208
49	0	135,112	11,033				0	27,824	160,705	46,168	334,674	380,842
50	0	221,735	98,273				0	39,778	20,327	0	380,113	380,113
51	205	80,000	334,914	2,499			2,499	140,781	11,357	553,181	569,551	1,122,732
52	0	197,390	787			2,764	2,764	131,757	3,091	16,582	335,789	352,371
53	3,023	128,486	0				0	54,278	600,011	1,211,291	782,775	1,994,066
54	0	138,110	1,200		50,000		50,000	0	42,520	0	181,830	181,830
55	10,607	272,116	11,204	4,720		7,500	12,220	0	14,326	0	347,646	347,646
56	0	161,004	2,845				0	680	0	0	176,749	176,749
57	0	89,485	7,222				0	9,605	2,878	0	109,190	109,190
58	0	254,274	46,432				0	12,140	18,612	0	331,458	331,458
59	6,190	37,113	17,898	152,626			152,626	0	2,205	0	209,842	209,842
60	0	208,504	60,344				0	9,975	11,175	57,659	296,188	353,847
61	1,281	98,518	23,297				0	300	3,778	413,443	125,893	539,336
63	0	163,500	31,000				0	4,500	95,611	0	294,611	294,611
64	0	57,329	36,431				0	35,475	5,342	43,585	139,420	183,005
65	0	119,026	0				0	0	2,775	17,729	124,368	142,097
67	0	140,428	65,288				0	0	4,871	100,350	144,450	244,800
68	0	56,048	0				0	8,344	16	5,275	218,931	224,206
69	0	141,675	0				0	43,692	46,591	0	126,381	126,381
70	0	82,673	0				0	0	6,096	0	102,705	102,705
71	0	47,314	26,926		50,000		50,000	582	6,096	0	130,918	130,918

Source: Figures supplied by the Surgeon General's Committee on Medical School Grants and Finances.
0 Indicates no income.
— Indicates income not segregated but kept in total.
No information on schools 4, 22, 25, 26, 34, 62, and 66.

Table 69. INCOME OF TWO-YEAR MEDICAL SCHOOLS IN FISCAL YEARS 1940–41, 1947–48, AND 1950–51

1940–41*

School No.	Tuition and Fees—Medical Undergrad.	Postgrad.	Total	Endowment	Gov. Federal	Gov. State	Gov. City or County	Gov. Total	Gifts and Grants from Private Sources	Other Income	Hospitals and Clinics	Total	Total Exclusive of Hospitals and Clinics
72	$4,015	0	$4,015	0	0	$40,985	0	$40,985	0	0	0	$45,000	$45,000
73	22,858	$2,839	25,697	$8,478	0	64,601	0	64,601	$13,775	$254	0	112,805	112,805
74	7,976	255	8,231	0	0	0	0	0	0	0	0	8,231	8,231
75	8,400	0	8,400	0	0	34,134	0	34,134	0	0	0	42,534	42,534
76	18,500	0	18,500	1,607	0	0	0	0	0	56,017	0	76,124	76,124
77	12,954	0	12,954	0	0	49,932	0	49,932	0	0	0	62,886	62,886

1947–48*

School No.	Tuition and Fees—Medical Undergrad.	Postgrad.	Total	Endowment	Gov. Federal	Gov. State	Gov. City or County	Gov. Total	Gifts and Grants from Private Sources	Other Income	Hospitals and Clinics	Total	Total Exclusive of Hospitals and Clinics
72	7,313	0	7,313	0	0	73,137	0	73,137	0	2,000	0	82,450	82,450
73	35,746	7,548	43,294	7,713	$16,252	171,620	0	187,872	10,350	177	0	249,406	249,406
74	28,375	0	28,375	0	4,000	100,000	0	104,000	0	0	0	132,375	132,375
75	22,000	0	22,000	0	2,400	111,393	0	113,793	1,357	4,450	0	141,600	141,600
76	26,225	2,725	28,950	1,631	0	1,200	0	1,200	10,850	112,309	0	154,940	154,940
77	21,632	0	21,632	0	0	89,221	0	89,221	0	0	0	110,853	110,853

1950–51

School No.	Tuition and Fees—Medical Under-grad.	Post-grad.	Other	Total	Endowment Medical School	University (for M.S.)	Total	Gov. Federal Re-search	Instruc-tion	Total Federal	State	City or County	Total Gov't.	Gifts and Grants—Private Re-search	Non-restr.	Total	Other Income	Hospitals and Clinics	Total	Total Exclusive of Hospitals and Clinics
72	$9,356	0	0	$9,356	$61,574	0	$61,574	$60,948	$5,000	$65,948	$312,377	0	$378,325	$83,480	$7,500	$90,980	$12,516	0	$552,751	$552,751
73	31,162	0	$1,500	32,662	0	$10,150	$10,150	59,850	5,000	64,850	248,303	0	313,153	16,950	0	16,950	0	0	372,915	372,915
74	43,694	0	0	43,694	0	0	0	15,647	14,848	30,495	195,000	0	225,495	0	0	0	10,002	0	279,191	279,191
75	24,000	0	0	24,000	0	0	0	0	0	0	140,000	0	140,100	8,328	0	8,328	5,927	0	178,355	178,355
76	16,200	$20,918	633	37,751	4,657	0	4,657	6,900	0	6,900	1,420	0	8,320	11,606	0	11,606	1,118	$39,242	102,694	63,452
77	14,698	0	900	15,598	0	0	0	7,400	5,000	12,400	184,400	0	196,800	0	0	0	0	0	212,398	212,398

* 1940–41 and 1947–48 figures supplied by the Surgeon General's Committee on Medical School Grants and Finances.

0 Indicates no income.

Table 70. BUDGETS OF FIVE MAJOR CLINICAL DEPARTMENTS FOR FISCAL YEARS 1940-41,* 1948-49,* AND 1950-51, IN 36 FOUR-YEAR MEDICAL SCHOOLS

School No.	Medicine 1940-41	Medicine 1948-49	Medicine 1950-51 Dept. Budget	Medicine 1950-51 Special Funds	Surgery 1940-41	Surgery 1948-49	Surgery 1950-51 Dept. Budget	Surgery 1950-51 Special Funds	Pediatrics 1940-41	Pediatrics 1948-49	Pediatrics 1950-51 Dept. Budget	Pediatrics 1950-51 Special Funds	Obstetrics and Gynecology 1940-41	Obstetrics and Gynecology 1948-49	Obstetrics and Gynecology 1950-51 Dept. Budget	Obstetrics and Gynecology 1950-51 Special Funds	Psychiatry or Neuropsychiatry 1940-41	Psychiatry or Neuropsychiatry 1948-49	Psychiatry or Neuropsychiatry 1950-51 Dept. Budget	Psychiatry or Neuropsychiatry 1950-51 Special Funds
										15 TAX-SUPPORTED SCHOOLS										
13	$70,399	$131,705	$155,175	$31,000	$54,815	$96,600	$106,680	$3,877	See Medicine				$12,830	$19,900	$20,500	0	$9,833	$21,900	$28,300	$5,000
11	41,509	46,361	46,361	102,147	41,337	25,450	25,450	27,400		23,862	23,862	48,669	26,056	16,920	17,714	9,000	19,950	149,464	60,900	39,008
3	16,926	137,879	141,618	28,786	15,536	105,012	109,895	23,599	47,775	53,405	13,455		8,832	36,189	13,100	6,000	See Medicine		159,163	150,326
28	34,020	141,618	42,360	31,960	28,500	47,300	57,400	0	11,400	11,700	0		17,580	12,600	13,100	3,000	See Medicine			
18		37,660	49,535	25,680		19,650	32,410	44,345	39,200	38,200	23,575		33,670	34,210	1,100	8,097	19,020	10,000		
24	10,650	47,125	23,000	11,600	16,300	52,780	23,550	7,000	16,500	15,900	0		12,800	14,300			See Medicine			
12	59,890	25,000	38,430	0	62,902	99,098	86,932	46,902	17,570	13,200	103,200		20,630	28,168		9,520	21,600	11,800		
5		28,112	178,706	261,633		121,463	104,344	35,200	39,479	46,143	18,257		20,318	36,867		8,500	10,000	16,490		
7		120,956	71,075	144,687		101,305	100,570	81,103	20,318	18,890‡	269,000†		28,317	5,240		63,961	23,186	108,900		
15	33,821	178,830	36,800	147,843	23,325	111,045	122,840	10,425	27,300	27,900	13,400		6,500‡	19,990	16,510	21,600	55,960	67,325		
6	48,040	34,700	102,000	36,050	29,710	120,923	134,870	9,000	58,559	78,000	85,558		20,100	34,265		27,040	73,425	34,333		
1	38,547	87,075	122,039	10,000	37,030	69,366	93,924	201,000	59,267	61,800	35,000		37,535	42,872	13,370	62,845	53,110	28,380		
8	14,795	105,766	156,337	89,716	10,455	31,923	54,439	94,089	69,959	42,000	13,400		39,256	56,287	29,200	44,020	See Medicine	60,505		
14		149,315	17,379	53,972			109,093	26,853	—	20,340			87,048	16,029	15,000	See Medicine	36,681			
4		62,213	118,000	125,000				38,852	15,220	35,738	63,755		12,769	48,650		834				
										21 PRIVATELY SUPPORTED SCHOOLS										
61	8,100	53,400	55,700	283,456	1,000	7,300	7,250	300	14,400	17,496	0		9,000	10,540	23,830	5,500	2,000	2,000	No Department	
32	283,487	553,382	689,786	485,300	176,749	377,897	231,771	272,400	105,134	101,791	86,585		78,637	108,230	110,850	62,875	51,026	88,995	See Medicine	
68	5,152	10,904	9,460	10,000	0	0	3,710	0			2,960		0		0		0	See Medicine		
65		74,000	74,000	—	0	0	24,600	0	7,185	7,665	4,890		0	0	9,000	0	0			
71	7,235	19,947	19,947	17,700	3,462	13,540	12,000	0	7,500	8,175			6,150	11,895	11,455	6,800	1,850	2,800	225	9,900
56	73,720	53,545	34,670	68,850	73,342	24,100	21,490	35,834	46,196	45,615	27,248		25,720	20,620	21,850	1,500	27,183	69,640	2,800	10,000
37		99,144	113,652	14,032	3,000	125,306	125,934	170,261	25,066	18,466	141,113			27,986	28,521	30,498	6,250	21,025	67,700	79,000
54	5,000	27,325	16,312	1,000	2,000	36,015	35,210	55,460	1,100	1,260	2,200		350	8,200	4,461		1,000	7,300	24,850	2,000
64		16,312	16,312	43,200		7,000	7,800	4,700	1,000	37,200	16,755			600	300			38,200	8,800	10,000
66		18,650	19,850	1,000	2,000	9,800	287,440	3,613	12,900	2,400	22,900		2,200‡	11,400	59,400	0	See Medicine	41,750	18,300	
70	55,100	31,000	105,170	51,150		287,440	55,500	16,200	37,230	50,558			34,061	18,100	24,520	0	4,540	35,500	35,382	
31	197,195	83,164	53,000	206,871	12,765	67,630	85,229	317,000	41,000	119,330	61,536		41,937	38,130	41,937	7,860	3,450	29,900	35,390	176,241
48	72,392	96,419	96,419	402,480	54,651	65,977	85,332	93,540	103,240	40,800	55,520		60,474	79,440	60,740	23,400	26,850	See Medicine		
57	15,634	202,459	179,140	92,150	197,975	180,235	91,393	99,836	27,682	750			17,120	26,402	43,392	0	2,525	12,600	43,834	62,509
41	39,845	87,401	21,842	35,040	52,510	68,289	29,300	10,000	750	37,150	21,970		2,560	5,628	7,820	9,593	52,733	36,840	47,500	
36	51,810	22,041	73,985	210,636	5,136	27,905	37,200	73,832	43,908	40,000	200,000		11,826	11,891	50,209	800	7,050	29,775	61,225	54,850
51	49,182	77,823	72,895	244,185	21,735	31,433	58,850	116,880	31,770	37,000	4,212		16,130	34,575	34,485		13,724	61,225	57,540	
35	82,407	59,952	46,710	98,188	30,810	34,890	47,040		32,868	108,679	54,434		19,805	24,470	26,950	31,232	59,274	114,618	94,050	151,565
38		47,110	145,580	387,819	47,645	46,470	47,040	125,240	77,516	26,300†	426,000†		42,353	58,150	56,705	24,641		800	4,200	87,886
42	35,308	21,970	47,000	97,320	4,948	1,500	5,805	73,588	28,425	2,450	1,800		3,730	24,380	60,650	9,390	5,645	13,515	12,332	26,804

The budgets of the five major clinical departments presented in this table are the figures reported to the Survey by the department heads. They do not reflect the organization of the various departments or the extent of their activities. The departments may or may not include medical and surgical specialties, and the budgets may or may not include such items as faculty earnings or contributions by teaching hospitals. In no case is allowance made for the value of the time contributed by volunteer faculty members. The figures are of interest in showing the growth of the departmental budgets over a decade and the relative size of medical school funds and special funds in 1950-51. Special funds are usually research funds although some teaching grants are probably included. Departmental budgets were not obtained from all the medical schools and departments studied.

* 1940-41 and 1948-49 figures supplied by the Surgeon General's Committee on Medical School Grants and Finances.
† Large department financed almost entirely by private gifts or research funds.
‡ Obstetrics only.
— Indicates figure not obtained.

Table 71. BUDGETS FOR MEDICAL BASIC SCIENCE DEPARTMENTS FOR

School No.	Anatomy				Biochemistry				Physiology			
	1940–41	1948–49	1950–51 Medical School	1950–51 Special Funds	1940–41	1948–49	1950–51 Medical School	1950–51 Special Funds	1940–41	1948–49	1950–51 Medical School	1950–51 Special Funds
15 TAX-SUPPORTED												
13	$ 29,250	$ 57,100	$ 60,120	$15,435	$15,375	$31,830	$41,220	$ 20,500	$27,314	$ 45,250	$ 54,604	$ 26,725
11	—	55,093	55,093	41,144	—	69,503	79,380	18,550	—	56,389‡	56,390‡	42,158‡
3	42,542	86,451	88,782	7,000	29,340	78,858	81,108	4,500	37,558	104,963	115,467	80,000
28	17,158	33,254	34,822	0	10,924	20,200	23,300	5,768	14,004‡	37,720‡	26,000	8,400
18	36,460	40,220	56,240	5,200	15,733	21,640	33,511	0	18,683	24,560	31,460	0
24	—	36,600	39,010	11,500	—	18,280	20,780	2,000	—	26,340	29,580	5,120
12	—	—	64,000	25,500	—	—	32,964	20,380	—	—	54,997	11,320
5	57,360	109,350	129,302	19,486	26,331	55,690	77,380	11,400	31,688	60,740	77,430	12,976
7	—	38,929	51,315	8,907	—	46,270	47,014	53,892	—	26,923	27,216	3,500
15	12,750	31,210	32,595	11,264	6,950	31,600	33,050	68,291	9,701‡	29,300	31,400	28,700
6	31,156	69,480	97,180	600	15,424	45,547	72,720	3,500	14,673	54,810	48,100	13,000
1	48,748	70,666	89,995	60,006	—	34,950	38,468	130,974	51,430	60,601	85,500	75,000
8	32,070	75,760	85,882	22,180	7,782	45,580	62,179	9,000	22,990	58,252	81,454	51,386
14	16,199	38,011	42,347	25,793	15,971	25,829	27,466	30,108	12,665	26,493	31,524	25,933
4	—	57,608	85,325	67,991	—	17,634	88,000	43,600	—	50,455¶	103,889¶	84,595¶
22 PRIVATELY												
61	19,260	34,100	44,550	0	9,686	34,260	25,000	9,000	13,810	40,400	49,350	32,150
32	31,059	70,631	84,369	62,065	13,604	20,393	72,497	52,400	14,648	37,139	78,159	125,125
68	18,932	26,614	39,576	18,800	12,927	19,369	27,710	10,387	12,783	18,948	23,561	0
65	13,906	74,660	78,300	1,125	8,849	34,000	36,600	0	12,087‡	57,500‡	44,900‡	5,100‡
71	—	15,150	27,570	3,545	—	4,870	17,620	90	—	16,240	17,740	1,500
56	11,161	19,850	22,750	7,500	16,899	26,620	26,520	10,688	16,652	23,650	26,050	10,000
37	42,085	58,334	56,594	67,130	33,600	56,840	66,580	37,882	68,260	52,060	59,056	74,790
54	23,197	40,105	41,176	333	14,098	23,440	23,140	0	18,549	34,587	32,062	2,100
64	23,000	33,680	38,080	5,500	17,190	32,480	38,040	0	21,980‡	33,120‡	36,650‡	52,813‡
66	—	23,075	18,500	1,750	—	18,180	32,800	21,800	—	30,900‡	37,800‡	46,825‡
70	3,720	20,500	18,250	0	5,060	39,636	34,911	15,397	6,905‡	21,800‡	40,700‡	0
33	35,481	43,350	44,062	16,500	28,332	30,750	35,300	43,000	37,232	42,000	64,888	94,966
31	104,427	113,040	142,230	4,000	76,958	61,866	78,640	151,334	72,093	102,171	108,700	40,258
48	42,540	59,927	63,350	29,816	—	—	17,500	55,000	31,020	44,132	53,150	18,507
57	16,035	40,020	55,065	10,000	6,593	21,410	24,050	21,600	10,154	28,830	29,770	21,000
41	40,798	59,436	63,000	78,382	14,740	62,950	61,200	74,680	21,730	39,041	42,760	88,281
39	36,330	53,561	68,340	0	32,780	45,760	50,730	57,350	35,310	44,210	57,105	29,862
51	26,860	28,260	29,060	13,024	19,668	20,400	44,660	35,350	21,455	29,900	29,900	9,700
35	50,591	66,155	65,918	8,295	28,933	46,918	49,331	22,629	30,350	49,255	49,295	9,200
38	—	96,660	97,600	33,180	—	56,464	67,209	103,519	—	67,100	73,017	26,208
34	—	58,966	50,000	58,000	—	87,918	69,000	14,000	—	42,196	54,868	17,300
42	36,212	54,530	62,840	36,474	16,291	30,625	41,575	38,242	60,640‡	54,125	59,310	1,500
3 TWO-YEAR												
75	7,463	19,675	24,494	3,820	5,000	19,040	24,750	1,800	7,667‡	26,525‡	25,263‡	8,025‡
78	16,661	23,458	26,043	300	9,169	13,773	15,560	10,000	16,620‡	35,795‡	43,100‡	0‡
73	13,394	29,355	45,815	33,000	8,131	18,100	28,420	5,950	22,903	23,750	28,500	35,700

Departmental budgets were not obtained from all the schools and departments studied.
* 1940–41 and 1948–49 figures supplied by the Surgeon General's Committee on Medical School Grants and Finances.
† Bacteriology and pathology.
‡ Pharmacology and physiology.
§ Bacteriology and preventive medicine.
¶ Physiology and biophysics.
— Indicates figures not obtained.

FISCAL YEARS 1940–41,* 1948–49,* AND 1950–51, IN 40 MEDICAL SCHOOLS

Pharmacology 1940–41	Pharmacology 1948–49	Pharmacology 1950–51 Medical School	Pharmacology 1950–51 Special Funds	Bacteriology 1940–41	Bacteriology 1948–49	Bacteriology 1950–51 Medical School	Bacteriology 1950–51 Special Funds	Pathology 1940–41	Pathology 1948–49	Pathology 1950–51 Medical School	Pathology 1950–51 Special Funds
SCHOOLS											
$12,682	$20,090	$29,671	$10,030	$14,477	$40,400	$ 56,208	$ 23,360	$ 17,650	$ 34,100	$ 51,045	$ 18,485
See Physiology				—	45,068	45,068	7,202	—	53,542	53,542	103,591
24,278	63,915	86,899	53,936	See Path.	86,861	68,350	17,000	61,961†	91,458	104,495	32,229
See Physiology		16,850	200	10,022§	20,620§	22,620§	20,000§	11,154	24,758	25,688	14,610
13,573	16,280	24,215	12,900	See Path.	36,980	45,560	0	35,230†	39,240	47,498	18,306
—	26,300	28,000	10,315	—	20,780§	29,380§	0§	—	37,390	40,560	14,505
6,880	11,636	20,622	0	—	—	62,653	146,324	16,460	35,704	46,789	0
21,140	40,360	61,588	72,106	34,594	68,950	97,840	44,434	29,834	61,770	87,835	5,780
—	20,464	26,313	9,600	—	31,952	30,145	16,962	—	31,425	45,366	7,325
See Physiol.	22,750	27,020	90,000	See Path.	27,020	28,620	115,035	13,750	30,540	—	—
20,590	25,620	33,060	9,200	14,942	46,660	65,490	1,300	22,115	52,280	101,560	4,698
19,463	28,376	41,250	18,100	38,870	74,950	92,334	62,209	28,460	53,993	—	—
19,040	32,702	41,551	19,850	15,210	39,315	63,507	17,850	27,451	62,650	67,377	22,000
6,617	17,459	19,148	4,870	8,371	26,727	30,863	11,425	22,269	44,050	56,632	72,266
—	31,674	65,902	9,852	—	76,734	130,908	63,532	—	39,985	178,710	77,040
SUPPORTED SCHOOLS											
9,910	44,600	30,908	38,125	9,725	19,420	22,540	2,000	21,680	42,300	36,999	20,422
16,087	15,530	32,000	45,000	16,742	50,763	93,946	45,485	47,923	87,297	87,384	38,636
18,264	21,039	22,065	5,600	See Pathology		24,040		11,650†	29,619†	26,496	2,000
See Physiology				0§	44,600§	46,800§	3,000§	8,577	39,500	43,000	13,198
—	17,300	20,500	200	—	16,520	17,360	4,514	—	25,900	28,900	100
8,901	18,700	19,550	34,345	16,915§	24,750§	27,820§	3,574§	19,946	25,800	24,060	0
19,090	36,465	30,420	38,725	46,210	46,776	48,606	86,818	51,912	62,168	80,582	138,065
13,863	22,977	26,400	2,400	18,938†	21,705	27,310	8,500	See Bact.	17,747	19,985	1,300
See Physiology				37,600†	71,000†	77,240†	7,500†	See Bacteriology			
See Physiology				—	32,850	32,000	0		24,720	95,000	31,800
See Physiology				8,800	18,520	23,400	4,207	8,200	19,000	14,260	0
0	7,974	10,543	50,000	42,558	46,576	55,622	24,878	42,028	46,706	48,631	25,696
31,320	49,212	59,620	30,400	82,944	97,290	113,700	96,983	101,437	119,599	150,435	81,683
23,570	27,910	31,220	30,050	34,221	45,575	52,350	15,000	29,422	42,602	—	—
9,004	22,260	25,800	68,112	10,302	24,707	54,766	22,865	12,900	14,810	18,340	4,000
16,702	48,850	46,800	70,580	19,795	44,000	40,000	58,194	23,423	35,544	81,540	79,700
32,125	51,695	46,151	62,026	41,346	54,394	39,380	105,745	39,550	60,699	59,945	0
18,892	18,892	24,992	39,489	See Pathology				36,562†	39,475†	42,535†	15,505†
28,661	45,057	45,021	37,559	See Pathology		24,000	0	47,543†	92,920†	73,200	15,553
—	38,070	36,184	50,513	—	34,031	38,898	19,609		70,168	67,488	65,456
—	24,471	33,644	27,182	—	67,938	82,958	65,649		60,536	48,726	36,518
See Physiol.	33,430	40,100	12,418	15,236	24,630	33,890	42,200	36,258	56,570	38,150	46,948
SCHOOLS											
See Physiology				4,556	20,650	20,700	13,000	3,982	20,790	24,668	5,000
See Physiology				See Path.	17,385§	20,500§	5,190§	22,828†	19,657	20,548	1,000
11,847	26,090	24,300	1,200	8,355	24,820	30,805	3,500	12,836	34,029	42,525	27,390

INDEX